ANIMALS
OF THE
WORLD

ANIMALS OF THE WORLD

DP
DEMPSEY
PARR

Authors
Martin Walters
&
Jinny Johnson

Editor
Steve Parker

Design and Project Management
Jo Brewer

Assistant Editor
Helen Parker

Artwork Commissioning
Susanne Grant & Lynne French

Picture Research
Kate Miles, Janice Bracken, Lesley Cartlidge, Liberty Mella

Production
Jenni Cozens & Ian Paulyn

Indexed by
Jane Parker

Proofread by
Penny Clarke

Art Director
Clare Sleven

Editorial Director
Paula Borton

Director
Jim Miles

The publishers also wish to thank
John Farndon and Branka Surla in the production of this book.

Color Reproduction
DPI Colour, Saffron Walden, Essex

First published in 1999 by Dempsey Parr
Dempsey Parr is an imprint of Parragon
Parragon
Queen Street House
4 Queen Street
Bath
BA1 1HE, UK

24681097531

Copyright © Parragon 1999

Produced by Miles Kelly Publishing Ltd
Bardfield Centre, Great Bardfield, Essex CM7 4SL

British Library Cataloguing-in-Publication Data
A catalogue record for this book is available from the British Library

ISBN 1-84084-414-0

Printed in Germany

Contents

A world full of animals

The world teems with animals. Almost everywhere we look, creatures are going about their daily lives. On a walk through the countryside we see birds high in the sky. Insects buzz around the flowers. Mice and voles scamper through the undergrowth. Rabbits race across fields. Worms burrow in the soil under our feet. Even in a busy city, pigeons flock and rats gnaw and cockroaches scuttle.

These are a tiny selection of the kinds of animals that live on Earth. No one is sure exactly how many there are. Nearly two million kinds, or species, have been studied and identified by scientists. But many remote mountains, rain forests, coastlines, and deep seas remain to be explored. The total number of animal species on Earth may be 10 million, 20 million, or even more. Most of them are likely to be small insects such as beetles.

The kingdoms of living things

Scientists used to divide the living world into two main groups, or kingdoms—plants and animals. Today, most experts agree that there are five kingdoms. Two consist of microscopic life forms, where each individual is just one living cell. One of these kingdoms is Monerans, including the germs known as bacteria. The other kingdom is Protists. Some protists are like tiny, one-celled micro-animals. They move around and eat food. So they are included at the beginning of this book (pages 12–15).

Another two kingdoms are Plants, such as flowers, trees, grasses, ferns and seaweeds, and Fungi, such as mushrooms, toadstools, and yeasts. The fifth kingdom, and the largest, is the Animals.

Mushroom

What are animals?

Animals are multicelled living things that get the energy they need for survival, and the nutrients they need for growth and repair, by feeding on other living things. In this way they differ from plants, which capture their energy from sunlight.

Puffin

Wild bee swarm

Most animals feed by eating or ingesting their food. Carnivores such as wolves and sharks eat meat. Herbivores such as deer and parrots feed on plant parts such as leaves and seeds. Detritivores such as worms and millipedes feed on dying, dead, and rotting bits of living things. Omnivores eat almost anything.

Most animals have sense organs such as eyes and ears, so they can detect changes around them. They also have muscles so they can move around, react to changes, find food, and avoid danger. However, very simple animals like sponges have few senses and cannot move. Some animals, such as mussels and barnacles, fix themselves into position when young, and stay put for the rest of their lives.

Manta ray

Boa constrictor

Caterpillars

How animals breed

The key feature of all living things is that they breed—they produce more of their kind. Animals do this in a huge variety of ways. Many, from butterflies to birds, lay eggs. Some, such as mammals, certain snakes, and some fish, give birth to babies. A few, such as some flatworms, starfish, and jellyfish, can split and grow into two new individuals.

Animals care for their offspring in different ways. Monkeys and apes look after their babies for months, even years. Most birds spend weeks tirelessly feeding the chicks that hatch from their eggs. Mouthbrooding fish shelter their young in their mouths. The gastric-brooding frog keeps its young

Horned grebe

Sea turtles

Evolution

Evolution is when living things change or adapt to their surroundings. The world is always changing, as weather and climate alter, seas rise and fall, volcanoes erupt, and earthquakes split the land. Living things change too, developing new bodily features and behavior, so they can survive better in the new and

different conditions. But survival is a continuing struggle. It is as if nature chooses or selects which plants and animals will survive, and which will die. This is evolution by natural selection.

Evolution has been happening since life first appeared on Earth some 4 billion years ago. It has meant that some kinds of animals have died out, or become extinct, while others have evolved to take their place. All of this usually happens over a very long time scale, thousands or millions of years. However, we have altered the world greatly in the last few hundred years. New types of living things can now be produced in a few weeks or months using the science of genetics. How this will affect nature in the future is very unclear.

Tuatara

Horned owl

tadpoles in its stomach! However, most animals lay or release their eggs, and have nothing more to do with the offspring.

Animal habitats

Animals live in almost every type of surroundings, or habitat. A waterless desert, an icy glacier, a wave-battered coastline, a deep and pitch-black cave—they are all homes to animals of one kind or another. Each type of animal has features that enable it to survive in its habitat. Glacier grasshoppers can be frozen alive, yet come back to life when thawed out. Desert creatures escape the drought and heat by burrowing underground and staying still or dormant until it rains once more.

Young male lion

Penguins and chicks

Harmful, helpful, and useful

Some animals have taken to living alongside people. We have covered much of the world with buildings, roads, factories, mines, ports, and dumps. These have become ideal habitats for animals such as cockroaches, rats, mice, foxes, and gulls. Some animals have become pests. Insects feed on cereal

Shrimp on a sea slug

grains and destroy our crops. Some creatures, such as flukes and mosquitoes, cause or spread disease.

But we have also found other animals helpful or useful. We have bred farm animals for meat, milk, fur and skins. Working animals pull plows and carts or carry goods. Horses, dogs, camels, falcons, frogs, and

Frog

others are used in sports and competitions. For some people, pets are their main companions.

Equal animals

When we talk about "animals and birds," some people think of furry mammals and fluffy chicks. But the animal kingdom contains a gigantic range of creatures—including insects, spiders, snakes, worms, slugs, snails, and other less appealing "creepy-crawlies." We may not want to pick them up and cuddle them. But they each have their rightful place in the world and their role to play in nature.

Backswimmer

Today, many animal species are in danger of extinction, due to our activities. We hunt them for "sport," kill them for collections, and eliminate them in case they are dangerous. Most of all, we take over their wild places so they no longer have anywhere to live.

Stinkbug

Habitat destruction is the major threat facing the natural world today. Without these animals, our world will be a far less exciting place.

Grouping animals

To study and understand the animal kingdom, we need to have some method of grouping or classifying its creatures. Those with important similarities are put together in the same group. The main division is between vertebrates and invertebrates. Vertebrates are animals with backbones and include fish, frogs and other amphibians, lizards and other reptiles, birds, and furry mammals. Invertebrates lack a backbone and include all other animals, from tiny flies to giant squid.

This book is organized into sections using the standard system of classifying animals. It begins with simple invertebrates such as sponges and jellyfish. It ends with mammals that have complex behavior, such as solving problems and using tools. Classification panels on the lower right of each right-hand page give details of how many species are in the group, where they live, what they eat, and other information.

The classification system is broadly based on the idea of evolution. For example, all birds are classified together in the group called Aves. They are probably all descended from very early birds that first evolved millions of years ago. So all birds are related to each other. On a wider scale, the first birds probably evolved from reptiles such as the dinosaurs. In this way, relationships spread throughout the animal kingdom.

It is tempting to see this system as a "ladder of evolution" with simple animals at the bottom, and apes and monkeys—and ourselves—at the top. But all animals have fascinating features and amazing adaptations. A penguin might not survive on its own in one of our large cities. But then, we would not survive on out own at the South Pole.

Hagfish

SIMPLE ANIMALS

The simplest of all life forms are not animals. They are protists. Each is just a single living cell. Some are like microanimals, because they eat tiny bits of food. Others are like microplants, using the sun's light energy to live and grow. Protists number untold trillions and are the basic food for many tiny animals, especially in the sea, where they form much of the plankton.

A simple animal is a creature with few uncomplicated body parts. The simplest of the life forms we call animals (page 8) are sponges. Each is little more than a collection of fairly similar cells, with no brain, heart, muscles, or similar body parts. Sponges live in rivers and lakes, and on seashores and ocean floors, around the world. Crawling and swimming among them are tiny animals smaller than pinheads, such as water bears and wheel animals. Floating above them in the sea are various creatures that resemble bags of jelly. They include comb jellies and jellyfish, all with long, stinging tentacles.

Close relatives of jellyfish are the sea anemones on the shore, and the anemones' similar but smaller cousins, coral polyps. All of these animals may have few and simple body parts. But they thrive in their millions. Indeed, coral polyps construct the largest animal-made structures on Earth—coral reefs.

The microworld of protists

PROTISTS ARE VERY SMALL. They are among the tiniest living things, and each is made of just one microscopic cell. An average protist is about 20 times smaller than the dot on this i. A very large protist might fit into this o. In the deep sea lives a gigantic kind of protist that grows to the size of your finger. Protists are living things, but they are not really animals or plants. They have a separate kingdom (major group) of their own, Protista. However some kinds, called protozoans, are like tiny animals (rather than tiny plants) because they can move around and they eat other living things— especially other protists! They are found in all watery or damp places, including seas, rivers, ponds, soil, and on and inside animals and plants. Some kinds cause diseases.

Protists come in many shapes. Some are almost perfect spheres, like these diatoms. Others are shaped like bananas or commas.

There are many different kinds of protists. Amebas are shaped like blobs and they can move around by changing shape as they ooze along like plastic bags of jelly. An ameba feeds by sending out armlike parts to surround a microparticle of food, and then merging the arms with its body to engulf the particle. After digesting what it can, the ameba simply oozes on and leaves the remains behind. A few types of ameba are real giants, growing almost to the size of shirt buttons.

Another group of protists is the ciliates, such as stentors and parameciums (page 17). They are known as ciliates because their bodies are covered by a "carpet" of miniature hairs called cilia. The cilia beat regularly, like rows of miniature oars, to make the protist glide through the water. However, some ciliates, like stentor, cannot move about. They are attached by a stalk to the pond or stream bottom. They beat their cilia to make water currents which bring tiny bits of food to them.

The amazing slime molds
Sometimes a slimy, slug-shaped blob appears on an old tree. It looks like jelly, but gradually, over several minutes, it moves! This is a slime mold. It is not a single creature, but a collection of hundreds of single-celled living things

Protist parts

An ameba is easily small enough to fit onto the head of a pin. It lives in water. It has no proper shape. It can spread out almost flat, extend armlike parts called pseudopodia, then form into a round ball and roll along.

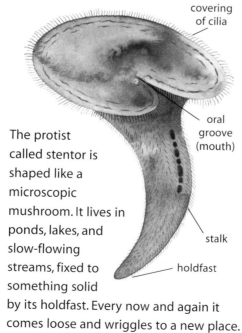

The protist called stentor is shaped like a microscopic mushroom. It lives in ponds, lakes, and slow-flowing streams, fixed to something solid by its holdfast. Every now and again it comes loose and wriggles to a new place.

covering of cilia

oral groove (mouth)

stalk

holdfast

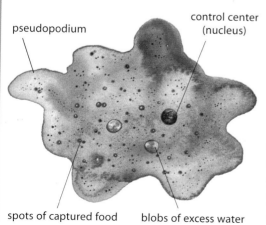

pseudopodium

control center (nucleus)

spots of captured food

blobs of excess water

Plasmodium and malaria

The protists that cause malaria grow through many stages in their lives. Some are in mosquitoes, some in humans. When a mosquito that does not have plasmodia bites a person who does have them, the mosquito sucks up plasmodia in its meal of blood. Then it bites another person and passes on the parasites.

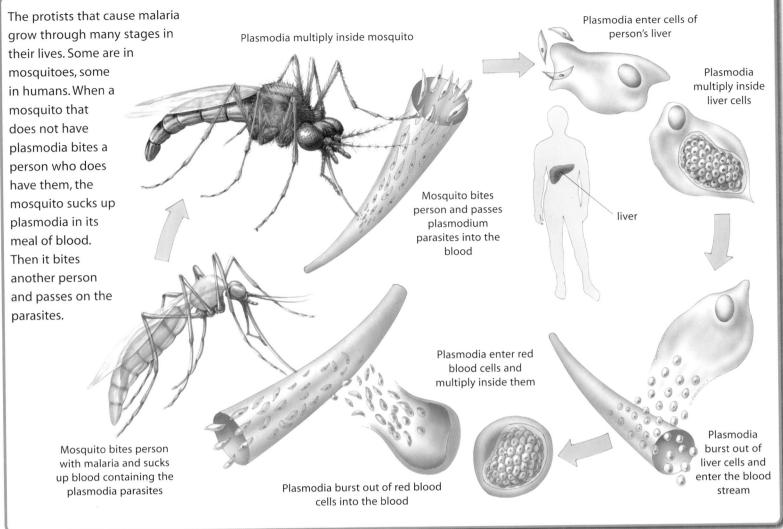

Plasmodia multiply inside mosquito

Plasmodia enter cells of person's liver

Plasmodia multiply inside liver cells

Mosquito bites person and passes plasmodium parasites into the blood

liver

Plasmodia enter red blood cells and multiply inside them

Mosquito bites person with malaria and sucks up blood containing the plasmodia parasites

Plasmodia burst out of red blood cells into the blood

Plasmodia burst out of liver cells and enter the blood stream

More than 200 million people around the world suffer from malaria. And more than two million people die from this disease each year—about one million of them in Africa. The name of the disease, *malaria*, means "bad air." This name came from the time when people thought the illness was spread by bad or stale air. Then it was discovered that malaria was caused by protists too small to see, carried by mosquitoes.

These blow away and hatch into new amoebas. A slime mold "slug" can weigh up to 2 pounds (900 g).

Protists and diseases

Many protists are parasites. They thrive on or in other living things, known as the hosts. The protist gains food and protection or shelter from its host. Some parasitic protists have hardly any effect on their hosts. Others cause great harm and serious diseases such as malaria and sleeping sickness. Malaria is common in many warm,

tropical regions. The protists that cause it are known as plasmodia. They are spread by mosquitoes. When a mosquito bites a person, but before it sucks up blood, it passes a few thousand plasmodia protists into the person's body. These plasmodia parasites multiply inside the person's liver and blood. Eventually they produce the sweating, shivering, headaches, and other symptoms of the disease malaria. People who visit tropical places where malaria is common can take tablets or have injections to prevent them catching it.

resembling amebas. They normally live separately in the soil and among leaves. They gather together into a sluglike lump to breed. After creeping about for a while, the "slug" grows a stalk that releases tiny, dustlike particles called spores.

Wow!

Many plant-eating animals, from rabbits to elephants, depend on protists to help digest their food. These animals have billions of protists in their guts. The protists make chemicals to dissolve the tough plant food. The protists take in some of the nourishment, and the larger animal has the rest.

PROTISTS
(Kingdom Protista)
- more than 60,000 kinds or species
- live in water, soil, other damp places, and inside creatures and plants
- most are microscopic
- single-celled (body made of only one cell)

Some main groups of protists:

Amebas
- 16,000 species
- move about and feed by changing shape
- some gather together and are known as "slime molds"

Ciliates
- 7,500 species
- move and feed by tiny hairlike cilia

Euglenas
- at least 1000 species
- mainly freshwater
- have one long, whiplike flagellum
- can capture the energy in sunlight, like tiny plants

Parasitic protists
- 5,000 species
- live inside other animals
- some cause diseases, such as malaria, sleeping sickness, and dysentery

Floating protists

MOST OCEAN CREATURES, EVEN GREAT WHALES, DEPEND ON TINY PROTISTS. These protists live in the upper layers of the sea. They form part of the plankton—a "living soup" of all kinds of tiny plants, animals and other organisms, drifting with the currents. Trillions of plantlike protists trap the sun's light energy and use it to live, grow, and multiply. In turn, they are food for millions of tiny animal-like protists. Both kinds of protists are eaten by small sea creatures, such as tiny fish and shrimps, as well as the larvae (young) of bigger animals. These are consumed by larger ocean creatures, and so on, building up the ocean food chains to huge sharks and whales.

Ceratium dinoflagellate

Gymnodinium dinoflagellate

Oily!
Crude oil, or petroleum, was formed from the remains of billions of tiny plankton organisms that lived millions of years ago. They sank slowly to the seabed in layers. The pressure of more layers above eventually turned them into oil.

In a drop of seawater, protists such as foraminiferans (pale and curled like spirals) and radiolarians (blue and ball-shaped) teem in their thousands.

Green plankton
Much of the plankton can make its own food using sunlight energy. Like trees and other green plants on land, the water-dwelling protists have a green substance called chlorophyll, which absorbs light energy. These members of the green plankton are sometimes called producers, because they produce food for themselves, rather than consuming it as animals do. Because strong sunlight

Rotalia foraminiferan

can only shine down about 100 feet (30 m) into the sea, the green plankton have to stay close to the surface to survive. Most live concentrated into the top 300 feet (90 m) of the ocean. A few can make weak wriggling movements, but most are at the mercy of ocean currents and they drift about in the endless circulation of seawater.

Diatoms

The diatoms are plantlike protists with beautifully shaped, sculpted, and patterned shells. They float in the upper levels of the sea, and also in lakes, as part of the plankton. A diatom's shell is double-layered and made of silica— the main mineral in sand (and also in glass). Some diatoms have ringlike flaps that help them float near the surface.

Miliota foraminiferan

Radiolarians

These protists are related to the amebas shown on the previous page. Like diatoms, they have silica shells. These are usually circular or spherical, with lines and patterns etched into the surface. Some have silica rods sticking out, like the spokes of a wheel.

Nodosaria foraminiferan

Foraminiferans

Another group of amebalike protists, the foraminiferans, also live inside shells. However, their shells are usually made of limestone or chalk rather than silica. Foraminiferans are very common in sea plankton, where they

float about, feeding on even smaller organisms. A foraminiferan sticks long, threadlike "arms" through the many holes, called foramens, in its shell. It grabs food particles with these arms. A few foraminiferans grow as large as a fingernail.

Dinoflagellates

These plankton protists have long, spinelike projections, which probably help to stop them sinking in the water, and which also deter predators. Some can use the sun's light energy, like plants. Others grab tiny bits of food. In certain

Spiroplecta foraminiferan

Haploozoon dinoflagellate

Polykrikos dinoflagellate

Noctiluca dinoflagellate

Shiny!

Some sea protists can make their own light. At night it makes the waves glow, or the water shine as people or boats pass through. This is often due to *Noctiluca* dinoflagellates. If you disturb water which contains large numbers of these protists they give off enough light between them to make the sea flash! Light production by living things is called bioluminescence.

conditions, especially a warm springtime, dinoflagellates cause "red tides" along the seashore. They multiply in such huge numbers that their bodies color the seawater bright red. Some kinds also produce poisons that kill other forms of life, such as fish.

Besides protists, the plankton contains eggs and young forms (larvae) of larger animals such as shrimps and crabs.

Some kinds of floating protists:

Diatoms
• 10,000 species
• live in the sea and in fresh water
• common in plankton
• have glassy, boxlike casings

Dinoflagellates
• 2,000 species
• live in the sea and in fresh water
• have two whiplike flagella
• some live inside other creatures, such as corals

Foraminiferans
• 3,000 species
• live in the sea and in fresh water
• have chalky shells with holes
• some capture food, others absorb sunlight

Moss animals

MOSS ANIMALS OR BRYOZOANS, SOMETIMES CALLED SEA MOSSES, DO NOT LOOK LIKE ANIMALS AT ALL. As their name suggests, they live in the sea and look more like a patch of moss or a similar plant, or even like a doormat. This is because the tiny moss animals live together in a group or colony and extend their tentacles, like hundreds of miniature sea anemones (page 32). The tentacles wave in the water and filter floating bits of food, which the moss animals eat and digest.

In the warm waters along the coast of South Australia these *Celleporaria* sea mosses have formed colorful branching colonies on an old piece of wooden jetty.

In some ways, moss animals are similar to coral animals (page 36). Each one is tiny, only about half a pinhead across. It lives inside a hard, stony case and puts its tentacles into the water to catch floating pieces of food. Hundreds or thousands of individual moss animals are connected together into a flat, branching structure which spreads and grows over an underwater object. This object may be a rock or stone, a piece of wood, a large frond of seaweed, or even the shell of another animal like a clam or mussel. In some kinds of moss

animal, the colony grows upward, like a plant, rooted at the base to a firm object. The cases of neighboring moss animals, known as zooids, are cemented to each other. The whole colony may widen like a fan or branch like a twig, and be brightly colored. It can have millions of individuals, resembling a piece of coral. However most moss animals are less spectacular. They live in small, flat, pale-looking colonies, rarely larger than coins.

Freshwater moss animals

Most types of moss animal live in the sea, but a few live in fresh water, especially if it is clean and unpolluted. In some kinds the protective case is flexible and jelly-like, rather than hard and stony.

In the late summer or autumn, both sea and freshwater moss animal colonies produce hard, egglike structures. These survive through the winter and

Inside a moss animal

A typical moss animal or bryozoan is about the size of a pinhead. It lives in a hard casing, shaped like a shoebox, that it makes around itself from hard, chalky minerals taken from the water. The bell-shaped ring of feathery tentacles surrounding its mouth filter tiny particles of food, like small algae (plants) and protists, from the water. These food particles are passed down into the mouth and digested in the baglike stomach. When danger threatens, strong strands of muscle pull the tentacles into the casing and then close and hold down the doorlike lid, the operculum.

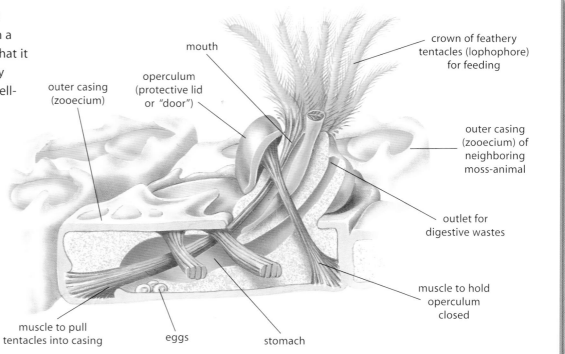

mouth

operculum (protective lid or "door")

outer casing (zooecium)

crown of feathery tentacles (lophophore) for feeding

outer casing (zooecium) of neighboring moss-animal

outlet for digestive wastes

muscle to hold operculum closed

muscle to pull tentacles into casing

eggs

stomach

Freshwater moss animals feed on protists such as paramecium, euglena, and volvox (below). Being single cells, these are far smaller than the moss animal. Sea-living moss-animals eat similar tiny food items. These include floating scraps of seaweed, marine protists as shown on the previous pages, and also the eggs and larvae (young) of larger animals like crabs, starfish and worms. The moss animal grabs its prey with its tentacles, which are covered with microscopic hairs called cilia.

Paramecium

Euglena

They live mainly in colonies and are fixed in one spot. Some grow on stones, others on seaweeds. A few live on other animals, including sponges, worms, crabs, and shellfish. Each entoproct animal has a horseshoe-shaped ring of about 40 tentacles for feeding, a cup-shaped body and a stalk fixing it to its host object.

Like moss animals and other tiny creatures, entoprocts are so small that they do not need a heart or blood

The animal cell

The bodies of all creatures, from moss animals to blue whales, are made of microscopic units known as cells. A typical animal cell is shown below. A protist is just one, all-purpose cell. A moss animal is about 5,000 cells. An elephant's body has 100 million million cells.

cell membrane (flexible outer "skin")

nucleus (control center)

mitochondria (provide cell with energy)

cytoplasm (cellular jelly)

system. Nutrients can easily seep through their bodies to reach all parts. About 150 species are known.

can resist freezing and drying out. The eggs may blow about in the wind, spreading the moss animals to new places. In the spring they develop into new colonies.

Sea mat and hornwrack
The sea mat is one common kind of moss animal. It grows on the fronds of kelps and similar brown seaweeds and forms flat, pale, lacy sheets that stand out well against the background of the seaweed frond.

Another common type of moss animal is called hornwrack. It grows about as long as a human hand and is found in deeper water along rocky coasts. Sometimes colonies of hornwrack are washed up on the shore after a storm, and they look like pieces of pale, lacy seaweed.

Entoprocts
Entoprocts are another group of tiny creatures, very similar to moss animals. The largest are only as big as rice grains.

Volvox is the main kind of food for freshwater moss animals. It is a protist that lives like a plant, trapping the energy in sunlight to live and grow. Each floating ball is made up of hundreds of volvox protists.

Dead or alive?
Tiny creatures such as moss animals, and the one-celled protists, eat the smallest living things—especially bacteria. Some bacteria hardly seem alive. They can be dried out, boiled, frozen, and even made into crystals in laboratory dishes (right). Yet they still become active when conditions are right.

Moss animals
(Ectoprocts or Polyzoans)
- about 4,000 species
- aquatic (live in water)
- mostly marine or sea-dwelling
- grow as rooted, branching colonies
- each animal has a bell-shaped ring of tentacles called the lophophore, for feeding
- most individuals are hermaphrodite (have both male and female sex parts)
- breed by releasing tough, egglike structures

Entoprocts
(Endoprocts or Kamptozoans)
- about 150 species
- aquatic (live in water)
- mostly marine or sea-dwelling
- grow as rooted, branching colonies
- each animal has a C-shaped ring of tentacles for feeding
- breed by releasing tiny, young forms or larvae

Water bears and wheel animals

WATER BEARS ARE AMAZING TINY CREATURES, WITH POWERS AS STRANGE AS THEIR APPEARANCE. A typical water bear has a plump body and four pairs of stumpy, clawed legs. It also has a faintly bearlike face, which might make it look cuddly—if it were not so tiny. Most water-bears are smaller than the dot on this i. They creep about in the soil and dead leaves, among plants such as mosses, in the fresh water of ponds, streams, and lakes, and also in the sea. They feed on the sap of plants, or on other creatures even smaller than themselves. Another group of very tiny creatures are wheel animals. Most look like miniature cups on stalks. They take their name from the ring of microscopic hairs, cilia, around the rim of what looks like the cup-shaped body—which is actually the creature's head. The cilia beat like tiny oars to create water currents, which bring tiny bits of floating food to the animal's mouth.

A water-bear has sharp claws on its eight stubby legs, to grip slippery plants or grains of mud and sand. It has mouthparts like sharp needles to pierce and suck food.

Kinorhynchs (left) are tiny, bristly, wormlike animals similar to hairybacks (page 19). They live in the sea.

Water bears are also known as tardigrades, a name that means "slow-steppers." They are very small—from one to 20 could fit on a pinhead. Some live in the sea, between particles of sand and mud. Others dwell in fresh water. But most live in places that are sometimes wet, and at other times dry—like muddy puddles, inside a moss plant, or in the rainwater gutters of buildings. They can survive here because, as the dampness dries out, the water bear turns into a special resting stage called a tun. It simply dries out, shrivels up to about one tenth its normal size, and becomes inactive, almost like an egg. This tun stage can

This wheel animal or rotifer has just eaten some food particles, and is starting to digest them.

Inside a wheel animal

- crownlike central tufts (lobes) of cilia
- head
- wheel-like ring of cilia (trochal disk)
- mouth opening
- small, simple brain
- jawlike mouthparts (mastax)
- muscle strands to pull in cilia
- main body
- sex organs
- stomach
- digestive glands
- bladder for waste fluids
- anus (outlet for digestive wastes)
- foot
- pincerlike toe

A wheel animal has a rounded head like a cup or bowl, a plump body, and a clawlike toe for gripping. Around the rim of the head are rings of hairlike cilia. These wave or beat to make a current in the water, which sweeps food into the creature's mouth. Some wheel animals can swim through the water by means of their beating cilia.

survive for many months, even years. When the moisture returns, the water bear "hatches" out of its tun stage, and carries on living!

A wheel head

Wheel animals are also called rotifers, which means "wheel-carriers." The wheel-like part is the head and mouth of the creature, with its tufts of hairlike cilia. The biggest wheel animals grow to about one eighth of an inch (3 mm) across, but most kinds are far tinier. Like water bears, they can survive drying out, and also being frozen or almost boiled, by shriveling up into a resting stage. The tough-cased, egglike resting stage of a wheel-animal is known as a cyst.

Hairybacks

Yet another group of extremely tiny animals are the hairybacks, also called gastrotrichs. A typical hairyback has a round, bristly head and a streamlined body with a forked tail. It glides along the bottom of a pond or stream, nosing in the mud to feed on even smaller bits of food such as single-celled plants and tiny protists. Kinorhynchs are similar small animals, resembling worms. They wriggle along like worms and live only in the mud and sand of the seabed.

This is a starlike group or colony of wheel animals as seen under the microscope.

The hairs of a hairy back (left) are really small knobbly outgrowths of the body, called papillae. The head is rounded and the tail forked.

Pedalia wheel animal

Collotheca wheel animal

There are many kinds of wheel animals with different body shapes.

Filinia wheel animal

Pieces of food can be seen inside the mouth and stomach of this branchionus wheel animal. The small dark spot between the brownish food particles toward the center and the ring of hairs to the far left is the eye spot. This simple type of eye detects the difference between light and dark. A wheel animal is either male or female. This is a female. The male is smaller, perhaps only one third the size of the female. He has a shorter body, shaped like a collar. Most wheel animals swim by waving their cilia. Some can loop along like a caterpillar, attaching first the head and then the tail. Others stay fixed to a solid object by the clawed foot.

Water bears (Tardigrades)
- about 400 species
- microscopic or nearly so
- four pairs of stumpy legs, with bristly claws
- live in damp places, some in fresh water, a few in the sea

Wheel animals (Rotifers)
- about 1,800 species
- microscopic or nearly so
- wheel- or crown-like tufts of tiny hairs (cilia) on the head
- live mainly in fresh water, a few in damp places and in the sea

Hairy backs (Gastrotrichs)
- about 450 species
- live in fresh and salty water
- microscopic or small, up to 4 mm
- scaly or hairy body, forked tail

Kinorhynchs
- only about 120 species
- living in sea mud or sand
- small, up to 0.1 inch (2 mm) long
- body seems to be divided into about 13 sections or segments

Sponges

SPONGES LOOK MORE LIKE PLANTS THAN ANIMALS. They grow on underwater objects such as rocks or plant stems. They cannot move around, although a few types twitch slightly at the surface when touched. They have no eyes or ears, brain or nerves, heart or blood. But they do catch their own food, by filtering tiny particles from water. The water enters the sponge through thousands of tiny holes, or pores, and then leaves through one of the few big holes. Adult sponges are fixed to the spot, but when they breed, they produce young ones or larvae, which swim actively. Eventually a larva finds a suitable place to settle down and grow into the adult colony of cells we call a sponge.

A brittlestar climbs across an orange sponge.

Tiny coral animals (polyps) grow around a sponge's oscule—the main exit hole for water. The tunnels are visible inside the sponge's main body cavity.

A typical full-grown sponge is not so much one single animal, more a collection or colony of animal-like cells. These form a flask-shaped body surrounding a central cavity. There are many tiny holes or channels in the body wall, linking the cavity inside with the sea water outside. Whiplike flagella on cells lining the cavity beat to make a current of water flow through the channels into the central cavity. The water brings with it tiny bits of food such as protists, tiny seaweeds and animal eggs and larvae. The water, and the sponge's waste products, pass out through larger channels, oscules, usually at the top.

How sponges breed
Like many plants, sponges can reproduce by growing small extra parts,

Breadcrumb sponges grow in several colours, including green (upper left). The hymenia sponge is usually blood-red (top right). Some solenia sponges are also red (top left). Column sponges can be purple or blue (center). Vase sponges are wider, with one large exit hole for water (lower left). The brain sponge is pink (lower right).

Different types of cup sponge grow in fresh and salt water.

Bath sponges

Most bath sponges are now made of plastic foam. But many years ago they were gathered from the sea. The common bath sponge lives on the seabed, in clear, warm water. It is rather slimy, and is a yellow or purple color. After it dies, its soft parts rot away to leave its flexible skeleton of fibers and spicules. This skeleton forms the sponge we use in the bath. Its thousands of tiny holes once let the living sponge suck in water. In some areas, such as parts of the Mediterranean Sea, so many bath sponges have been gathered that this animal is now very rare. It takes perhaps 20 years for a new bath sponge to grow.

buds, which come away and grow into new sponges. Or they can breed sexually, like animals. Each sponge is both male and female, so it can make both sperm and eggs. An egg and sperm join, or fertilize, and develop into a tiny sponge larva which swims away. It lives in the open sea for a day or two, before settling on the seabed to grow into a new adult sponge.

How do sponges survive?

Sponges have no obvious defenses. They cannot bite or sting. They cannot run off or swim away. So how do they protect themselves? The bodies of many sponges are full of tiny, sharp spikes or shards of hard minerals, such as lime, chalk, or silica (the same substance that glass is made from). These spiny spikes,

Clean!

A large sponge can sieve water at the rate of a full bathtub every hour. This makes sponges useful in fish tanks and other aquaria. They work as living filters, helping to keep the water clean and clear.

called spicules, make up the sponge's skeleton. They give its body firmness and stiffness. They also help to deter animals who might try to eat the sponge. In addition, many types of sponges have an unpleasant smell or a horrible taste, which also puts off their predators.

Placozoans

These tiny animals, which grow to about the size of an ant, resemble giant amebas. However their bodies are not just one cell, like an ameba, but about 1,000 cells. Placozoans ooze and move like slugs. There are only a couple of species known and both live in the sea.

These pink sponges, on an old jetty support, form a network of chambers and holes used by worms, fish, and other creatures.

Purple column sponges form tall tubes, while red and yellow breadcrumb sponges spread over the rocks.

Sponges (Poriferans)	Placozoans
• about 10,000 species	• only a few species
• most live in the sea, a few in fresh water	• live in the sea
• many have spiky inner skeletons	• crawl along like slugs or giant amebas
• body full of holes	• about one eighth of an inch (3 mm) long
• some grow to 14 feet (4 m) across	

Comb jellies

COMB JELLIES ARE STRANGE, PALE, GHOSTLY SEA ANIMALS THAT ARE SIMILAR IN SOME WAYS TO JELLYFISH. They have mainly see-through or transparent bodies, which are soft and squashy, and they drift or swim with the ocean currents. There are only about 100 different kinds, or species, of comb jelly, but some of these are amazingly common. They float in their thousands in the upper layers of the sea, as part of the surface plankton. In the twilight zone more than 1,500 feet (450 m) down, they are even more abundant and drift in huge swarms, millions strong. In fact, in the deep oceans, comb jellies are some of the most numerous of all animals.

Comb jellies vary in color depending on the angle of the sun, the color of the seawater, and also on what they have eaten.

Comb jellies range in size from smaller than a baked bean to as long as a human arm. Most are round and ball-shaped or long and slim like sausages. One of the most common kinds is known as the sea gooseberry. It has a pear-shaped body, about the size and shape of a grape, and is completely transparent.

Rows of combs
Running around the body of a comb jelly, like stripes, are eight bands or rows of what look like tiny combs—which is

The lampea comb jelly is one of the sausage-shaped types. The comblike groups of tiny hairs are on ridges along the sides of the body. In some types of comb jelly the hairs are fused or joined to each other to form one broad, flap-shaped surface. If a comb jelly is washed up on the beach, it loses its shape and soon dries out and dies.

how these animals got their name. Each comb is made up of groups of minute hairs known as cilia. These can beat in rhythm, like rows of oars. By beating its cilia, a comb jelly can swim through the water. Usually it swims straight up or down as part of its daily feeding routine, rising at night and sinking back to the depths by day. But, like many jellyfish, comb jellies are at the mercy of strong ocean currents.

Sticky tentacles
Trailing from the comb jelly's body are two long, sticky tentacles which dangle in the water. Smaller animals of the plankton, including tiny shrimps and the young forms of crabs, starfish, and worms, become entangled in and stung by these tentacles. The sea gooseberry then brushes its tentacles across its mouth and swallows its prey.

Glowing in the dark
Although most comb jellies are transparent, if the sun catches them they shimmer in the water with iridescent rainbow colors. At night, some kinds can glow with multicolored lights.

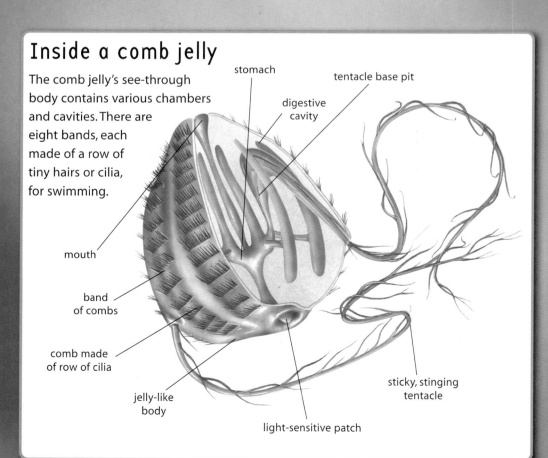

Inside a comb jelly
The comb jelly's see-through body contains various chambers and cavities. There are eight bands, each made of a row of tiny hairs or cilia, for swimming.

stomach

tentacle base pit

digestive cavity

mouth

band of combs

comb made of row of cilia

jelly-like body

light-sensitive patch

sticky, stinging tentacle

These come from lines of glowing spots inside the comb jelly, which shine through the transparent body, making the creature visible from a distance. It is possible that the lights attract other animals toward the comb jelly, which then catches and eats them. (The ability of some creatures to make their own light is known as bioluminescence, page 15).

Venus' girdle

Most comb jellies have rounded bodies. An exception is the remarkable Venus' girdle, which has a lacy, ribbonlike body about the size and shape of a yardstick. It is like a normal comb jelly that has been ironed flat! Venus' girdle swims by wriggling from side to side, rather like a snake.

Another unusual comb jelly is coeloplana, which looks like a slug with a tentacle at each end. It creeps over rocks and seaweeds in search of prey.

A comb jelly can pull or retract its two main tentacles into base pits or cavities in the sides of the body, when it is swimming or not feeding (above). To catch food, the comb jelly lets its tentacles dangle in the water (left). They form a sticky drift net to catch small prey.

A comb jelly opens its mouth, which leads into the stomach region and the many-branched digestive cavities.

Comb jellies (Ctenophores)
- about 100 species
- most have transparent, rounded bodies
- many have a pair of long tentacles
- live only in the sea
- range in size from 0.2 inch (5 mm) to more than 3 feet (90 cm)

The "nettle animals"

JELLYFISH, SEA ANEMONES, AND CORAL POLYPS (the tiny creatures that build coral reefs) all belong to the animal group called cnidarians. This name means "nettle animals." It comes from the tiny stinging cells on the tentacles and other parts of these creatures. The stings are used to capture, paralyze, and kill prey; some are strong enough to give a painful sting to humans. However a few cnidarians have such venomous stings that they can kill people. Cnidarians are also known as coelenterates, which means "hollow gut," because their bodies are almost all stomach, like a hollow bag. Most of these animals live in the sea, and have a circular body shape.

An underside view of a jellyfish reveals the billowing tentacles called oral arms that stick onto prey and pass it into the mouth.

The body of a jellyfish or other cnidarian has a single opening. This is both a mouth, to take in food, and an anus, to get rid of undigested leftovers. It is surrounded by the animal's tentacles. These are usually long and thin, and may number more than one hundred. They are coated with microscopic stinging cells (shown on page 27).

Most cnidarians have soft, squashy, floppy bodies, containing a large, bag-like stomach or gut cavity. The body wall is made of a jelly-like substance. Some types, like the corals, build hard, stony, cup like skeletons around themselves for protection. Jellyfish have an extra-thick jelly layer which makes up the bulk of the body.

Two body shapes
There are two basic types of body plan among the cnidarians. These are the medusa and the polyp. Some cnidarians spend most or all their lives as one form. The jellyfish, for example, are

The soft body or bell of this doughnut jellyfish is buoyed up in the water.

medusas, while coral animals and anemones are polyps. However, some cnidarians are first polyps, then change shape and become medusas—or the other way around.

The polyp
The typical polyp has a soft, cylinder-shaped body. The long lower part or stalk is attached at its base to a rock, seaweed or other object. At the top of the stalk is the polyp's mouth, surrounded by the ring of grasping, stinging tentacles waving upward. Sea anemones spend all their lives as polyps. They have no medusa form.

These purple striped jellyfish are hardly visible, as they drift like ghosts in the hazy waters of the sea.

The branching stomach cavity and reproductive parts can be seen inside the body of this pencillate jellyfish.

The medusa
A typical medusa is like a polyp that has had its stalk removed and then been turned upside down. Its body is shaped like an umbrella or bell, with the stinging tentacles dangling downward from the edges or rim. The mouth is in the middle of the tentacles. A medusa is usually the floating or free-living form, while the polyp is the attached or fixed form. Jellyfish spend most or all of their lives drifting or swimming slowly through the oceans, as medusas.

Pale or colorful
Some jellyfish, sea anemones and corals are pale or milky white, especially in cooler seas. But many tropical types are beautifully colored, often in shades of pink, red, yellow, and orange.

When the tide is out, anemones on seashore rocks may look like dull blobs of jelly. But as the tide comes in they spread out their flower-like tentacles, which resemble soft, waving plant petals. They are sometimes called "flowers of the sea." But of course, anemones are animals (page 32). Like all their cnidarian cousins, they may look innocent and harmless, but they are deadly predators.

Inside a jellyfish

A jellyfish is mostly a hollow stomach or gut cavity, where its meals are digested and dissolved. It has no proper eyes or ears. But it can detect touch, temperature, patches of light and dark, and water currents.

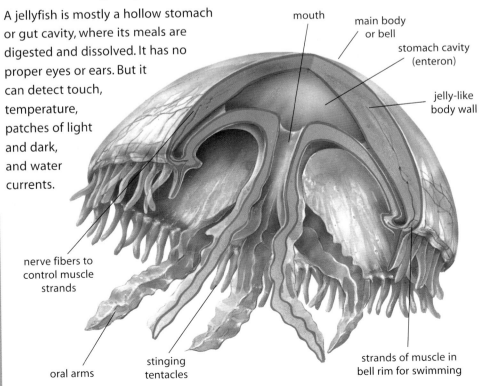

mouth
main body or bell
stomach cavity (enteron)
jelly-like body wall
nerve fibers to control muscle strands
oral arms
stinging tentacles
strands of muscle in bell rim for swimming

JELLYFISH AND RELATIVES (Cnidarians or Coelenterates)
- about 10,000 species
- mostly sea-living, some dwell in fresh water
- have a circular body
- central mouth surrounded by tentacles
- most are soft-bodied, but some (like corals) make hard, stony, protective cases or skeletons

There are two main sub groups:

Anemones and corals (Anthozoans)
- about 6,000 species
- live in the sea
- stalklike body attached at the base, with tentacles above (polyp form)

Jellyfish and hydroids (Medusozoans)
- about 4,000 species
- most live in the sea, some (like hydras) live in fresh water
- both free-floating medusa and fixed polyps
- a few have stings that are dangerous to humans

Jellyfish

JELLYFISH RANGE IN SIZE FROM SMALLER THAN THE TIP OF YOUR FINGER, to giants larger than a patio sunshade umbrella, measuring more than six feet (1.8 m). But most are about the size and shape of a breakfast cereal bowl. Some types can swim weakly by making pulsing movements of the main body or bell—like opening and closing your fingers. But these swimming motions are weak and most jellyfish are at the mercy of strong ocean currents. They are often washed up helpless onto the shore after a storm. Their floppy bodies collapse, and these creatures soon dry out and die.

The body of the lion's mane jellyfish can grow larger than a beachball. The long, thin tentacles around the rim of the bell do the stinging. They can cause great pain to a person.

Stauromedusans, or stalked jellyfish, are jellyfish that think they are anemones. There is a stalk on the top of the bell with a sticky end that attaches to a piece of seaweed or sea grass.

Swimming jellyfish

Around the rim of the jellyfish's main body, or bell, is a ring of muscle fibers. These can be shortened or contracted to squeeze the bell like a purse-string and make pulsating movements, which propel water out of the bell and so push the jellyfish through the water. Usually a jellyfish swims upward, to rise closer to the surface. When it stops swimming, it sinks down again. Using these movements the jellyfish can follow its prey, the small animals of the plankton, as they rise near the surface at night and sink to mid water during the day.

How jellyfish breed

Jellyfish reproduce by releasing tiny young forms, or larvae. These swim off and settle on the seabed, where they turn into small polyps. At this stage they resemble tiny see-through sea anemones, smaller than this o. Jellyfish polyps often spend winter in this form. In spring, each polyp form grows "buds," rather like a plant. Each bud develops into a very small, star-shaped version of the adult animal. This is released and drifts away into the plankton.

Largest

The biggest jellyfish is the Arctic form of the lion's mane jellyfish, *Cyanea capillata*. It can grow to 7.5 feet (2.3 m) across and may have hundreds of tentacles, dangling down over 130 feet (40 m)! !

A balancing act

Jellyfish have no proper eyes. But they have special sense organs which can detect light or dark, and which also tell them which way is up or down. These pinhead-size sense organs are spaced around the edge of the bell. The animal uses them to tell the difference between day and night, and also to change its swimming direction according to the position of the sun.

The moon jellyfish (aurelia) is one of the most common jellyfish, found in seas throughout the world.

The cnidarian sting

A jellyfish has thousands of microscopic stinging cells, nematocysts, all along its tentacles. The cell "fires" a barbed dart that carries either a sticky, gluelike substance or a poison (venom). Each stinging cell has a lid covering the dart. Near the lid is a tiny trigger. When a prey animal touches the trigger, the lid springs open and the dart shoots out. Each stinging cell can only be used once, after which it breaks down, is absorbed into the jellyfish's body and replaced by a new stinging cell.

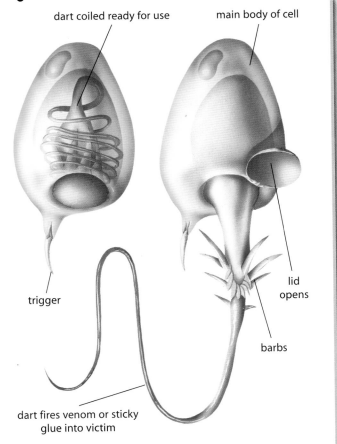

dart coiled ready for use

main body of cell

lid opens

trigger

barbs

dart fires venom or sticky glue into victim

Predators

Even though jellyfish have poisonous stings, some animals eat them. Jellyfish predators include various kinds of fish, squid, and especially sea turtles. However, because many jellyfish are pale or transparent this probably makes them harder for predators to see and catch.

Floating moon

The moon jellyfish, aurelia, grows to about 16 inches (40 cm) across and has a bluish tinge. It is very numerous and can be seen in bays and estuaries close to shore, as well as in the open ocean far from land. Moon jellyfish feed on small members of the plankton, such as tiny shrimps and other crustaceans, and also on fish. These get stuck on the stinging cells, the lower surface of the bell and the frilly oral arms, and are then transferred to the jellyfish's mouth.

Haliclystus is a stalked jellyfish that lives in sheltered rock pools, clinging to seaweed.

The moon jellyfish has a fringe of short stinging tentacles and four much longer feeding or oral tentacles. The pink horseshoe-shaped parts in the middle of its main body are its reproductive organs.

Stalked jellyfish

These unusual jellyfish (shown opposite and above left) live attached to rocks or seaweeds. They are small, growing only to the size of your little finger. They look like jellyfish that have turned upside down and become stuck by the top of the body, which is underneath. Stalked jellyfish can move to a different place by slowly cartwheeling along. They feed on tiny prey such as worms and copepods.

True jellyfish (Scyphozoans)
- about 200 species, all in the sea
- the main form or stage in the life cycle is the free-floating medusa
- the body is circular
- four-part symmetry, with four mouth or oral tentacles and four sets of reproductive organs
- sexes separate—a jellyfish is either female or male

More jellyfish

PROPER OR TRUE JELLYFISH ARE SHAPED LIKE FLOPPY BELLS OR UMBRELLAS. There are other cnidarians that look like true jellyfish, but are not, although they are close relatives. Some of these jellyfish-like cnidarians have bodies with different shapes, such as boxes or balls. Others, like the man-o'-war, look like a single animal, but each body is really lots of cnidarians all linked together and living as one. These are called colonial cnidarians.

Box jellies such as the sea wasps (above) have more angular, flat-sided bodies than true jellyfish.

In true or proper jellyfish, the body is rounded and shaped like an umbrella, and consists of a single cnidarian animal. There are several kinds of similar creatures which are often called jellyfish, but they are not true jellyfish. However they are still cnidarians, and so close relatives of jellyfish.

Box jellyfish
These jellyfish take their name from the shape of the body. This is not rounded, but box-like, with flat, square sides. Box jellyfish are found only in warm, tropical seas. They have thin, trailing, stinging tentacles, and they feed on small shrimps, fish and other animals floating and swimming in the plankton. The stings of some box jellies are especially powerful and can cause great pain to a person. Also, box

The man-o'-war (left) is a cnidarian—or rather, lots of them. It is very different from true umbrella-shaped jellyfish (right and below). It is a floating group of cnidarian polyps known as siphonophores.

jellyfish sometimes gather together in huge swarms, as they drift through the sea. If they are swept inshore by winds and currents, these box jelly swarms can be very dangerous to people swimming and wading. Swimmers trapped in a swarm of these cnidarians have been stung to death.

Even when box jellies are stranded on the shore and dead, their tentacles can still produce very painful stings. In some parts of Australia, box jellyfish are a particular hazard and beaches may be closed if a swarm drifts near.

Floating colonies
Some kinds of cnidarian live in floating colonies. From a distance, they look like a single animal—usually like a jellyfish. But they are really dozens or hundreds of creatures, polyps, all living together. These jellyfish-like colonies of polyps are known as siphonophores. They usually float at the surface of the ocean, rather than drifting or swimming below the surface, like true jellyfish.

Plastic!

The peculiar dried-out bodies of the by-the-wind sailor are sometimes found on the beach, after strong winds. Only the skeleton of the disk-shaped float and triangular sail remain. They look and feel like thin plastic.

Floating hotel

One of the best-known siphonophores, or colonial cnidarians, is the man-o'-war. It is also called the sea bluebottle. It consists of about 100–200 individual polyps, of different shapes and sizes, who all depend on each other.

The bluish-purple, gas-filled, balloon-like float at the top of the colony is one large individual polyp. It catches the breeze, like a sailing ship, to move the colony along. This float polyp buoys up the whole colony of other polyps beneath.

For the good of the group

Each type of polyp in the man-o'-war is specialized to do a different job for the whole colony. Stinging polyps each have a single, very long tentacle trailing as far as 100 feet (30 m) down into the sea. The tentacles stick to and sting prey such as fish, squid, and shrimps. The venom is very strong and can seriously hurt a person. The paralyzed victim is then passed to the feeding polyps. These eat and digest the meal and share the nourishment through the whole colony. Another group of polyps do the job of reproduction, releasing eggs and sperm.

Natural sailboat

The by-the-wind sailor or velella, is another remarkable colony of cnidarians. Like the man-o'-war, it is a colony of polyps, acting together almost as a single animal. It too has a purplish gas-filled float, but above this is a hard skeleton which acts as a mast to support a thin sail. The sail catches the wind and moves the colony along. Short tentacles in rings beneath the float catch small items of food. By-the-wind-sailors grow as big as your hand and live in huge swarms, especially in the North Atlantic.

The innocent-looking box jellyfish (above) can inflict extremely painful stings. It is known as the southern sea wasp, or jimble and is common in Australian waters.

This massive pink jellyfish floats in the warm waters of the Pacific Ocean, near the Philippines. It looks dangerous but its venom is not harmful to humans.

JELLYFISH-LIKE CNIDARIANS

Colonial jellyfish (Siphonophores)
- members of the hydroid group (see next page)
- body looks like a single creature but is made of many individual cnidarian animals or polyps
- some polyps sting and kill prey
- some digest prey
- some act as floats
- some carry out reproduction

Box jellyfish (Cubomedusans)
- resemble true jellyfish but have a more angular, box-shaped body
- have four single or branched tentacles
- extremely strong venom
- include sea wasps

Hydroids

THE HYDROIDS ARE CNIDARIANS THAT MAINLY RESEMBLE SEA ANEMONES. Each animal, or polyp, has a stalk-shaped body and a flowerlike ring of tentacles. However, some hydroids live as colonies of polyps, almost like a single, large "superanimal." Many of these colonies branch and spread over any solid surface. The man-o'-war and the by-the-wind sailor (pages 28–29) are also hydroids. However, they are unusual, since they are floating rather than fixed, and they resemble jellyfish.

The hydroid obelia grows in many branched groups. The individual animals or polyps are joined by their stalks.

The typical hydroid is a colony of small polyps, each less than about 0.2 inch (5 mm) tall, all connected and growing together. They attach to and spread over a rock, a frond of seaweed, or even the shell of a larger animal. Such hydroids are often known as sea firs. They are most common on sheltered, rocky seashores. At a glance, they look very much like moss animals or bryozoans (page 16). But the tentacles of individual hydroid polyps are not covered with tiny hairs or cilia.

Mini sea trees
Some of the best-known colonial hydroids are obelias. Several different kinds or species of obelia live along the coasts of the Atlantic Ocean and Mediterranean Sea. Some grow to more than a foot (30 cm) in height and have zigzag stalks. Others have branching stems and look like miniature trees growing on the underwater rocks.

Two types of polyp
There are two different kinds of polyp in each obelia colony. The feeding polyps live inside hard, protective cups. They stretch out from these when active. The polyp uses its stinging tentacles in the normal cnidarian way to catch tiny animals from the water. Because the polyps are all connected together at their stalks or bases, food can easily pass around the colony.

The other kind of polyp is for reproduction. It is flask-shaped and has no tentacles. Tiny medusas, like miniature jellyfish, grow inside each reproductive polyp and are released to

Like corals, hydroids form colorful colonies on reef rocks in tropical and subtropical seas. Some grow over and around sponges and moss animals, forming crusty coverings with all creatures crammed together.

In fresh water

In almost any pond or slow stream, on stones and among the leaves of water plants, live small green or pale brown animals that look like miniature sea anemones. These are hydras. They are not anemones, but hydroids that live in fresh rather than sea water. A hydra feeds in the typical cnidarian way, using its tentacles to catch tiny animals such as water fleas. It can grow buds on its stalk that turn into miniature versions of itself. These eventually separate from their parent and become new individual hydras. This type of reproduction is called asexual or vegetative, because it resembles the way that vegetables and other plants produce buds. Hydras can also reproduce in the usual animal way.

swim away in the sea. The medusas produce eggs and sperm, which float in the water. An egg and sperm join to form a tiny larva, which floats in the plankton and then settles and changes into a single polyp. This produces smaller versions of itself attached to its body, like plant buds. In this way the single polyp soon develops into a hydroid colony, and so the life cycle is complete.

Sea firs grow like tiny fir trees and ferns on rocks along the shore below the low-tide line. The branches of the colony bear feeding polyps with their stinging tentacles. Larger sea firs, known as sea ferns and sea hairs, are dried for flower decoration.

More! More!

The fresh water hydroid called hydra has amazing powers of recovery and regeneration. If it is sliced in two, each half can grow into a complete animal, regenerating all of its missing body parts. This helps when a piece of a hydra is nipped off by another animal such as a small fish. Hydras have even been turned inside out, yet they still recover and repair their bodies.

Inside a hydroid

Most ponds and streams are home to hundreds of the tiny hydroids called hydras. Each has a stalk like body with new individuals branching and growing from it, like buds from a plant stem. At the top is a circle of six or eight tentacles around the mouth.

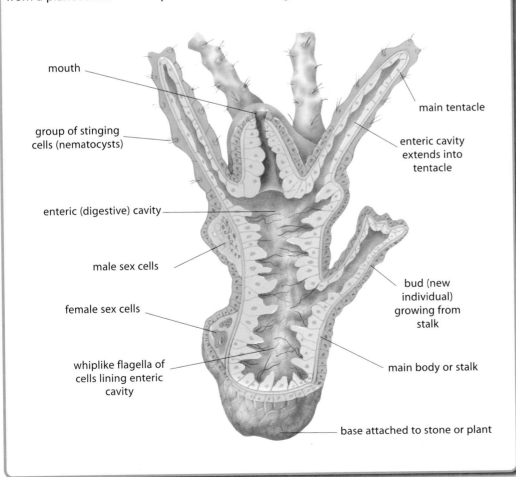

- mouth
- group of stinging cells (nematocysts)
- enteric (digestive) cavity
- male sex cells
- female sex cells
- whiplike flagella of cells lining enteric cavity
- main tentacle
- enteric cavity extends into tentacle
- bud (new individual) growing from stalk
- main body or stalk
- base attached to stone or plant

Fire corals

These colonial hydroids resemble true corals (page 36). Each individual, or polyp, has a hard, chalky casing or skeleton and a ring of stinging tentacles to catch prey. Fire corals can inflict painful, hot-feeling stings on humans. This is how they got their common name. The fire coral known as millepora can resist pounding by waves and often forms the highest parts of coral reefs. Millepora grows in various colours, from white and pink to yellow and orange. It is known as elk's-horn coral due to its antler-like shape.

HYDROIDS (Hydrozoa)

- most are marine, living in the sea
- a few, like hydra, live in fresh water
- most live together in colonies, with connections for passing nutrients among themselves
- some, like hydras, live as individuals
- some colonies, like the man-o'-war, float at the surface of the sea (page 28)
- some, like obelias, live in stalked colonies
- many have powerful stings
- includes the fire corals

Sea anemones

SEA ANEMONES AND CORALS ARE TOGETHER CALLED ANTHOZOANS, OR "FLOWERLIKE ANIMALS." They form the largest group of cnidarians, with some 6,000 species. Most of these are different kinds of coral, shown on the following pages. More familiar to many people are the sea anemones. These are mostly quite large (for cnidarians). They live singly, rather than in colonies, along coasts and in shallow water. They attach themselves to rocks, plants, shells or other firm surfaces, and usually stay put. Yet sea anemones can move around, by shuffling or gliding on the base of the stalk. If they are in a hurry, they may cartwheel or somersault. A few can even swim, by waving their tentacles or bending their bodies. But usually the only movements we notice are when the anemone's tentacles gentle sway in the water—or when they sting and grab their prey.

The dahlia anemone's short, squat stalk is covered with wartlike lumps. Bits of gravel, shells, and weed stick to these lumps. When the tide goes out and the anemone draws in its tentacles, its stalk is camouflaged as a small pebble.

The orange ball anemone has bright, rounded, yellow-orange tips to its pale blue, see-through tentacles.

In deeper water

Lower down the shore is the snakelocks anemone. It has as many as 200 long, coiling tentacles, usually bright green in color. This type cannot stand being out of water at low tide for as long as the beadlet anemones. The dahlia anemone is another common type, named after the dahlia flower. It is patterned in pink,

Sea anemones are cnidarians but they have no medusa—the floating, jellyfish-like stage. Anemones live their entire lives as polyps. They resemble the hydroids shown on the previous page, but most anemones are larger and more heavily built, and they live alone rather than in groups. The stalk is fatter, and the tentacles around the central mouth are shorter and sturdier. Also, many sea anemones are brightly colored in shades of red, yellow, pink, brown, blue, and green. These colors may be warnings to other animals that the anemone is not good to eat and that it can sting with its tentacles.

Multicolored beadlets

One of the most common types is the beadlet anemone. It lives on rocks between the low-and high-tide marks, and in rock pools. It is usually bright red, but some beadlet anemones are brown, orange, or green.

Largest

The biggest sea anemone is a type of discoma. It can reach 2 feet (60 cm) across. It lives among corals on the Great Barrier Reef in Australia.

!

white, and red. The plumose anemone (page 35) has a much longer stalk than the snakelocks or dahlia anemones. It grows up to 20 inches (50 cm) tall and has 200 fluffy-looking tentacles.

Feeding and food

Most sea anemones feed by trapping small fish, shrimps, and similar animals in their tentacles. The stinging cells or nematocysts on the tentacles (shown on page 27) kill or paralyze the prey. Sea anemones have no eyes, so they cannot see a victim coming. But they can detect touch, and they shoot out their poison stings when their tentacles make contact. They can also detect substances released by the body of any animal they catch and injure. This makes more and more tentacles arch over, to help secure and disable the prey. The nematocyst barbed darts of most common anemones are not large or strong enough to pass into human skin.

Jewel anemones have pale knobbed tentacles. But their bright, shiny bodies glisten like gem stones in the water.

The orange sea anemone has strong, sturdy tentacles around its central mouth.

An anemone's tentacles are usually arranged in widening rings, based on the number six or eight.

Old!

Some sea anemones have lived for as long as people. They have survived in large seawater tanks or marine aquaria, protected and well fed, and with clean unpolluted water, for 70 years or more.

Big mouth

The mouth of an anemone lies at the centre of its tentacles. It is wide and can stretch even wider, so an anemone is able to swallow prey almost as big as itself! The meal goes into the large stomach cavity in the stalk, where it is slowly dissolved and

digested. Any leftovers are pushed back out later, through the way they came in.

Anemone enemy

Few animals feed on sea anemones because of the stinging tentacles and their horrible-tasting, jelly-like flesh. But creatures called sea slugs (page 56) do not seem to mind. They swallow the stinging cells and use the venom to make their own bodies taste terrible.

Sea anemones make more of their kind in the same way as hydras, by budding off new individuals from their bodies. Or they can produce eggs and sperm in the usual animal way. A sperm and egg join and become a swimming young form, or larva. This seeks out a suitable place and settles down to grow into a small new anemone.

Fighting anemones

Sea anemones may not look aggressive. But they try to get the best place in the rock pool. They push and shove against each other in slow-motion trials of strength. They may even try to tip rivals off the rocks into the mud or sand.

Anemones and corals (Anthozoans)
- about 6,000 species, all living in the sea (page 25)
- stalklike body attached at the base, with tentacles above (polyp form only)
- circular body with tentacles, sex organs, and other parts based on the numbers six or eight

Anemones and partners

SEA ANEMONES ARE SIMPLE CREATURES. They have no proper brain, only a few nerves to control the movements of their tentacles and stalk. They can only do the simplest actions, such as detecting and eating prey, and gliding along the rocks to a new place. Yet anemones have many "friends" on the seashore. They live in partnerships with other creatures such as fish, shrimps, crabs, and worms. These other creatures have thick shells or coatings of body mucus (slime) that protect them from the anemone's stings. Usually, both partners benefit from being together. For example, the anemone feeds on leftovers from the food of its fish friend, while the fish is safe hiding in the anemone's tentacles. This type of helpful partnership in nature is called symbiosis.

Shrimps are at home among anemones.

Clownfish and their anemone partners are popular in tropical saltwater aquaria. The fish's thick coating of slime protects it against the anemone's stings.

Symbiosis happens between many types of creatures, such as cleaner fish and bigger fish, and oxpecker birds and cattle. But it is especially common among sea anemones. It has probably evolved, or developed gradually, over millions of years of evolution.

Tolerant partners

As a result, the anemone has become used to the presence of another creature in its tentacles. It can detect this partner by the chemical substances that the partner gives off, and so rarely tries to sting it. At the same time, the partner has evolved some kind of protection against the anemone's stings, and is hardly ever hurt.

Types of partners

Clown or anemone fish, usually striped orange and white, form symbiotic partnerships with anemones. So do various kinds of banded shrimps, and crabs. Some hermit crabs allow calliactis sea anemones to live on the large sea snail shell that the crab uses as a mobile home. The anemone gets carried around and probably has more chance of finding prey. Meanwhile the crab is protected by its stinging partner. When one catches food, the other can share the

The sunstar above is not an anemone friend, but a victim. The large dahlia anemone is slowly pulling the sunstar, a type of starfish, into its mouth.

This tiny porcelain crab is safe among the tentacles of an anemone. It scavenges small bits of food and keeps the anemone clean.

Plumose anemone

This type of sea anemone can stretch itself tall and thin, or pull down its stalk or column to be shorter and fatter. The anemone pictured here is halfway between these two positions. Plumose anemones occur in many colors, from almost perfect white through cream, yellow, and brown to orange and red. They live in seashore pools, especially under rocky overhangs, and on and under breakwaters, piers, and jetties. They can catch larger prey, but they mainly feed on tiny bits of floating food filtered from the water by the feathery tentacles.

fine stinging tentacles

mouth

group (plume) of tentacles

stalk or column

slimy covering to stalk

muscle strands in stalk

adhesive (sticky) base

leftover bits and pieces. The calliactis anemone is sometimes called the parasitic anemone. But it is not really a parasite, since it rarely does the hermit crab any harm. The two are usually equal partners, so a better name would be the symbiotic anemone.

More partnerships

Other crabs may grab anemones in their pincers, like underwater flaming torches. The crab waves the anemone, to scare away enemies or to try and sting possible prey. Again, both crab and anemone benefit from the relationship.

Corals

THERE ARE MORE THAN 5,000 DIFFERENT KINDS OF CORAL. A coral animal or polyp is usually small, less than one centimetre tall, and looks like a miniature sea anemone. In fact, corals are very close cousins of anemones (page 33). Most types are found in tropical seas. Some coral polyps live singly, as individual animals. But most live with others of their kind, linked or connected into huge groups or colonies. Some of them build stony protective casings around themselves. This is how the rocks of a coral reef gradually build up, as shown on the following pages. Sea fans are coral polyps that make tough, horny skeletons which branch into a tree or fanlike shape. The protective cases of soft corals are more like spongy, rubbery jelly.

Red-tipped soft corals

The reef rocks made by coral polyps have many holes, crevices, caves, and overhangs. These are ideal places for larger animals to hide.

Coral animals are cnidarians and they catch their prey with sticky or stinging tentacles, like sea anemones and jellyfish. But, unlike jellyfish, corals do not have a medusa or floating stage in their lives. Like anemones, all coral animals are polyps. In a coral colony, each polyp is connected to its neighbor by living tissue, usually at its base. So the whole colony is joined, almost like one giant multi-animal. Each polyp can catch its own tiny victims, but the food may then be shared among the nearby members of the colony. This is

This bright coral reef scene shows various kinds of coral, their relatives the anemones, and sponges and fish such as seahorses and wrasses. By day the coral polyps are mostly drawn into their protective cases.

At breeding time, coral animals release clouds of eggs and sperm that drift away in the seawater.

important because in some corals, certain polyps in the colony cannot feed for themselves. Instead, they help to protect or support the colony, by building cases or outer skeletons.

Hiding from enemies

In stony corals, each polyp makes a cup-shaped skeleton beneath itself, from rock minerals that it takes out of the sea water. When danger threatens such as a polyp-eating fish or starfish, the polyp withdraws its tentacles and retreats into this protective cup. It emerges again later when the danger is past.

How corals eat

A feeding polyp spreads its little tentacles in the sea water. It relies on currents and waves to bring fresh supplies of food, usually with each tide. It catches tiny protists and animals as they drift past. These stick to the tentacles and are then passed to the mouth at the centre, just as in the larger anemones. Many coral polyps come out to feed only during the night.

Inside a coral polyp

A coral animal is like a miniature sea anemone. Its stalk is almost all stomach or digestive cavity. Folds of flesh called mesenteries stick into the cavity, forming a larger surface area for absorbing digested nutrients.

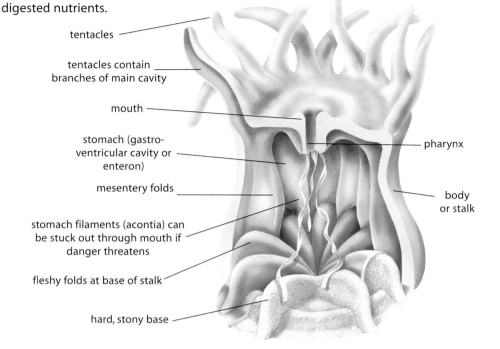

- tentacles
- tentacles contain branches of main cavity
- mouth
- stomach (gastro-ventricular cavity or enteron)
- mesentery folds
- stomach filaments (acontia) can be stuck out through mouth if danger threatens
- fleshy folds at base of stalk
- hard, stony base
- pharynx
- body or stalk

This is when the plankton of the sea rises nearer the surface. The polyps wave their shiny tentacles and make a patch of coral rock look like a glistening, multicolored, living carpet. By day, the polyps withdraw into their cases and the rock looks dead and bare.

Some soft corals form colourful, branching, finger-like structures that are tough and leathery.

Breeding

When the conditions are right, usually on a calm night when the moon is full, all the corals in one area release their eggs and sperm into the sea. These float near the surface in great clouds. Each sperm joins with, or fertilizes, an egg. The fertilized egg develops into a tiny coral larva that floats in the sea for a short time. Then it swims down to the seabed to find a resting place. The larva sticks itself firmly onto a rock, and grows into a tiny coral polyp, complete with a ring of tentacles. After several weeks, if the single original polyp survives, it has sprouted or budded several new polyps. These remain joined together. As their numbers increase and spread, they gradually form a new coral colony.

Types of coral
- stony or hard corals, usually colonial—some are reef-builders
- soft corals
- gorgonian corals, also called sea fans and sea whips (types of soft coral)

Coral reefs

A CORAL REEF IS A HUGE LUMP OF ROCK MADE BY MILLIONS OF TINY ANIMALS—coral polyps, as shown on the previous page. Reef-building coral polyps make small protective cases, or skeletons, for their soft bodies from chalky minerals they take out of sea water. These cases are shaped like cups, disks or boxes. Each group or colony of coral polyps grows and spreads in its own pattern or shape, as the older polyps form "buds" that grow into new ones. As the older polyp animals die, they leave their empty, stony cases. But more polyps grow above and beside them. In this way, over years and centuries, thousands of rock-hard polyp cases build up to form the stony, strange and beautiful shapes of the coral reef.

Corals are usually named after the shapes formed by their thousands of empty skeletons. These build up in patterns according to how the polyps grow and reproduce. The bulges and wrinkles of brain coral look like a human brain!

Gorgonian corals form delicate, lacy, fernlike shapes (left). Finger coral looks like a human hand (below left). There are many different shapes of mushroom corals (below).

Reef-building coral polyps make the hardest, strongest most massive structures formed by any animals. But they are delicate little creatures. They can only thrive in warm, clear, clean, shallow, sunlit seawater. This is partly because each polyp contains, inside its body, hundreds of microscopic living things called dinoflagellates. These are protists (page 15) and they need sunlight to grow. They live in partnership with the coral polyps. The polyp provides shelter, minerals and raw materials for its protists. In return the protists use the sun's light energy to make food for themselves, which they share with their polyp. So coral polyps need sunlight to survive. This type of helpful partnership is known as symbiosis (page 34).

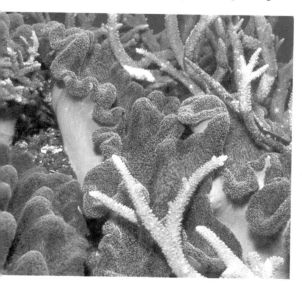

Corals grow in all colors of the rainbow, like this blue coral from the Caribbean.

Largest

The Great Barrier Reef stretches more than 900 miles (1,500 km) along the coast of Queensland, northeast Australia. It has taken millions of years to reach this size. The Great Barrier Reef is by far the largest structure built by living things (including us!). Many of its 3,000 smaller reefs are now marine parks, where the coral environments are protected.

(!)

Diverse reefs

Coral reefs are some of the richest wildlife habitats on Earth. The front of the reef slopes down steeply into the sea, and this is where the wave action is fiercest, especially during storms. But behind the reef ridge or crest, there is usually a shallower, calmer area, protected from the biggest ocean waves. This is the reef flat, or lagoon. The crevices and caves in the reef rocks provide homes for a multitude of fish, shellfish, worms, crabs, shrimp and other animals, and also for plants such as seaweeds.

Rich!

Coral reefs are second only to tropical rain forests in the richness and diversity of their wildlife. They are home to half a million different kinds of animal—including one third (more than 7,000) of all fish species.

Problems on the reef

Coral animals are quickly affected by any changes to their surroundings. Pollution in the sea, such as oil spills from ships, kills the coral polyps and the many animals that eat them. Another threat is mud and silt from worn-out farm fields and cut-down forests far inland. This is washed into rivers and carried to the sea. The mud makes the water cloudy, so sunlight cannot reach the plantlike protists on which the coral polyps depend. Also, in many parts of the world, the rock-hard coral shapes and patterns are cut away by people, and sold to tourists. This trade is destroying some reefs at an alarming rate.

The reef-eating starfish

More natural enemies of coral, especially in the Indian and Pacific Oceans, are crown-of-thorns starfish. These large, spiky predators eat polyps. One crown-of-thorns can destroy 50 square feet (4.6 sq m) of coral in one year. In some reefs, these starfish have increased hugely in numbers—either as part of a natural cycle, or due to changes made by people.

A colony of soft coral polyps extend their frilly red-tinged tentacles to grasp bits of food.

Coral reefs grow only in shallow tropical or subtropical seas, where the average water temperature is more than about 68°F (20°C).

WORMS, SNAILS, & STARFISH

Many long, thin, soft, slimy, wriggly creatures are called worms. They are not very appealing to most people. Yet worms are some of the most varied and important members of the animal kingdom. There are at least 20 major groups of worm, ranging from common earthworms that keep the soil fertile, to tiny parasitic worms that cause horrible diseases, to giant tubeworms as thick as your arm living in pitch blackness at the bottom of the sea.

The mollusk group is not well known to many people. Yet it is second only to insects, in the number of different species. Most mollusks have a hard protective shell around the soft body. The group includes limpets and whelks on the seashore, snails in gardens, and water snails in ponds. Some mollusks are eaten as food, such as oysters, mussels, scallops, and clams. A few, like cone shells, are deadly poisonous. And one of the largest of all animals, the giant squid of the oceans depths, is a mollusk.

Yet another enormous group of sea-dwelling animals is the echinoderms, meaning "spiny-skinned." Starfish, urchins, brittlestars, featherstars, and sea lilies are all echinoderms. One of the strangest is the sea cucumber. It looks like an animated sausage eating slimy ooze on the sea bed. If it is attacked, it sicks up sticky threads from its stomach and squirts them out of its mouth!

Earthworms and leeches

THERE ARE AT LEAST 30 DIFFERENT GROUPS OF WORMLIKE CREATURES. The main group is the annelids or segmented worms, also called true worms. An annelid worm has a body divided into lots of similar ringlike sections called segments. There are 12,000 species of annelid worms, including familiar earthworms, lugworms and ragworms on the seashore, and leeches. Although these animals are amazingly numerous, we rarely see them because most worms live only in water or under the ground in damp mud, sand, or soil. This is because worms absorb oxygen through their thin, moist skin. If the skin dries out, the worm dies. Worms are also soft, slow-moving and vulnerable, so they gain some protection from living in tubes and tunnels.

Most of these tropical fanworms (page 44) are hidden in purple-tinged tubes. Two have spread their spiral yellow feeding tentacles.

Earthworms spend nearly all their lives underground, burrowing in the soil. They push aside some earth and swallow the rest. The earth passes through the worm's gut and nutritious bits like pieces of dead leaves are digested. The remains pass out of the worm's rear end as fine-grained droppings. These are left as curly worm casts at the surface. Millions of earthworms keep soil fertile. They break down and recycle plant and animal remains. Their burrows allow air and moisture into the soil, for plant roots to use, and to help water drain away.

Mating in the grass

An earthworm has no obvious head. The front or mouth end is slightly more pointed than the rear end, and it has simple detectors that can distinguish between light and dark, but which cannot form an image like proper eyes. One obvious feature of the earthworm is

Biggest

The world's largest earthworms are giant Gippsland earthworms of South Africa. Most are over 3 feet (90 cm) long. Some grow to more than 20 feet (6.5 m) long.

(!)

a part called the saddle or clitellum, where several segments seem to be enlarged and fused together. When two worms meet to mate, they put their saddles next to each other. Each earthworm is an hermaphrodite—it has both male and female parts. So each passes sperm to the other, to fertilize its eggs. Each then goes on to form a parcel or cocoon of eggs around the saddle. The cocoon slips off and is left in the soil, and baby worms hatch from it.

Water worms

A cousin of the earthworm that lives in fresh water is the bright red tubifex or sludge worm. It is sometimes called the bloodworm because of its color. The bright red is due to a pigment (colored substance) that is specialized to take in oxygen from the water, through the skin

Two earthworms partly emerge from their tunnels on a damp night, to mate. They lay side by side and exchange sperm.

A spiral fanworm's feathery tentacles are covered with sticky mucus, which traps tiny bits of food and flows slowly into its mouth.

Delicious worms

Worms have few defenses against predators, except their underground lifestyle and ability to breed in great numbers. Birds such as thrushes and blackbirds depend on plentiful supplies of worms for themselves and their chicks. Some birds even trample on the soil to mimic the patter of raindrops, which brings the worms to the surface.

into the worm's body. (Our own blood is red because of a similar substance.) In the sludge worm it is so plentiful that this worm can live in stagnant water that is very low in oxygen. Hundreds of sludge worms build tubes of sticky mucus in the mud and wave their tails in the water to obtain oxygen.

The bloodsuckers

Leeches are like flattened types of worms. They have muscular bodies which can shorten or lengthen, and a sucker at each end. Some leeches prey on smaller worms, insect grubs, and similar creatures. Others are parasites, sucking the blood of fish or other animals,

The horse leech grows to 30 cm long. It swallows tiny animals whole.

including people. The hungry leech clamps itself onto the animal as it passes, perhaps while coming to water to drink. It then rubs into the skin with three sets of tiny teeth and gorges itself, sucking in five times its own weight of blood and fluids. It can then last for weeks before another meal.

A leech moves by "looping." It stretches forward while anchored by its back sucker, and sticks down the front one. Then it detaches the rear sucker, shortens its body, attaches the rear sucker again, and so on.

Sludge worms can survive in stagnant ponds and ditches.

ANNELID WORMS
• about 12,000 species
• tube-shaped soft body
• divided into segments

Three main subgroups:

Earthworms
• 3,000 species
• most live in soil or fresh water
• hermaphrodite (each individual is both male and female)
• includes most earthworms, also sludge worms (bloodworms)

Leeches
• 500 species
• many are leaf-shaped
• mostly freshwater, some in the sea or on land
• some are bloodsuckers
• hermaphrodite

Bristleworms
Described on page 44

Bristleworms

BRISTLEWORMS ARE NAMED FROM THE STIFF BRISTLE-LIKE HAIRS, known as chaetae, sticking out all over their bodies. More than half of the types of segmented worms (page 42) belong to the bristleworm group, also called polychaetes. In some types the bristles are attached to paddle-like flaps. Bristleworms live mainly in the sea, and use these flaps as oars, to paddle over the bottom or dig into sand and mud. Some kinds live inside tubes.

Compared to earthworms, most bristleworms have an obvious head and tail end. The head usually has tentacles, which may look like thin fingers, or be arranged as a frilly ring or a feathery crown. Some types of bristleworms also have simple types of eyes that can pick out shapes. There may be a pair of long threadlike feelers at the tail end.

Bristleworms on the shore include ragworms and lugworms. Ragworms often live in burrows lined with their own hardened mucus (slime), in the

At the bottom of the sea, giant white tubeworms live near cracks or vents that pour out scalding, sulfur-rich water. They are 10 feet (3 m) long and as thick as your arm. They take in the sulfur chemicals, and bacteria in their bodies and use the chemicals to make food, which they share with the worm.

Ragworm

muddy silt that collects at the bottom of a rock pool. When the tide is out, the ragworm stays hidden. When the tide comes in, the ragworm emerges from its burrow to feed on the surface of the mud. It can wriggle like a snake, or swim by rowing with its paddle-like flaps.

Ragworms eat a range of food, from dead animals and small creatures like shrimps to seaweeds. Their strong jaws can easily bite chunks of flesh from a carcass—and even draw blood through human skin. They can also shed their slimy body covering and eat it, to take in the microbes in the slime.

Fan-feeders

The main body of a fanworm stays hidden inside a protective tube set into the sea bed, which it builds from mud or sand particles glued together with its own slimy mucus. Fanworms are named for their stiff, feathery feeding tentacles, which they stick out from the top of the tube and spread out like a fan. One of the most beautiful fanworms is the peacock worm. Its tube may be 10 inches

Feeding fanworms

(25 cm) long. When safe, it extends the tentacles like the tail of a peacock bird, and waves them in the water. The tentacles are coated with a thin layer of sticky mucus that catches any bits of food floating past. They also work as gills for breathing. If a fish or other predator swims nearby, the peacock worm whisks in its tentacles and pulls itself down into the safety of its tube. Sometimes peacock worms and other fanworms live in groups, looking like a carpet of flowers. When danger appears, they are gone in a flash, leaving the seabed looking bare and lifeless.

Hard tubes

Some bristleworms build much tougher, more rigid tubes from chalky minerals, either in the sand or on rocks. The hard, white, wiggly tubes on seashore weeds and boulders belong to bristleworms called keelworms. When the tide is in, the keelworm pushes its tiny crown of feeding tentacles from the end of the tube, to gather food.

Lugworms hide under the sand in U-shaped burrows (right). The worm wriggles to make water flow through its burrow, so it can breathe. The tubes of peacock worms partly stick up from the seabed (below).

The mouse worm

The sea mouse is not a mouse at all, but a type of bristleworm. It grows about 8 inches (20 cm) long. Its plump, humped body is covered with gray-brown, hairy flaps, almost like the fur of a real mouse. Sea mice live mainly on muddy or sandy seabeds, in the Atlantic Ocean and Mediterranean Sea.

Sand casts

Little mounds of sand or mud on the shore are the casts of lugworms. These worms are 6-8 inches (15–20 cm) long, soft, and thicker at the front end. They feed like earthworms, by eating the sand or mud, digesting any nutrients, and then passing out the remains as the familiar worm cast.

Continued from page 43:

Bristleworms
- 8,500 species
- most live in the sea
- body has bristles or flaps
- sexes separate (male or female)
- includes lugworms, ragworms, fanworms, peacock worms, sea mice, scaleworms, catworms

Flatworms

FLATWORMS ARE THE SIMPLEST OF ALL WORMS. They are indeed flat and smooth, resembling leaves or ribbons. They lack the ringlike body sections or segments of annelid worms (page 42). There are more than 13,000 species of flatworms. But they are less familiar than earthworms, because most are too small to see easily, while others live in water, and some are parasites inside other animals. Most free-living flatworms are found in the sea, among weeds, or the pebbles on the shore. Some live in fresh water and a few in damp soil.

Large tropical flatworms crawl through dead leaves in rain forests.

Flatworms that can move around freely, rather than being parasites inside animals, are called turbellarians. The freshwater turbellarians, or planarians, are streamlined animals, with an obvious head and tail end. Some species even have several small eyes around the front end, while others have two larger eyes on top of the head. Some also have a pair of feelers on the head, to help them feel objects and detect scents as they move about.

Flatworms in the sea are larger and more varied than the freshwater species. Some are brightly patterned or colored.

The underside of a flatworm is covered in tiny hairs, cilia, which wave smoothly to and fro to glide the worm along. Flatworms can also move by rippling their muscular undersides. Many feed on smaller animals, or on the dead and decaying bodies of other creatures. When some flatworms find their food, they push part of the gut out from the body (opposite), then slowly suck the food and the gut inside again.

Shrink!

Some flatworms can reproduce by splitting themselves into two. Each half then regrows the missing portion and two separate flatworms result. They can also feed on themselves if food is in short supply, absorbing their own bodies and gradually shrinking in the process.

Flatworms of pond and stream

Planarians are common in ponds and streams all around the world. But they hide among pebbles and weeds by day, and they are mostly only fingernail-sized or smaller, so they are seldom noticed. They are active mainly at night. In the dark water, they glide smoothly along the surfaces of

Many freshwater planarians have an obvious head end with eyes.

plants, or slither across submerged logs and stones. Sometimes they even slip upside down along the underside of the water's surface, feeding on tiny creatures trapped by the surface film.

Different types of these free-living flatworms are suited to particular freshwater habitats. The crenobia planarian lives in cold upland streams or springs. It has earlike feelers and a pair of large eyes. The polycelis planarian is also found in running streams, but it has many tiny eyes around the edges of its head. The dugesia planarian has a triangular head with two large eyes on the top. It lives in ponds and streams, but it cannot cope so well with fast currents as the other two species.

How flatworms breed

Most flatworms are hermaphrodites. This means each has both male and female sex organs. So any two flatworms can come together and mate, each passing on sperm to the other. Each of the pair then goes on to develop and lay its eggs.

The eggs are sticky when first laid, and are attached beneath stones or underwater logs. After a few weeks, the eggs hatch out into tiny baby flatworms that gradually grow into adults. This is quite different to parasitic flatworms (page 48), where the young forms or larvae often differ in shape from the adults.

Inside a flatworm

Flatworms have very simple bodies. On the outside is a layer of cells called the epidermis. On the inside there is another layer of cells, the endodermis, arranged in tubes to form the intestine (gut or digestive tract). The only way in and out of the intestine is the mouth, which may be at the head end, the tail end, or part way along the underside. In between the epidermis and the intestine are masses of cells called the parenchyma. These make up the flatworm's muscles, glands, nerves, and reproductive organs.

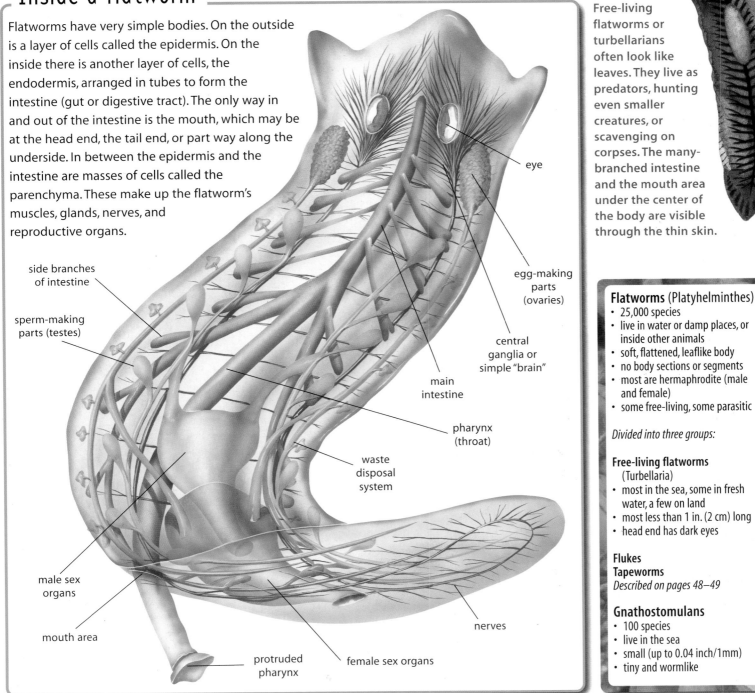

side branches of intestine

sperm-making parts (testes)

male sex organs

mouth area

protruded pharynx

female sex organs

nerves

waste disposal system

pharynx (throat)

main intestine

central ganglia or simple "brain"

egg-making parts (ovaries)

eye

Free-living flatworms or turbellarians often look like leaves. They live as predators, hunting even smaller creatures, or scavenging on corpses. The many-branched intestine and the mouth area under the center of the body are visible through the thin skin.

Flatworms (Platyhelminthes)
- 25,000 species
- live in water or damp places, or inside other animals
- soft, flattened, leaflike body
- no body sections or segments
- most are hermaphrodite (male and female)
- some free-living, some parasitic

Divided into three groups:

Free-living flatworms
(Turbellaria)
- most in the sea, some in fresh water, a few on land
- most less than 1 in. (2 cm) long
- head end has dark eyes

Flukes
Tapeworms
Described on pages 48–49

Gnathostomulans
- 100 species
- live in the sea
- small (up to 0.04 inch/1mm)
- tiny and wormlike

Flukes and tapeworms

FLUKES AND TAPEWORMS ARE FLATWORMS (page 46) that mostly live as parasites, on or inside other animals and people. Many flukes can live both inside their host—in its intestine, liver, or heart—and on or under its skin, gripping by special leechlike suckers. Tapeworms live right inside their host's gut, for months at a time. The host is not always aware of the worm's presence, but it may feel ill since the worm steals its nutrition or damages its body parts. Tapeworms tend to live in larger mammals. Flukes live in nearly every kind of animal, from insects and crabs to fish, reptiles, birds, and mammals.

Most flukes are leaf-shaped and about an inch (2.5 cm) long, although some are more rounded, like other worms. At the front end, the adult fluke has a sucker which it uses to hang onto its host. There may be another sucker farther down its body, to give the fluke extra sticking power.

The outside of an adult fluke is covered with slimy mucus. This protects it from the host's body fluids and digestive juices, which would otherwise attack and kill it. The adult fluke feeds by sucking up the blood and other fluids from its host animal. One kind of fluke lives inside the bodies of frogs and toads. When the host returns to water to breed, the flukes release their

A tapeworm has a head called the scolex, with tiny hooks for clinging to the inside of the host's gut. The rest of its body grows steadily in baglike parts behind the head. These are not proper segments, but sacs containing sex organs with their eggs and sperm.

Long!
Tapeworms can grow very long. One kind found in whales may reach 66 feet (20 m) in length. Tapeworms have been a problem for people as long as there have been people. Ancient Egyptians suffered from these parasites.

eggs into the water as well. Then the tiny fluke larvae attach themselves to the frog's tadpoles, infecting the next generation of amphibians.

A complicated life
Many kinds of flukes have complicated life cycles. They live on or in different hosts at different stages of their lives. Some flukes even move from one host to another four times. Typically, a fluke would spend most of its adult life in the body of a large vertebrate animal such as a fish, reptile, bird or mammal. But it would transfer its eggs or larvae to the body of an invertebrate, such as a snail or a slug, when it breeds.

This fluke is less than 0.04 inch (1 mm) long. It lives in the blood of many animals.

Fluke diseases

Liver flukes infest the livers of sheep and cattle, and cause disease. As an adult, the liver fluke feeds on blood in the sheep's liver. Its eggs pass out with the sheep's droppings and lie in the pasture. They only develop further if they hatch near a water snail. When the young or larval fluke finds a snail, it burrows in and lives there for a while. Then it leaves the snail and attaches itself to plants at the water's edge. If a sheep eats a plant with one of these larvae on it, the sheep becomes infected and the fluke larva grows into an adult—and the cycle is complete. Sheep that graze in damp pasture near plenty of water snails are at risk of infection by flukes.

In East Asia, a type of liver fluke lives inside people and makes them ill. The host species is a water snail, followed by a freshwater fish of the carp family. If a person eats the infected fish, especially raw, he or she may become infected with this fluke.

Tropical disease flukes

Bilharzia or schistosomiasis is a terrible tropical disease caused by a blood fluke called schistosoma. These flukes live inside the veins near the host person's intestine or bladder. The eggs are released near the gut, and some pass out of the host's body with the feces. If these eggs get into water, they can infect the second host, a type of water snail. After living inside the snail and developing, the next stage of fluke larva escapes into the water. If these larvae end up on human skin, they burrow into the person and enter the blood.

The liver fluke is a flatworm that burrows into the livers of animals such as sheep.

Tapelike worms

Tapeworms get their name from the tape- or ribbon-like bodies of the adult worms. The body is flat and can be very long—30 feet (9 m) or more, looped back and forth several times inside the host's intestine. The adult is divided into units called proglottids. These are almost like a row of individual worms. They break away, pass out of the host, and release their eggs to infest new hosts.

Most tapeworms live as parasites inside the intestines of large carnivorous animals, including people. At the front end, the tapeworm secures itself to the gut wall of its host with hooks and suckers. The tapeworm has no mouth or gut of its own. It feeds by absorbing nutrients through all the surfaces of its body. It has plenty of food—all around it, provided by its host.

People badly affected by tapeworms become very thin, even though they eat normally. This is because the worms "steal" their food. One kind of human tapeworm has the pig as a second host. Another species infects cattle. If someone eats pork or beef infected with tapeworm larvae, he or she may become infected as the tapeworms are taken in and grow. In the past, the pork tapeworm was a common human parasite due to eating raw or under-cooked pork. Cooking or curing the meat kills any tapeworm eggs or larvae.

Flatworms continued from page 47:

Flukes (Trematoda)
· parasites, some causing diseases in animals and people
· most small, less than 2 inches (5 cm)
· leaf-shaped body

Tapeworms (Cestoda)
· parasites in animals and people
· long (30 feet (9 m) or more)
· ribbon-shaped
· tiny head with hooks
· no mouth or intestine
· egg bags look like segments

Life cycles of flukes and tapeworms

Many flukes infest two, three, or four hosts during the different stages in their lives. For example, certain kinds of flukes live inside a person, in the intestine, liver, or bladder. They produce tiny eggs, which pass out in the host person's urine or feces. Only if the eggs find their way into the correct type of snail, water flea or similar aquatic animal, do they develop into larvae. Then this host of the fluke larvae must be eaten by the right type of fish, for the next stage to happen. Finally a person eats the poorly cooked fish and takes in the fluke larvae, which mature into adults.

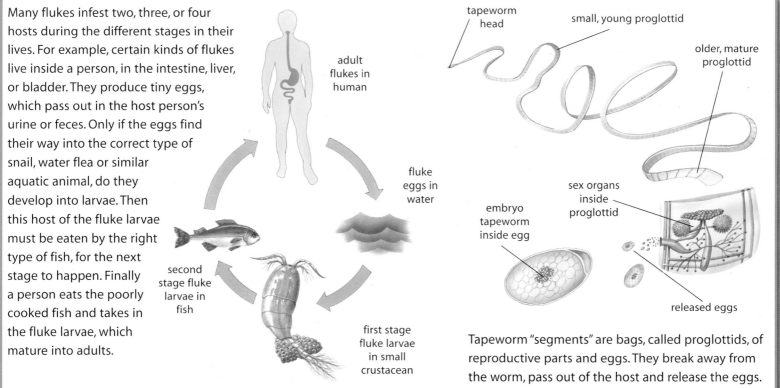

adult flukes in human

fluke eggs in water

second stage fluke larvae in fish

first stage fluke larvae in small crustacean

tapeworm head

small, young proglottid

older, mature proglottid

sex organs inside proglottid

embryo tapeworm inside egg

released eggs

Tapeworm "segments" are bags, called proglottids, of reproductive parts and eggs. They break away from the worm, pass out of the host and release the eggs.

Roundworms

ROUNDWORMS ARE FOUND ALMOST EVERYWHERE, IN VAST NUMBERS. Most are tiny and live in water or soil, so we rarely notice them. Others are parasites and cause disease and suffering. They include eelworms, hookworms, threadworms, filarial worms, and a host of other species. A typical roundworm has a long body that tapers toward each end, is round like a tube, and does not have sections or segments. Roundworms are also known as nematode worms.

The strongyloides roundworm is a parasite in sheep. It bores through the skin into the blood and ends up in the intestine.

About 20,000 different kinds of roundworms or nematodes have been discovered. But the true number is probably far higher—perhaps half a million. Because they are so plentiful, roundworms are very important in the balance of nature. By feeding on dead and decaying animals and plants, they help to break these down and return the goodness to the soil, recycling vital nutrients. Tiny roundworms living between grains of sand at the seaside feed on bacteria, and by doing so, help to keep the beaches clean!

Everywhere
Roundworms live in just about every habitat on the planet. There is a story that if everything on Earth were magically removed, except for the roundworms, you would still be able to make out most natural objects and places because of the roundworms left! Despite being so common, most are so small that we cannot see them. Most free-living (nonparasitic) roundworms are usually less than 0.04–0.08 inch (1–2 mm) long. A single spadeful of soil in the garden may contain half a million.

When we do notice roundworms, is when they are parasites in plants and animals, and cause enormous damage.

Some types of roundworms colonize plants and ruin crops. Certain kinds cause hard swellings known as galls. Others puncture plant cells and suck out the sap. Still others infest animals of all kinds. No creature is safe, even other worms. These tiny roundworms are eating their way into an earthworm.

Roundworms not only do damage themselves. They may also carry viruses that infect the host. A common plant parasite is the eelworm, which attacks the roots of several crops, notably potatoes, tomatoes, and sugar beet. A single potato plant may have 40,000 eelworms infesting its roots.

The dreaded hookworm
Hookworms are particularly harmful parasitic nematodes. They are among the most common causes of human illness, affecting more than 1,000 million people, especially in tropical Asia. Newly hatched hookworms burrow through the skin of a person and get into the

The lives of parasites

Many kinds of roundworms, flukes, tapeworms, and other worms live as internal or endo-parasites. They obtain shelter and nutrients from their hosts, and usually cause harm in return. The life of a schistosoma parasite (a fluke, page 48) is shown here. Worms are suited to the parasitic way of life. Their thin, flexible bodies can squeeze through the host's blood vessels, intestines, and other parts. A worm can also absorb nutrients and oxygen easily through its thin skin.

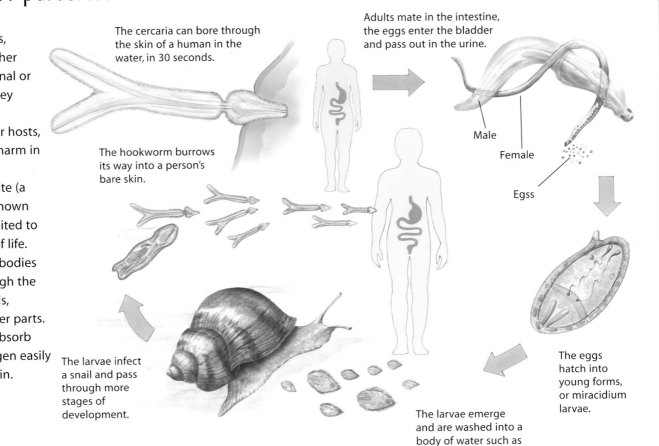

The cercaria can bore through the skin of a human in the water, in 30 seconds.

The hookworm burrows its way into a person's bare skin.

Adults mate in the intestine, the eggs enter the bladder and pass out in the urine.

Male

Female

Egss

The larvae infect a snail and pass through more stages of development.

The larvae emerge and are washed into a body of water such as a pond or lake.

The eggs hatch into young forms, or miracidium larvae.

bloodstream. They then travel around the body and settle in the intestine, where they feed and grow. They have a very weakening effect on people they infest. Children, especially, suffer from anemia (shortage of red blood cells). An infected person becomes pale and weak, and the legs and abdomen swell. If not treated quickly with drugs that kill the worms, death may be the result.

Filarial worms

Another unpleasant tropical parasite in humans is the filaria roundworm, wucheria. It gets into the body's lymph tubes and glands, which carry fluids around the body and fight germs. As the worms grow and multiply, they block the lymph system and cause terrible swellings, especially in the limbs, known as elephantiasis.

The filiaria roundworm is spread by flies and mosquitoes. The worm's young are released by the mother and make their way to the surface blood vessels. When a mosquito bites the person's skin, it takes up the filaria with the blood. The worm

grows inside the mosquito's head. Then, when the mosquito bites another person or animal, the worm enters through the wound and infects the new host. Some roundworms have several hosts in their lives, as flukes do (page 48).

The threadworm (pinworm) is a common human parasite. It is harmful in large numbers.

Giant roundworm

The Guinea worm is another tropical parasite on humans. It lives in the bodies of its victims, and it may grow more than 3 feet (90 cm) long. It causes pain and disfigurement, and ulcers develop when the worms release their eggs through the skin.

The pig roundworm, ascaris, has the typical roundworm body—long and thin, pointed at both ends, with no obvious head or tail.

So many!
Some kinds of roundworms are found in such vast numbers, they are hard to imagine. One rotting apple may have 90,000 roundworms inside it. More than 20 million roundworms have been found in one wheelbarrow-load of seaside mud. Some soil roundworms are predators of even tinier creatures, sucking their juices.

Roundworms (nematodes)
- 20,000-plus species
- all habitats
- most are free-living, some are parasites
- body rounded, but without segments
- many are tiny
- largest are up to 3 feet (90 cm)

Other worms

BESIDES THE MAIN GROUPS OF WORMS (segmented worms, flatworms, and roundworms), there are many other types of worms. They include ribbon worms, spoon worms, arrow worms, and acorn worms. They are not necessarily close relatives of the main worms, or of each other. But all have the main worm feature—a long, soft, wriggling body.

Ribbon worms live among rocks and stones on the shore and under the sea. They hunt tiny animals for food.

Ribbon worms or nemerteans live mostly in the sea. They have soft, slimy bodies which are slightly flattened, especially toward the head. Some are very long and ribbon-shaped, hence their name. The smallest ribbon worms are about 0.02 inch (0.5 mm) long. But the bootlace worm can exceed 30 feet (9 m), and is on record as the world's longest creature. Some ribbon worms are black or dark, others are brightly striped or banded. Most are predators.

Horsehair worms or hair worms often live in groups and look like a mass of living, writhing hair. They often coil themselves almost into knots. Adults live in damp soil or water and do not feed at all. They just reproduce their kind. The young horsehair worms live as parasites, inside the bodies of insects and similar hosts.

Longest

The longest known animal is a type of ribbon worm—the bootlace worm. It often grows to 15 feet (4.5 m) long, but lengths of 100 feet (30 m) have been recorded.

!

Horsehair worm

Peanut worm

Spiny-headed and peanut worms

Spiny-headed worms are all parasites and live inside larger animals, especially fish. Their mouthparts are equipped with spiny hooks which they use to attach themselves to their hosts.

Peanut worms are cylinder-shaped, with a flexible stalk-like proboscis at the top that can be extended or pulled back inside the body. The proboscis has frilly tentacles at the end, which are used for feeding. Peanut worms range from pinhead size to more than 28 inches (70 cm) long.

Spiny-headed worms

Spoon worms

Spoon worms include some of the strangest of all animals. Most have pear-shaped bodies, with hooks and a proboscis at the head end. They live in the sea, either in mud burrows or crevices in the rocks. In one kind, the bonellia spoon worm, the female has a body about 6 inches (15 cm) long. But her enormous proboscis stretches 3 feet (90 cm) in length, and is forked at the end. She is vivid green in color. Yet the male is almost microscopically small compared to the giant female. Bonellias are quite common in the Mediterranean Sea.

Beard worms

Beard worms live in the ocean depths, in tubes almost buried in the mud. They have long, thin bodies, just a "matchhead" across, but 3 feet (90 cm) or more long. At the front is a beardlike tuft of 100 or so tentacles. These worms were only studied in the 1960s. They have no stomach or intestine, absorbing nutrients through the body surface.

Priapulid and horseshoe worms

Priapulid worms burrow in the mud on the seabed or shore. They resemble the peanut worms, but the stalklike proboscis at the head end has a ring of teeth rather than tentacles. Priapulid worms have frilly appendages on the tail. These probably work as gills for breathing. This is one of the smallest of all animal groups, with only about ten known species.

Horseshoe worms are another very small group in terms of numbers of species. But the worms themselves can be very abundant in muddy sand. They live in tubes which they make for themselves. Some kinds burrow into limestone rocks. The animal itself is long and wormlike, but at its top or head end it has a fanlike swirl of tentacles. When feeding, only the spreading tentacles can be seen at the top of the tube.

Tongue worms

Tongue worms are parasites, living inside the nose passages and lungs of mammals, birds, and reptiles. The tongue worm has no obvious features except for its head end, which has five fingerlike parts sticking out. The middle one of the five has the tongue worm's mouth at its tip.

Priapulid worm

Arrow worms

Arrow worms are transparent, arrow-shaped animals about an inch (2.5 cm) long, with small "fins" at the sides and tail. They live in the upper layers of the sea and hunt small fish and animal plankton such as copepods, using spines near the mouth to grasp their prey.

Arrow worms

Arrow worms (above right and below) live in the tropical oceans in huge numbers. They feed mainly on smaller animals of plankton, including fish fry.

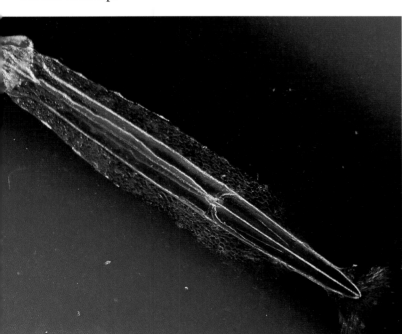

Acorn worms

Acorn worms are yet another group of soft-bodied, worm-shaped animals which live in burrows in mud and sand on the sea bed. They are found mainly in shallow water near the coast. They range in size from about 1 inch (2.5 cm) to 20 inches (50 cm) long. Between the proboscis and the rest of the body is a distinct collar. In some, the proboscis is short and looks slightly like an oak tree's acorn, giving the group their name. Acorn worms are very fragile creatures, and out of their burrows, they easily fall to pieces!

Ribbon worms (Nemertea)
- 900 species
- most are marine
- long and ribbon-shaped
- sexes separate in most species

Horsehair worms (Nematomorpha)
- 250 species
- water or damp soil, some marine
- long and hairlike
- sexes separate

Spiny-headed worms (Acanthocephala)
- 1,000 species
- parasitic
- spiny mouthparts

Peanut worms (Sipuncula)
- 350 species
- marine, in sand and mud
- cylinder-shaped
- mouth with frilly tentacles

Spoon worms (Echiura)
- 150 species
- marine, in burrows in mud or sand
- sausage- or pear-shaped
- long fingerlike proboscis

Beard worms (Pogonophora)
- 100 species
- marine, in the deep sea

- beardlike tentacles on head
- sexes separate

Arrow worms (Chaetognatha)
- 70 species
- marine, in plankton
- long, transparent body, with flaps or fins
- most are transparent
- extremely numerous

Priapulid worms (Priapula)
- 10 species
- marine, live on the sea floor
- tube-shaped

Horseshoe worms (Phorona)
- 20 species
- marine
- live in hard tubes
- have head tentacles

Tongue worms (Pentastoma)
- 100 species
- mainly parasites of reptiles, mammals, and birds
- four short tentacles around head end

Acorn worms (Hemichordata)
- 100 species
- marine, on the sea floor, mostly in burrows
- fingerlike proboscis on head

The range of mollusks

SNAILS AND SLUGS, AND SEA CREATURES SUCH AS WHELKS, COCKLES, CLAMS AND MUSSELS, ARE ALL MOLLUSKS. So are octopuses, squid, and cuttlefish. Indeed, there are nearly 100,000 species of mollusk, and they are the second largest of all groups of animals, after insects and other arthropods. They vary tremendously in size and shape, but all of them have soft bodies, and many have hard shells. Unlike insects, mollusks do not have limbs with joints. Instead, most mollusks move about on a large, flat pad, called the foot. The head of a mollusk often has soft, bendy tentacles, to feel its way about or grasp food. The main mollusk groups are described on the following pages.

The octopus trails its tentacles behind it as it jets through the water.

Sea slugs look like multicolored snails without their shells. They crawl around on the seabed looking for food.

mantle ooze a liquid, mineral-rich, shell-building substance. This hardens, and the shell grows with its owner.

Some shells are round and smooth. Some are coiled into tight spirals, or spread out like fans. A bivalve's shell is two flaplike shell halves, called valves, hinged together. In mollusks such as slugs and cuttlefish, the shell is inside the body. If there is no shell, the mantle forms a leathery cover around the body.

Many mollusks look little more than squishy blobs. But the body is quite complicated inside, with many of the usual important parts such as a brain, heart, and kidney. Muscles can pull and squeeze the body into almost any shape.

Most mollusks live in the sea. Only certain species of two groups, the bivalves and the snails, live in fresh water. Some snails are even able to live in damp conditions on land. There are seven main groups of mollusks. The three most familiar are the gastropods such as snails, limpets and winkles, the bivalves such as mussels, clams, oysters, and razorshells, and the cephalopods such as octopuses, cuttlefish, nautiluses, and squid.

All mollusks have a large, cloaklike part around the main body, called the mantle. In many mollusks, this makes a hard protective shell on the outside, which the creature can withdraw into, to avoid danger. The shell grows as the edges of the

The beautiful colors and patterns of tropical sea slugs warn that they are bad to eat. The knobs and frills help in breathing.

Mussels are fixed to seashore rocks by strong, stringy byssus threads.

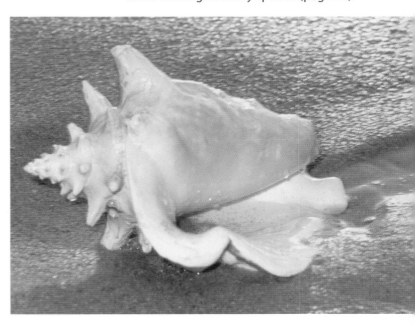

Tusk shells have long, curving, tapering shells that look like an elephant's tusk. The shell is open at both ends, and the tusk-shell lives half buried, head-down in the sand. It feeds by spreading its thread-like tentacles into the sand.

Scallops are bivalve molluscs, which means they have two shell parts. The scallop can snap its shell shut to swim jerkily.

The mollusk's foot

The mollusk's large, muscular, padlike foot is used for many tasks. Squid and octopuses have developed the foot into tentacles to catch prey. A limpet uses its sucker foot to cling to rocks. A snail slides about on its foot. A clam's foot is like a strong finger that pokes and digs into the sand or mud. A razorshell's foot is so powerful, it can dig the animal down into the seashore mud, almost as fast as a person could dig with a shovel.

The mollusk's radula

One special feature of mollusks is a filelike "tongue" called a radula, covered in rows of hard teeth. The mollusk uses this to scrape away at its food, perhaps

tiny seaweeds covering a rock, or lettuces in the vegetable garden. Not all mollusks feed in this way, however. Squid and octopuses are active predators, tearing up their prey with a beaklike mouth.

Food from mollusks

All over the world, mollusks such as clams, oysters, cockles, mussels, scallops, abalones, winkles, octopus, and squid are eaten by people. They are usually an important source of food, especially in coastal places and on islands. However, some mollusks have become rare or even endangered as a result of being over-collected for food.

Many mollusk shells are incredibly beautiful, especially when wet from the sea. The tropical conch shell is especially attractive. Empty, it has been used as a trumpet to make sounds for thousands of years. However, the souvenir trade in mollusk shells endangers many species (page 60).

Chitons are oval in shape and have a shell divided into eight arched plates, making them look as if they are protected by chain-mail armor. The alternative name for this group is "coat-of-mail shells." They graze on the film of seaweed covering rocks in shallow water at the coast. Chitons can curl up tightly if dislodged from their rock.

MOLLUSKS
- up to 100,000 species
- most live in the sea, some in fresh water, a few on land
- soft body in cloaklike mantle
- many have hard shell around body
- many have large, muscular base or foot
- some have flexible tentacles

Main groups of mollusks:

Tusk shells
- 350 species
- marine
- burrow into sand
- single shell shaped like elephant's tusk

Slugs and snails
- 70,000 species
- marine, freshwater and land-living
- most have a single shell, often coiled
- head has tentacles
- glide on muscular foot

Bivalves
- 20,000 species
- most are marine, some freshwater
- hinged shell of two parts (valves)
- foot rounded, not flattened
- most burrow, or live attached to rocks

Squid and octopuses
- 650 species
- live in the sea
- long tentacles around mouth
- large eyes, big brains
- hide in rocks or swim in the sea

Chitons
- 550 species
- live in the sea, on rocks on the shore or in shallow water
- body oval and domed (like a woodlouse), with eight plates
- no eyes

Slugs and snails

LAND SNAILS AND SEA SNAILS, LAND SLUGS AND SEA SLUGS, along with limpets and whelks, are all gastropods—mollusks with soft, squidgy bodies. The name gastropod means "stomach-foot," because these mollusks seem to slide along on their stomachs. But it is really the same muscular foot possessed by all mollusks. Many snails and limpets have a hard shell, so gastropods are sometimes called univalves (meaning "one shell"). But a slug's soft body is exposed to the world.

Few mollusks are more familiar than the common garden snail (above right). After a heavy rainstorm, snails emerge as if from nowhere in the damp conditions. They rasp their way through many kinds of leaves and plant bits on the ground.

Most snails are little bigger than cherries. But a few, such as the giant ram's-horn snail of ponds and lakes, can be 4–6 inches (10–15 cm) across.

Largest

The biggest snail is the African giant snail, whose shell can be almost 10 inches (25 cm) across.

!

Shells and survival

Snails seem to live everywhere, not only in all parts of the oceans, but in almost all habitats on land. Like all mollusks, the snail needs plenty of moisture to survive. So land snails stay in or near moist places. If the weather is too cold or too dry, the snail makes a seal of slime over its shell entrance. This hardens into a kind of temporary door. In autumn in temperate regions, many snails settle down for the winter in this state. As it gets warmer in the spring, the snail breaks open the seal and emerges again. In hot, dry weather, snails also seal themselves in their shells and wait for cooler, moister conditions. Surviving heat or dryness like this is called estivation.

When a gastropod slides along the ground, its large, flat stomach-foot spreads out underneath. Muscles in the foot ripple backward and forward. As they move, land snails and slugs ooze a trail of slime to ease the way forward and reduce friction.

The shell's trapdoor

On the back of the foot, most sea snails and some land snails have a flap called an operculum. When danger threatens, the snail retreats into its shell and pulls the operculum over the opening, like closing a trapdoor, for protection.

Many gastropods have two pairs of tentacles on the head. One pair is feelers that help the animals to find their way by touch. The other pair of tentacles are often stalks with eyes at the tip. But many gastropods have no eyes at all.

Slugs like this keeled slug have a great appetite for all kinds of plants, including potatoes. The keeled slug often burrows under the soil, especially to eat plant roots and to hide during the day.

Some sea slugs have large hairlike tentacles on their backs. These can be equipped with stings, like the tentacles of anemones, or horrible-tasting fluids.

This Indonesian sea slug can swim by undulating its capelike foot. The gills are tall, yellow and spiky. Sea slugs eat seaweeds and small animals such as sea mats and corals that coat rocks.

Male and female

Snails are hermaphrodite, which means that each animal is both male and female at the same time. When they mate, each snail passes sperm into the body of the other snail. Each partner goes on to develop and lay a clutch of leathery eggs. There may be dozens of eggs in a single clutch, and eventually many tiny snails hatch. Except for their size, they look very like the adults, each with its tiny shell. It takes about two years for a snail to reach maturity.

Slugs

Slugs are like snails that have lost their protective shells, although some slugs do have small shells inside their bodies, just under the skin of the back. Some even have a tiny shell on the back. To protect themselves, slugs produce large quantities of very sticky slime, which puts off many predators. The slime also helps to stop the slug from drying out. However, some birds, such as thrushes, and some mammals, including hedgehogs, can cope with this slime. They eat large numbers of slugs. Song thrushes can even tackle snails. They bash the snail against a hard object, like a stone, until its shell breaks open. Then they quickly eat the tasty flesh inside.

Slugs at sea

The marine relatives of snails and slugs include some of the most beautiful of all sea creatures. Like land slugs, sea slugs are mostly without shells. Many of them have feathery gills and bodies covered with amazingly bright, almost glowing patterns and colors. There are sea slugs in shades of orange,

pink or blue, and with the tufts of vividly brilliant gills on their backs. The bright colors warn predators that they should be left alone. Sea slugs taste horrible, and some even have poisonous stings on their backs.

Sea slugs are also called nudibranchs. This yellow-spotted red nudibranch is from the seas around the Philippines.

Jelly babies!

Water and pond snails lay their eggs in a string or blob of jelly, usually stuck to the stem of a water plant or stone. The jelly helps to protect the eggs from being eaten, and also stops them drying out if the water level in the pond or stream changes. In an aquarium tank water snails often lay their eggs on the glass. This allows a clear view of the tiny baby snails developing inside.

Groups of slugs (continued from page 55):

Land and freshwater snails, slugs
- 20,500 species
- on land and in fresh water
- spiral or coiled shell (not in slugs)

Sea slugs
- 1250 species
- mostly sluglike, lacking shells
- bright colors
- frilly gills

Seashells

THE VARIETY OF SHAPES AND COLORS IN SEASHELLS FROM AROUND THE WORLD IS AMAZING, making these some of nature's most beautiful and intricate objects. Most seashells are the hard homes made by various kinds of mollusks (mainly sea snails) when they were alive. After the sea snail has died, all that remains is its shell, and this may get washed up on the beach. But most shells are fairly brittle, and they get broken by the action of the waves. Even on the beach, wind and waves, and rain and sand, gradually crack and wear the shell into fragments. Finally it is ground up and its chalky or limy minerals are recycled.

Spider conch shell

Some shells, such as scallops, cockles, mussels, oysters, and razorshells, belong to bivalved mollusks. In life, these shell parts are joined in pairs, at a hinge, but they often get washed up as single items on the shore. The insides of some shells, especially those of some bivalves, are lined with mother-of-pearl. This is a smooth, shiny substance which glints and shines with a pearly sheen.

Tower shells
Tower shells are long and tapering spirals. A common species on the European coast is the auger shell, which can grow to 2 inches (5 cm) in length.

Harp shells have intricate ridges, grooves, and stripes.

Top shells
Some of the most colorful sea snail shells are top shells (page 58). The European top shells are quite small, ranging from about an inch (2.5 cm) in height. But many are patterned with glorious streaks or zigzag markings, on a colored background which may be cream, orange, red, or gray-green, depending on the species. Some tropical top shells are much larger, reaching well over 6 inches (15 cm) in height, and they are even more colorful in bright hues of red and pink or vivid green and blue.

Strawberry topshell

Cowries
Cowries have perhaps been prized for longer than any other seashells. Cowrie necklaces have been found in the tombs of Ancient Egypt.

The largest and most impressive cowries live in the warm seas of the tropics. The tiger cowrie of the Indian and Pacific Oceans, for example, grows to 4 inches (10 cm) or longer. Its shell is beautifully blotched in orange or brown, on a cream background. Cowries are smaller and much less common in temperate regions such as northern Atlantic shores. The spotted cowrie shell can sometimes be found on a sandy beach.

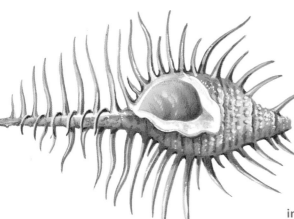

Venus's comb is the shell of a sea snail from the Pacific Ocean. The shell has delicate spines, like the teeth of a comb. The spines are longer in females of the species than in males.

Lampshell shells look like bivalve mollusks but they are a different animal group, brachiopods.

Conches

The conches are some of the largest of all sea snails. In North America, a "conch" is usually a queen conch, common off the coast of Florida. Queen conches are valued not only for their shells but also as tasty seafood and as fish bait.

Screw shell

Conch shells are among the most prized of all shells with collectors, because of their delicate patterns and colors and their glossy sheen. Like other seashells, they may be burned to make lime minerals, or ground up to make porcelain. Sadly, queen conches have been collected in such numbers that they have become quite scarce.

The largest sea snail shell is that of the trumpet conch of Australia, which can be over 30 inches (75 cm) long and 3 feet (90 cm) across the spines. The smallest seashells are almost microscopic, even when the animal is fully grown.

The abalone or ear shell is valued for its pearly lining as well as the tasty contents.

WORLD WATCH

Should people collect seashells? Taking one or two that have been washed up on the beach may seem to do no harm, since the original animals have passed away. But collecting the living animals for their shells is having devastating effects on many species. Abalones are some of the many mollusks that have been over-collected in certain parts of the world. The very survival of this beautiful creature is threatened.

Bivalve mollusks

BIVALVE MEANS "WITH TWO VALVES." Bivalve mollusks have a shell in two halves, called valves. The valves are usually joined together by a flexible hinge, so that in most species, the animal can open and shut them rather like a small suitcase. The soft, fleshy body of the bivalve mollusk is inside, protected by the hard shell, which few predators can lever or crack open. Most of the creatures we call "shellfish" belong to this group. They are shelled, but they are not fish! They are well known because they are eaten as seafood. Examples are cockles, mussels, oysters, scallops, and clams.

Like all bivalves, giant clams (above) usually stay open to feed—clamping shut when danger threatens. Their breathing tubes or siphons (left) are like small cones.

Most bivalve mollusks cannot move round easily, and some are stuck to their rocks. So they let the water bring food to them, by filtering out edible particles from it. The water is sucked into the body through a tube called a siphon. Inside, food is filtered by the comblike or feathery gills, which also take in oxygen. The water leaves through another siphon.

Bivalves galore
Cockles have pale, rather rounded shells, with furrows radiating outward. They live in sand and mud on the lower shore, using the muscular foot to burrow down below the surface. Mussels stick themselves to rocks and breakwaters (groynes) with strong threads called byssus threads. This means they are not rolled around and damaged by the waves. At low tide they are exposed to the air, but they keep their shells tightly shut and are soon covered again as the tide returns.

Oysters have gray shells, which are irregular and flaky or scaly. They are highly prized as seafood in many parts of the world. They are farmed on boards or fences in some estuaries, so that natural populations can be saved.

The cockscomb oyster is a red oyster that looks like a cockerel's (rooster's) comb.

Scallops can swim away from danger by quickly opening and closing the shell, squirting out water to move along jerkily. The tiny dots around the mantle are simple versions of eyes which detect light and dark.

Scallops are among the few bivalves that can move fast. They swim by flapping the two valves of the shell open and shut. As in many bivalves, the mantle forms a fleshy covering to the edges of the valves. It may have waving tentacles and tiny eyes.

Open wide!

Some animals are able to break into the hard shells of bivalve mollusks. Birds such as the oystercatcher have hard, chisel-like beaks to lever open mussel and oyster shells. A big lobster may be able to use its larger, crushing pincer to crack the shell. The walrus opens the shell with its tusk.

Razor or pod shells often turn up on the beach. They are named after the old-fashioned barber's "cut-throat" razor, because of their narrow, rectangular shape, up to 8 inches (20 cm) long. They burrow into the lower shore.

Freshwater bivalves

Although most bivalves live in the sea, some have adapted to life in fresh water, mostly in rivers or lakes. One of the largest is the swan mussel, which can grow to more than 8 inches (20 cm) long. It is common in muddy lakes or slow rivers. The pearl mussel is another large species, and famous for its pearls. Pearl mussels like large, fast sandy rivers, with soft water.

The pea mussel really is the size of a pea, and is very common in rivers. Most bivalves are either male or female, and breed by casting their eggs and sperm into the water, to mix and develop. Pea mussels are hermaphrodite (both male and female). The tiny young develop inside the mother-father, and are born fully formed.

The razor shell (razor clam) uses its muscular foot to burrow into the seabed. It pushes the foot, like a pink finger, down into mud. The foot tip swells to anchor itself, then the razor shell shortens the rest of the foot to drag itself and its narrow shell deeper.

What are pearls?

In oysters and many other mollusks, the fleshy, shell-forming mantle makes a special substance called nacre, which lines the inside of the shell. It forms a smooth, white, mother-of-pearl lining called the nacreous layer. A foreign substance, such as a bit of grit or a tiny parasite, may enter the shell. If the mollusk cannot get rid of it, it is gradually covered in nacre. This builds up in thin layers until the grit is completely wrapped in a ball of shiny white nacre—a pearl. The finest pearls come from pinctada pearl oysters, that live in the Pacific Ocean. The world's largest pearl came out of a giant clam. It was 5 inches (12 cm) across.

The file shell's tentacles filter food from the water.

Boring into wood and rock

Some bivalves use their hard shells to make holes, even drilling into wood or soft rock. Piddocks and shipworms have shells with rough surfaces, which they use to rub and grind away at rock or wood. Eventually, the mollusk has dug a small burrow for itself, where it can live unmolested by predators. A colony of shipworms (right) can cause great damage to wooden boats and breakwaters.

Another group of mollusks:

Bivalves
- 20,000 species
- most are marine, some freshwater
- hinged shell of two parts, called valves
- fingerlike foot
- most burrow, or live attached to rocks

Squid, octopuses, and cuttlefish

THE MOST FASCINATING OF ALL MOLLUSKS ARE SQUID AND OCTOPUSES. They are called cephalopods, a name that means "head-footed," because their molluskan foot is at the head end and has lots of long tentacles. They have the typical mollusk's soft body, but only the squid has a shell, which is small and rod-shaped, and inside the body. These creatures are fierce predators. Squid swim very fast, and octopuses hide away in caves and holes in the rocks. Squid and octopuses can also squirt out an ink-like liquid if they are attacked. This makes the water cloudy, allowing the mollusk to escape to safety.

Squid (above) and cuttlefish prey on quite large fish, grasping them with the suckers on their tentacles

A cuttlefish holds its tentacles together for streamlining as it swims.

Squid are narrow and streamlined, with flaplike fins at one end to keep them steady in the water. They have large eyes and good vision, to track their prey in the ocean. To catch food, they use a long pair of tentacles, which have adhesive suckers at the end. They have eight shorter tentacles too, also with suckers. Squid move slowly by rippling their fins, or dart suddenly using a kind of jet-propulsion, squirting water rapidly out of the siphon (breathing tube).

Cuttlefish

Cuttlefish are like small, flattened squid, with a fin running around all sides of the body. Even more than squid, they are the chameleons of the sea, able to change color and pattern in a split second. The cuttlefish skin contains tiny spots of different colors—yellow, red, brown, and black. The animal can control the size of these by muscles, and make many different shades by mixing the amounts of each color.

Largest

The giant squid of the ocean depths is the largest mollusk, and also the largest animal without a backbone. It reaches a maximum length of about 56 feet (17 m) from the tip of its outstretched tentacles to its tail end. Its eyes are the largest in the animal kingdom, at more than 16 inches (40 cm) across. The smallest squid are only about 0.4 inch (1 cm) long.

Some kinds of squid can produce lights inside their bodies. They have special body parts to create the light, and some can even direct the light like a flashlight. This is very useful in the deep, dark sea.

The pearly nautilus may sit on a rock to rest (above left), or float slowly in mid water with its tentacles pulled in (above right).

The blue-ringed octopus of the Indian and Pacific region is only small, but it has a very poisonous bite. The rings on its body glow bright blue if it is threatened.

The nautilus

Only one kind of cephalopod has a proper external shell like other mollusks. This is the nautilus, which has a shiny shell curled over its body. It swims along the seabed, using its 35 or so tentacles to find prey. Unlike its cousins, it cannot squirt ink to hide and escape danger.

Octopus tentacles are covered in suckers, which they use to hold their prey and to move over the rocks.

different shapes and patterns, choosing the correct one to obtain food. They can also remember simple tasks such as how to open their food box.

The common octopus of the Atlantic varies in size, but can reach about 3 feet (90 cm) in body length, with a tentacle spread of 10 feet (3 m). Octopuses are rarely seen. They spend most of the day holed up in their lairs—caves or crevices in the rocks. They come out mainly during the night, to hunt for other mollusks, crabs, and similar prey. They also scavenge for dead meat.

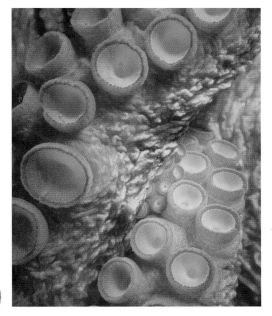

Octopuses

An octopus has a sacklike body, large eyes and eight long, spreading tentacles to catch prey. Like other cephalopods, its beaklike mouth is hidden in the middle of the ring of tentacles, where they join the body. Octopuses have complicated behavior and are often called the most intelligent of invertebrate animals. They can tell apart

The paper nautilus or argonaut looks like the pearly nautilus, but it is really a type of octopus. The female makes a thin, papery shell to shelter herself and her eggs, and sometimes her much smaller male partner.

Cephalopod mollusks

Octopuses, squid, and cuttlefish
- 650 species
- marine
- streamlined shape (squid and cuttlefish)
- ten tentacles in squid and cuttlefish, eight in octopus

Nautiluses
- 6 species
- marine
- large spiral shell
- many tentacles

Starfish and seastars

STARFISH AND THEIR RELATIVES ARE CALLED ECHINODERMS. This means "hedgehog skin," and many of them are indeed very spiny. These creatures are numerous and widespread, but they all live in the sea, so many are unfamiliar. They have a body built around a radial plan, like the spokes of a wheel, rather than the bilateral or two-sided bodies of other animals. They also have tiny, flexible tube feet that end in suckers, for walking and feeding. As well as starfish, this group includes feather stars, sea lilies, sea urchins, and sea cucumbers.

Starfish look slow and harmless enough, but they are all predators.

Most groups of sea animals have a few species adapted to life in fresh water or even dry land. Echinoderms do not. These creatures are quite large, and many are brightly colored. This means that they are easy to notice in the water, especially as they are slow-moving. However, the nearest that most people get to an echinoderm is a dead, stiff starfish or the ball-like body case of a sea urchin, washed up on the shore.

Many arms

Starfish are flat, and have arms which spread out from the center in a starlike pattern. Many species have five arms, but some have seven, and others as many as 14. The upper side of the body usually has small, hard plates or spines embedded in the skin, for protection. Underneath, each arm has rows of tiny tube feet, like miniature sucker-ended fingers. These bend to and fro so that the starfish can glide across the sea bed.

Starfish are very strong and can prise open the shells of clams and other bivalve mollusks. When attacking its victim, the starfish arches over it and clamps a couple of arms onto each side. It then pulls with great strength and stamina. As the two parts of the mollusk's shell begin to gape, the starfish turns its stomach inside out, through its mouth and into the gap in the shell. It then begins to digest the prey's flesh. Eventually, the shell opens wide and the starfish completes its meal.

Cushion star

Sun star

This starfish is humped over its prey, dissolving and absorbing its flesh.

Some types of starfish

Common starfish are indeed common. They sometimes gather in huge numbers covering a square mile (2.5 sq km) of seabed, all moving slowly along as they feed on a range of sea creatures such as bivalves and other mollusks, worms, crabs, and also other echinoderms. These vast marauding columns of starfish leave a trail of dead and dying seabed animals in their wake.

The sand star lives on fine sand, where it often lurks, half buried. It has a beautiful star shape, and its five arms are edged with spines. The common sun star is bright red, with as many as 14 short arms, spreading out sunlike from its large central disk. Its prey includes the common starfish.

Poisonous coral eater

The crown-of-thorns starfish eats the small coral animals called polyps. Sometimes these starfish gather in such large numbers that they eat away an entire coral reef. They are covered with sharp, poisonous spines as defense.

The Pacific blue star has the usual starfish number of five arms. Like its relatives, it is a slow-motion but very effective predator.

Writing arms

The brittlestar (shown on page 20) is indeed brittle and easily damaged. Parts of its long, delicate arms often break off. These arms are very curly and narrow, and spread out from a small circular disk at the center. The five arms can twist and turn, looping back on themselves. Brittlestars move very fast for echinoderms, writhing speedily across the sea bed.

Most brittlestars live below the tide zone, in deeper water. They can sometimes be found piled up in huge

heaps, with as many as 1,000 individuals on just one square metre of sea bottom. Most brittlestars feed by gathering up small edible items from the mud, or by filtering them from the water. The common brittlestar of the Atlantic and Mediterranean regions is a filter-feeder. It lives in dense colonies and each animal waves its spiny arms around in the water, to catch anything edible that may float past.

Feathery arms

Feather stars are similar to starfish and have feathery arms, used for both feeding and swimming. Many have ten arms, but some species may have

Armed!
If a starfish is damaged, and loses part of an arm, it can re-grow the missing piece again. The new part is often slightly smaller. Sometimes it branches into two, giving a six-armed starfish!

almost 200! The rosy feather star is a ten-armed type, with the arms banded in pink and white. The feathery plumes along the arm edges give it a plant-like appearance. Feather stars grasp onto rocks or seaweeds and can also creep about. They feed by waving their arms in the water to filter out edible particles.

Lilies in the sea

Sea lilies are close relatives of feather stars and feed in a similar way. Each animal is attached by a stalk to the seabed, usually deep in the ocean. The stalk may be more than 3 feet (90 cm) long. These echinoderms look like flowers on stalks, hence their name.

Sea lily (crinoid)

ECHINODERMS
- 6,250 species
- live in the sea
- five-rayed (spoked) body plan
- inner skeleton, often spiny
- tiny tubelike feet

Three of the main groups:

Starfish
- 1,500 species
- flat and star-shaped
- usually five arms (sometimes more)

Brittlestars
- 2,000 species
- flat and star-shaped
- usually five arms (sometimes six, or branched)
- arms long and brittle

Feather stars and sea lilies
- 625 species (mostly feather stars)
- either swimming (feather stars) or stalked (sea lilies)
- feed by filtering seawater

Sea urchins and sea cucumbers

SEA URCHINS, SAND DOLLARS, AND SEA CUCUMBERS are echinoderms, like starfish (page 66). Yet they look quite different from starfish. However, they have the same echinoderm feature of tiny tube feet, and many species bristle with spines. These are for protection, and sea urchins also tilt their spines to move along, as if on stilts. In some types of urchins, the spines are tipped with poison.

The largest kind of sea cucumber, the stichopus sea cucumber, lives in seas around the Philippines. It can grow more than 3 feet (90 cm) long and nearly 6 inches (15 cm) wide.

Sessile sea squirts look like see-through bottles attached to the rocks (below). Flask-shaped planktonic sea squirts swim and drift along (left). Some sea cucumbers have frills and flaps along the body (bottom left).

Sea urchins and sand dollars have rounded bodies, either ball-shaped, or flattened. The scientific name for their group is the echinoids, which means "hedgehog-like." It refers to the spiny covering of many species. Echinoids, like starfish, have a five-rayed body plan. But the arms are curled up and over and joined at the top to

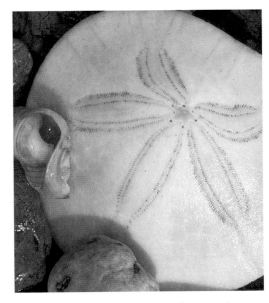

Sand dollars take their name from their resemblance to coins, being round and flat or disk-shaped. They move around just below the surface of the sand.

Sea squirts or tunicates have very special features. These include a main nerve or nerve-cord, and a stiff tube called a notochord—a very simple version of our own backbone.

make the balllike body. Urchins use their spines to lever themselves along slowly, and they can also climb by using their very long and flexible tube feet.

Sea urchins feed by grazing on the seaweeds and small animals, such as moss animals, that grow on the surfaces of underwater rocks. Some urchins, known as heart urchins, have a more streamlined and almost heartlike shape. This helps them to burrow beneath the sand. One type is known as the sea potato. Its brownish, potato-shaped empty shell, known as a test, is sometimes washed up on the shore.

Sea cucumbers

Sea cucumbers are named after their warty, sausage-shaped bodies, which look similar to a cucumber. Unlike most other echinoderms, sea cucumbers have soft bodies, although the skin is tough and leathery. The mouth at one end is surrounded by tentacles, which can be pulled back inside the animal. Sea cucumbers have three rows of tube feet and crawl slowly along the seabed.

The rosy feather star (above left) waves its filter-feeding arms to catch tiny bits of food. The sea potato or sand urchin (below left) is a hairy-looking urchin that lives in a burrow under the beach. Lancelets (near left) are long, pale creatures that filter-feed in seabed sand and gravel.

When disturbed or attacked, some sea cucumbers can shoot out parts of their insides, including their stomach and intestine. This sticky mass entangles and puts off most predators, even lobsters. The sea cucumber then regrows the missing parts.

Squirts in the sea

Sea squirts are not echinoderms, but members of a group called the tunicates. They resemble blobs of jelly. They are called sea squirts because, when the tide has gone out to leave them exposed on the shore, they sometimes squirt out jets of water. These creatures may bridge the gap between the two great groups of animals, the invertebrates (animals without backbones) and the vertebrates.

These sea squirts are barrel-shaped, with jellylike bodies. They feed by filtering tiny creatures from the water as it flows through them. Other types are shaped like tiny tadpoles and live inside a "house" that they build for themselves from jellylike material.

A sea squirt larva looks like a tadpole and has a very simple rodlike version of the backbone, called a notochord, inside its body. But this breaks down as the larva grows into an adult. Sea squirts live stuck to rocks or seaweeds along the tide zone and in the shallows, and filter food from the water.

Lancelets are fishlike creatures that also possess a notochord. However, unlike fish, they have no proper backbone, jaws, eyes or fins. They live half-buried in sand or gravel, filtering food from the water. Lancelets grow to about 4 inches (10 cm) long, and they can swim weakly if they need to escape from a predator. They live in shallow water, in most temperate and tropical seas.

More groups of echinoderms (from page 67):

Sea urchins and sand dollars
- 950 species
- ball-shaped body, may be spiny
- no arms

Sea cucumbers
- 1,150 species
- body long and sausage-shaped
- no arms
- tentacles around mouth

Other sea creatures:

Tunicates (sea squirts)
- 1,400 species
- attached to rocks or swimming
- tadpole-like young or larvae

Lancelets
- 25 species
- small, about 4 inches (10 cm)
- fish-shaped body
- no eyes or fins

INSECTS & OTHER ARTHROPODS

There are at least 10 million different kinds, or species, of animals. And at least 99 out of every 100 species are insects. They range from tiny gnats and fairy flies, almost too small to see, to fist-sized beetles, and moths with wings as long as your hands. Three key features of insects help to make them so successful, widespread, and diverse. These are: a hard outer body casing (exoskeleton), wings for flying, and six legs with flexible joints for fast running.

Other animals have a tough outer body casing and jointed limbs, too. They include eight-legged spiders and scorpions (arachnids), and multilegged centipedes and millipedes. Insects do not live in the sea. But another huge group of joint-limbed creatures does—crustaceans such as crabs, lobsters, prawns, shrimps, and krill. Most people are not familiar with creatures of the open ocean. So they rarely see one of the world's most numerous kinds of animal—the small flealike crustaceans known as copepods.

All of the above creatures belong to the animal group known as arthropods. This name means "jointed legs" as opposed to animals such as octopuses, which have flexible tentacles. The arthropod's body casing and limb design have allowed this group to conquer all the Earth's habitats—from the highest mountains, hottest springs, and saltiest lakes, to the darkest caves and deepest seas.

The world of bugs

THERE ARE PROBABLY MORE THAN FIVE MILLION DIFFERENT KINDS, OR SPECIES, OF ANIMALS. Of these, about eight out of ten are bugs and other insects. The insects belong to a larger animal group known as the arthropods, a name that means "joint-limbed." This describes the leg structure of an arthropod. The leg has rigid sections linked by flexible joints—similar to our own arms and legs. Insects and other arthropods also share another main feature. This is the hard outer covering to the body, called the cuticle. It forms a tough, strong, protective casing known as an exoskeleton, which covers the arthropod's body like a jointed suit of armor. Ants, beetles, bugs, cockroaches, flies, fleas, bees, and other insects, which all have six legs, are arthropods. So are the eight-legged arachnids such as spiders and scorpions, the multi-legged centipedes and millipedes, and crustaceans like crabs, lobsters, and shrimps. These are all so numerous that for every human being alive today, there are probably at least one million insects and other arthropods.

Dragonflies are the biggest flying insects.

Mites are tiny arthropods related to spiders. Some live in soil. Others are parasites and suck blood from animals.

Inside an insect

An insect's body is divided into three main sections—head, thorax (chest), and abdomen. Most insects have three pairs of legs and one or two pairs of wings, all attached to the thorax. (The worker ant, as shown here, lacks wings.)

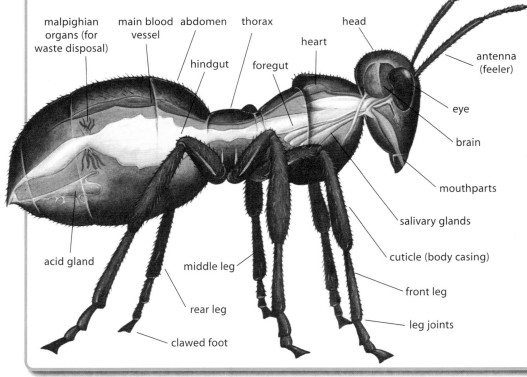

malpighian organs (for waste disposal)

main blood vessel

abdomen

thorax

head

heart

hindgut

foregut

antenna (feeler)

eye

brain

mouthparts

salivary glands

cuticle (body casing)

acid gland

middle leg

front leg

rear leg

leg joints

clawed foot

Arthropods are mostly small. But they affect people the world over. Some are harmful. Termites eat away wooden buildings and bridges. Locusts devastate vast areas of crops. Wasps annoy us with their stings, and lice with their blood-sucking bites. Poisonous spiders and scorpions can cause great pain, even death. Serious diseases are spread by some arthropods, such as malaria by mosquitoes, plague by fleas and Lyme's disease by ticks.

Useful arthropods

Other arthropods are useful. Bees make honey and carry pollen for flowers. Predatory insects such as lacewings eat plant pests like aphids (which are also arthropods). Silkworms are really moth caterpillars that spin silk. Dung beetles help to recycle animal droppings. Small flies called fruit flies, drosophila, have been used as insect "guinea pigs" to unlock the secrets of how genes work.

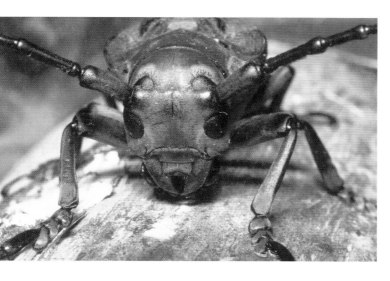

Senses

Most arthropods have keen senses, especially sight, smell, and touch. Each eye is made of a cluster of separate units, each with its own lens. This design is called a compound eye. Arthropods cannot see as much detail as we can, but most are excellent at detecting small movements, and many insects can see different colors.

Arthropods use their feelers or antennae to smell and even "taste" the air or water around them, detecting tiny particles of scents and odors. The antennae and the tiny hairlike bristles on the body and legs can also detect the slightest touch and movements such as wind or water currents.

Where insects live

Insects are found in almost every corner of the Earth, on land and in the air—in forests and grasslands, deserts, marshes and wetlands, streams and lakes, even high on mountains and glaciers, and deep in pitch-dark caves. Our parks and gardens, and even our houses, also buzz and crawl with insects. They include houseflies and ants, fleas on pets and silverfish in dark cupboards. However, there are almost no insects in the sea.

Other arthropod habitats

Spiders, scorpions, centipedes, and millipedes thrive mainly in warmer countries, especially among the dead leaves of the tropical forest floor and high above among the tree leaves. Most crustaceans, from tiny copepods to huge crabs and lobsters,

Crickets and grasshoppers have powerful chewing "jaws." In most insects these move from side to side rather than up and down.

Social insects live in groups, often in huge nests like this termite mound. Other social insects are ants, bees, and wasps.

live in the sea. Some, like crayfish and water fleas, dwell in fresh water. A few, like woodlice, can survive in damp places on land.

An arthropod's covering

The arthropod's body is covered by the cuticle, which is thin and light, yet strong and tough. It is made mainly from a substance called chitin. In land arthropods such as insects, the cuticle has a waxy, waterproof covering. In order to grow, an arthropod must shed its cuticle, and grow a new, bigger one underneath. This process is known as moulting or ecdysis.

The cuticle

An arthropod's cuticle is like a thick, stiff outermost layer on the skin. It forms a rigid casing, the exoskeleton, to support the soft inner body parts.

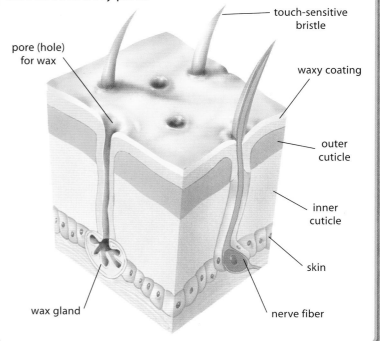

- touch-sensitive bristle
- pore (hole) for wax
- waxy coating
- outer cuticle
- inner cuticle
- skin
- wax gland
- nerve fiber

Insects
- more than one million species
- body divided into three main parts
- three pairs of legs
- most have two pairs of wings
- live on land and in fresh water

Crustaceans
- 43,000 species
- body divided into three main parts
- many have a hard, shell-like casing
- several pairs of legs
- two pairs of feelers
- most live in the sea

King Crabs
- 5 species
- heavy, rounded outer shell
- long tail spine
- large eyes
- live in the sea

Arachnids
- 80,000 species
- body divided into two main parts
- four pairs of legs
- jaws with fangs
- most are land-living

Centipedes
- 3,000 species
- body long and flattened
- one pair of legs per body segment
- long feelers
- jaws with fangs
- run fast
- live on land

Millipedes
- 10,000 species
- body long and rounded
- two pairs of legs per body segment
- short feelers
- walk slowly
- live on land

Beetles and weevils

BEETLES AND THEIR SMALLER COUSINS, WEEVILS, MAKE UP THE LARGEST SUB-GROUP OF INSECTS. They are called the Coleoptera. There are almost half a million known kinds, or species, of coleopterans, making up about one third of all animal species. And hundreds of new species are found each year. Most insects have two pairs of wings, but in beetles the front two have become hard and strong, like a shield over the top of the body. They are called wing cases, or elytra. The wing cases form a protective covering for the delicate second pair of wings. These are folded under the wing cases when the beetle is at rest. As it takes off, the beetle lifts the hard wing cases and then unfurls its thin wings, which it flaps to fly away. Beetles are the most widespread of all insects. They live in almost every habitat and region of our planet except the sea. Some are almost microscopic, others are nearly as big as your fist.

There are hundreds of kinds of dung, scarab and minotaur beetles. They are known as detritivores because they feed on detritus—animal droppings and dead bits of animals and plants. Many dung beetles roll the dung into balls and lay their eggs in it. The larvae hatch out and eat it, helping to recycle minerals and nutrients.

This cockchafer or maybug flies with its brown wing cases held up, to allow it to flap its large wings.

Beetles are not only incredibly numerous, they are also extremely varied. The familiar ladybugs in parks and gardens are brightly colored to warn other animals which might try to eat them that they taste horrible. Predators such as birds soon learn to avoid these small beetles.

Tiger and ground beetles are active hunters, with large eyes to see their prey and long legs to race after it. One kind of green ground beetle, the bombardier, uses a type of chemical warfare. It can squirt a spray of hot stinging chemicals from its rear end at an attacker.

Weevils

The weevils form the largest sub-group of beetles, with more than 60,000 species. They feed on plant parts, especially seeds, fruits, and flowers. A weevil has a long, curved snout, which looks like a tiny elephant's trunk. This snout is called the rostrum.

Night lights

On hot summer nights, flashes of pale green or yellow light can sometimes be seen among bushes and trees, or on the forest floor. These are fireflies and glow worms. They are not flies or worms, but kinds of beetle. Fireflies flash to attract each other in the mating season. Their worm-like larvae also give off light, but for a different reason. The larvae are warning predators, such as shrews, that they have a nasty taste and so should be left alone. In some kinds of beetle, the adult females have no wings and are also called glow worms. They flash to attract the winged males as they fly nearby.

Old beams and other wooden objects often have round holes we call woodworm. These are the work of the furniture beetle. The adult beetles lay their eggs on wood, including trees in the wild, and also our furniture.

Female fireflies and glow worms have no wings and small wing cases, showing the segmented main body or abdomen underneath. The males are much smaller and fly to the females.

Heaviest

The heaviest insect is a kind of beetle, the goliath beetle of Africa. It can weigh up to 4 ounces (108 g), which is almost as heavy as two ordinary hen's eggs. **!**

Strongest

The strongest insect is the rhinoceros beetle, also called the hercules beetle. It can lift and support more than 800 times its own weight. **!**

When the larvae hatch from the eggs they tunnel into the wood, feeding on it as they go. These larvae change into adults which eat their way out to the surface and fly away, leaving the small, round flight holes and a network of tunnels and powdered wood inside. The larvae of longhorn and deathwatch beetles also tunnel through wood, eating and weakening it as they go.

Nature's undertakers

Sexton or burying beetles are the undertakers of the natural world. They have a keen sense of smell and are attracted to rotting bodies, such as dead birds or small mammals like mice and rats. First the beetles mate, then they set to work to bury the corpse, by digging out the soil beneath it. They then lay their eggs in a chamber dug into the soil next to the body. When the larvae hatch, they feed on the decaying flesh of the corpse.

Water beetles

Some beetles live in fresh water. Diving beetles use their hairy legs as oars to row themselves through the water. The larva of the great diving beetle is a fierce predator with sharp, curved jaws. It catches tadpoles and small fish to eat. Tiny whirligig beetles swirl about like tiny wind-up toys on the surface of a pond. They can see both above and below because each eye is divided into two parts. One looks up into the air, the other down into the water.

The great diving beetle (left) must come to the surface every few minutes to gather air to breathe. It has strong mouthparts and can bite hard.

A typical weevil has a long trunk like snout. In some species this can be curled under the head. Some weevils are pests, eating wheat, other grains and flour, or crops such as apples, carrots, nuts, and clover.

Oldest

The record for the longest-lived insects is held by the larvae (grubs) of jewel beetles. They can live inside trees for more than 35 years, before emerging as adult beetles. **!**

Green tiger beetles (below) are truly the tigers of the insect world. They stalk and then rush after victims, killing them with a powerful bite from the strong, fanglike jaws.

Beetles and weevils
(Coleoptera)
- almost 500,000 species
- front wings are hard wing cases
- biting mouthparts to eat small animals or plant food
- most are active, fast runners

Butterflies and moths

AFTER THE BEETLES, THE SECOND LARGEST SUB-GROUP OF INSECTS IS THE BUTTERFLIES AND MOTHS, with about 175,000 species. They live wherever there are trees and flowers, being most numerous in tropical parts of the world. They are known as Lepidoptera, a name that means "scaly winged," because their large, papery wings are covered with tiny scales. Sometimes these scales brush off in a shower of fine powder. The bright patterns on the wings are made by different colors and patterns of scales, like a living mosaic. What are the differences between a moth and a butterfly? Most moths are active at night; butterflies usually fly by day. Most moths are dull browns and grays; many butterflies are brightly colored. Most moths have feathery feelers (antennae); butterflies have thin, club-ended feelers.

The peacock butterfly (above) has large eyelike patches on its wings. These are called eye spots. They are normally hidden. When the butterfly is in danger it opens its wings to show the eyes. They look like those of an owl or cat and frighten away predators.

Tropical zebra butterfly

Blue morpho butterfly

Butterflies and moths are insects which go through a drastic change in body shape as they grow up. This is called complete metamorphosis. The life cycle begins when an adult male and female mate, often flitting about in a courtship flight. The female usually lays her eggs on the food plant—the plant that the caterpillars will eat when they hatch. She places them carefully, either in groups or singly, on the undersides of leaves. For the brimstone butterfly shown opposite, the caterpillars' food plant is buckthorn. In fact,

A butterfly or moth, like this large white butterfly, has a long, tube-shaped mouth. This is normally coiled up under the head like a watch spring. To sip nectar from deep in a flower the butterfly straightens its mouth and uses it like a drinking straw to sip up the sugary fluid.

Longest

The giant agrippa moth has the biggest wingspan of any insect, up to 12 inches (30 cm) from tip to tip. The birdwing butterfly of New Guinea is second. Its wingspan is about 11 inches (28 cm).

!

caterpillars do little else except eat. After growing and molting its skin several times, each caterpillar changes into an inactive, hard-cased chrysalis. This seems to rest for a few weeks, or even through the winter. But inside, its body breaks up into a kind of thick, living soup.

Some caterpillars, like those of the monarch butterfly, have bright colors and stripes. These warn predators that the caterpillar tastes horrible and should be left alone.

The life cycle of a butterfly

When a young butterfly or moth hatches from its egg, like this brimstone, it is a long, worm-shaped creature called a caterpillar, grub or larva. This crawls, eats, and grows, molts its skin, eats and grows again, and so on, molting perhaps seven times. Then it sheds its last skin, forms a hard case around itself, and becomes an inactive chrysalis or pupa. Inside this case the creature's body undergoes amazing changes. Finally the adult butterfly emerges from the case, stretches its crumpled wings and flies away. These changes in body shape while growing up are called complete metamorphosis. The beetles and weevils, the bees, wasps, and ants, and the two-winged flies go through the same four stages of egg, larva, pupa, and adult. Other insects, like grasshoppers (page 86), have a less drastic metamorphosis.

egg (first stage of life cycle)

caterpillar (second or larval stage)

empty chrysalis case

imago (fourth or adult stage) of brimstone butterfly

chrysalis (third or pupal stage)

Moths usually hold their wings out sideways at rest.

This reforms into the wings, legs, feelers and other parts of the adult butterfly or moth. The adult emerges from the chrysalis case and flies away to search for its own food, usually the sweet, sugary fluid called nectar in flowers. Some butterflies and moths migrate long distances as adults, to avoid dry or cold seasons and find more sheltered places. In North America, monarch

WORLD WATCH

During the 19th century butterfly and moth collecting became a popular hobby. Millions of brightly colored specimens were killed, dried and put on display in glass cases. This made some species of butterflies and moths extremely rare. Many are now protected by law. But illegal collecting continues in some places, especially tropical regions. The large, bright butterflies are sold to collectors and tourists.

The hawkmoths, like this elephant hawkmoth, are fast and powerful fliers with narrow, V-shaped wings.

Moths usually have hairy, plump bodies. The feathery antennae of a male moth can pick up the female scent from more than 600 yards (1 km) away.

or milkweed butterflies fly south in late summer from Canada to Mexico. This journey of more than 2,000 miles (3,200 km) can take up to four months. In southeast Australia, bogong moths shelter in caves in the cool uplands during the hot, dry summer, and return to the lowlands to breed in autumn.

Bad taste

The bright colors of some butterflies and moths, especially in the caterpillar stage, warn animals who might try to eat them that they taste horrible. Others are brightly colored to attract mates.

Clearwings are day-flying moths that look more like butterflies, with their bright colors and slim bodies.

Butterflies and moths (Lepidoptera)
- 175,000 species
- adults have four wings, often colorful
- adult has long, tubular mouth
- most feed on flowers
- larvae are leaf-eating caterpillars

Bees, wasps, and ants

BEES, WASPS, AND ANTS MAKE UP THE THIRD LARGEST SUBGROUP OF INSECTS. They are known as Hymenopterans. They include the familiar honeybees, also bumblebees and carpenter bees, many kinds of wasps and hornets with their dangerous stings, black and red ants in the garden, and columns of army ants marching through tropical forests. They also include more than 100,000 species of tiny parasitic wasps that live on and in plants or other animals.

Ants, wasps, and bees are the main kinds of social insects. They live together in colonies or nests, helping each other by doing different tasks such as fetching and distributing food, cleaning, or defending the colony from attack. Some bumblebees live in colonies of only a few individuals, perhaps four or five. A typical wasps' nest numbers 2,000 individuals. A honeybees' nest or hive has up to 50,000 members. Driver ants and army ants have no permanent nests. They march through the forest in columns half a million strong, killing and eating anything in their path and setting up a bivouac camp for their overnight stop.

Queen and workers

In a typical wasps' or bees' nest, there is just one female who lays eggs. She is the queen. A queen honey bee lays up to 1,500 eggs each day. She is

Bees, wasps, and hornets make their nests from chewed wood, which dries as thin paper.

looked after by workers called courtiers. Forager workers fly off to collect food, mainly pollen and nectar from flowers. All of these workers are females. As well as laying eggs, the queen bee also controls the colony by preventing workers from developing into queens themselves. Her mouthparts produce a special chemical called queen substance, which spreads through the nest. If she dies, the queen substance fades away. Then some of the grubs, developing in their six-sided compartments, or cells, in the nest, develop into young queens. Others develop into male bees or drones. The young queens and drones mate. One new queen takes over the existing colony. The others fly off to found fresh colonies elsewhere. Wild bees nest in holes in trees and rocks. Honeybees have been domesticated in hives for more than 3,000 years.

Bees gather nectar and pollen from flowers, chew and predigest it, and "sick" it back up as honey. This feeds the grubs (larvae) in the nest.

Bees and wasps like this common wasp have four wings. But the two wings on each side are hooked together so they flap up and down as one.

Helping flowers too

Honey bees help us not only by making honey. Our fruit orchards, farm crops, and garden plants depend on insects, especially honeybees and bumblebees, to carry pollen from one flower to another. This enables the seeds and fruits to develop. At least 150 different main crops depend on bee pollination. One bumblebee may visit more than 200 different flowers on a single feeding trip.

Insects within insects

Some parasitic wasps lay their tiny eggs on or inside the bodies of other insects. Even the eggs of insects are not safe from attack by these tiny wasps. The smallest of all insects are called fairy flies. About ten would fit on a pinhead. But they are not flies; they are

This sphinx moth caterpillar is host to maggot-like parasitic wasp larvae, who will eat it alive.

minute wasps. They lay their eggs inside the eggs of other insects. When the grubs hatch out, they are surrounded by the nutritious contents of the egg, which they consume before emerging.

Termites

Termites are sometimes called "white ants." But they are not in the ant group;

they have their own insect group, Isoptera. However, like ants, termites live in nests or colonies. Some burrow into wooden structures such as timber buildings. Others make nest mounds of hard, sun-baked mud. Termites have the largest and most complicated colonies of any insect. There may be more than five million in one nest, all controlled by a king and queen. Worker termites fetch and carry food, and special soldier termites with large jaws guard the colony. The queen termite lays 30,000 eggs each day, and she can live for 15 years!

Lacewings and ant lions

Another subgroup of insects includes lacewings and ant lions. Lacewings take their name from their delicate, veined, lacy-looking wings. The adults have a weak, fluttery flight and are often attracted to lighted windows or lamps at night. They and their pincer-jawed larvae eat smaller creatures such as bugs. Adult ant lions look similar to lacewings. They are found mainly in warm countries.

The female great wood wasp has a long, sharp "sting" which is really an egg-laying tube or ovipositor. She drills through tree bark to the grub of a wood-boring wasp or beetle within, and lays an egg in it. When this egg hatches, the wasp larva feeds on the host larva, gradually killing it and finally emerging as an adult wood wasp.

The lacewings are large-winged insects that prey on smaller, soft-bodied bugs such as aphids (greenflies and blackflies).

The ant-lion larva has enormous spiked mouthparts to grab prey. It eats small creatures such as worms, caterpillars, and ants, and even fierce predators such as spiders and centipedes.

These insects are named after their fierce larvae. The ant lion larva digs a cone-shaped pit in loose soil or sand and waits at the bottom, part-buried, large jaws at the ready. When a small insect tumbles into the sand pit, the ant lion scrabbles and slides the sand, and the prey, down into its huge jaws.

Ants follow an invisible trail of scent, or pheromone, as they forage for food.

These bumblebees have opened a cell in their nest to clean the pupa. Like butterflies, hymenopterans go through four stages in their lives—egg, grub, or larva, the pupa in its cocoon or case, and the adult.

Bees, wasps, and ants
(Hymenoptera)
- at least 130,000 species
- four thin wings, joined on each side
- chewing mouthparts
- ants mainly wingless
- many can sting
- many feed from flowers

Termites (Isoptera)
- 2,250 species
- live in large colonies

- workers are wingless
- feed on rotting wood
- live mainly in warm countries

Lacewings and ant-lions
(Neuroptera)
- 5,000 species
- lacelike veins in the large wings
- larvae and adults catch and eat other insects
- live mainly in warm countries

Flies

THE COMMON HOUSEFLY IS A WELL-KNOWN, BUZZING NUISANCE IN THE KITCHEN OR AT A PICNIC. It is a member of the insect subgroup called the true or two-winged flies, Diptera. This has more than 90,000 species around the world. It includes gnats, midges and mosquitoes, craneflies, horseflies, botflies, hoverflies, fruitflies, bluebottles, greenbottles, and dungflies. The main feature of all these flies is that they have just one pair of proper wings, rather than the usual two pairs of most insects. The second or rear pair are small, thin, and club-shaped. They are called halteres and help the insect to balance as it flies.

Dungflies roll animal droppings into balls and lay their eggs in it, so the maggots (larvae) can feed on it when they hatch.

The two-winged or true flies are the supreme aerobats of the insect world. A hoverfly can not only hover in midair, it can also fly sideways and backward. The wing of a fly or similar insect is a thin flap that contains no muscles. The fly moves its wings by changing the shape of its thorax, the part of the body where the wings are attached. It does this by using muscles inside its thorax to make the wings click up and down. The wings are attached to the body by elastic, rubbery hinges, making them bounce back up at the end of each down stroke. Using this method, most insects can beat their wings more than 300 times every second. Some midges and hoverflies flap them more than 1,000 times a second. The speed of flapping creates a sound that we hear as a drone, buzz, hum, or whine.

What flies eat
Many flies eat very different foods in their young or larval stage, called a

A mosquito has a long, needle-like mouth to suck blood.

maggot, and in the adult stage. Hoverflies are expert flower-feeders and they especially like the flat flowers of plants in the carrot family. Yet their larvae eat aphids and other bugs, or dung, or even survive as "guests" in the nests of ants and wasps, feeding on the debris and rubbish.

Midges and mosquitoes bite us to suck our blood. They can be a great nuisance and spread diseases such as malaria and yellow fever (page 13), especially in wet and marshy areas where they breed.

Biting!
Mosquitoes, gnats, and midges bite people to suck their blood. But only the females do this. They need the concentrated nourishment from blood to help their eggs develop. Male mosquitoes and midges feed harmlessly on nectar from flowers.

They lay their eggs on the surface of ponds and pools. The clusters of tiny, waxy eggs stick together and float on the surface like miniature rafts. Then the comma-shaped larvae hatch out and swim down into the water by wriggling, to feed on tiny plants and animals.

The five species of tsetse fly (*Glossina*) live in Africa. They feed by sucking the blood of people and animals such as cattle, but as they feed they spread the microscopic protists called trypanosomes. These breed in the blood of a person and cause a serious disease called sleeping sickness.

Several kinds of flies are attracted by a rotting rat carcass. A tiny gnat, with feathery antennae (at the far left of the scene) watches a buzzing green-eyed horsefly (center). The tsetse fly (above left), with blue eyes, spreads the disease sleeping sickness. Stages in the fly life cycle are eggs on the rat's eyes, larvae or maggots in its body, and pupae or cocoons just below the horsefly.

Horseflies

The large, powerful horseflies can inflict painful bites on people, cattle, and horses with their bladelike mouthparts. The wound itches, bleeds and swells up, but horseflies rarely spread disease. Their larvae also bite fiercely and suck the body juices from worms, grubs, and other small, soft-bodied animals.

Flesh-eating grubs

Some kinds of fly, such as the botfly of tropical America and the tumbu fly of Africa, lay their eggs on the skin of large animals, including people. The maggots or larvae of some species burrow through the skin and eat the living flesh beneath. They can cause serious infections.

Horse botfly larvae get into a horse's mouth when it licks itself while cleaning its coat. The larvae then grow inside the horse's stomach. They eventually pass out with the horse's droppings, although some may burrow into the horse's blood vessels and spread around its body.

The sheep nostril fly really does lay its eggs inside the nose of a sheep. Its larvae live and feed in the nose passages of the sheep. They can bore their way through to its eyes and even into its brain.

Different types of biting midges suck the blood or body fluids of many animals, especially mammals and birds, also amphibians and even insects.

Dribbling onto its food

The housefly buzzing around the kitchen may have fed last on rotting garbage or animal droppings. It dribbles saliva (spit) from its spongelike mouthparts onto its food to make it dissolve into a liquid. Then it paddles around in and sucks up this "soup."

Germs stick onto its legs and mouthparts. Then it buzzes off—and lands on your meal! Houseflies can spread various illnesses, including diarrhea and various types of food poisoning.

Craneflies (left) are also called daddy-longlegs. The fruit fly (right) has red eyes, while three dung flies (below right) have distinctive red faces.

Flies
- at least 90,000 species
- worldwide, especially tropical
- one pair of transparent wings
- larvae are legless maggots

Dragonflies and damselflies

WITH WHIRRING WINGS, A DRAGONFLY DARTS FROM ITS PERCH NEAR THE POND, grabs a tiny gnat in midair, and returns to the twig to eat. There are some 5,000 species of dragonfly and damselfly, known as Orthopterans. Each has a long, slender body, two pairs of long, large, vein-patterned wings, and very big eyes for seeing prey. Damselflies are usually smaller and slimmer than dragonflies, and their flight is slower and less direct. The dragonfly is one of the champion insect fliers, able to cruise at around 3 miles per hour (5 km/h), dart ten times faster in a short burst, then stop almost at once and hover. Dragonflies and damselflies usually hunt over ponds, swamps and slow rivers. In fact, these are the places where they grow up. The young stages of these insects, called larvae or nymphs, live underwater. They grow and develop for up to five years in the water, depending on the species, before climbing out, shedding their skins and becoming adults.

A mayfly larva has three tail filaments, which help it swim. It also has small, non-flapping wings.

All the insects shown here have one feature in common. Their young, or larvae, live in fresh water—often for two years or more. The larvae are usually brown or gray and creep around in ponds, lakes, streams, and swamps. Dragonfly larvae are large, and like their parents they are very strong hunters. They feed by

Some caddisfly nymphs make their body cases from bits of water plant leaves (left). Others use tiny pieces of gravel (above) or snipped-off lengths of plant stems (right).

grabbing other water creatures, such as tadpoles and even small fish, with their enormous pincerlike jaws. The larva sheds or molts its skin many times. Finally it climbs up a reed or plant stem, and the adult crawls out of its last larval skin. Its wings spread and harden, and its body becomes slim and colorful. Then the adult dragonfly dashes off to catch its first victim, in the air rather than in the water.

Keep out!
An adult male dragonfly takes over a length of riverbank or lakeside as his breeding territory. He defends it fiercely by chasing off other males that

stray nearby. He may even fly at people walking past to get a good look and make sure they are not rivals. When a female appears, he holds her behind her head, using the claspers at the end of his tail, and she swings her abdomen forward to mate.

Adult mayfly

Mayflies
A mayfly lives for a year or more as a larva in a stream or river, eating tiny plants and other bits of food. It sheds its skin up to 25 times—a record for an insect. Then it crawls up a plant stem into the air and sheds its skin twice, first

The emperor dragonfly has a blue patterned body and wings 4 inches (10 cm) across. It holds them out to the sides while resting.

A dragonfly has its legs together in a basketlike trap to catch prey in flight.

Damselflies hold their wings over their backs at rest. Males and females link together at breeding time to form a "mating chain" that may be five or six damselflies long!

Caddisflies are usually active at night. Like moths, they may fly toward electric lights.

The stonefly has two long feelers on its head and two long tail filaments. It is a weak flier and usually crawls over plants and rocks near water.

becoming a winged sub-adult, and then a proper adult, able to breed. Yet after all this, the adult mayfly lives for only a few hours. It has just enough time to breed and die. Adult mayflies often emerge in swarms on the same day. They "dance" over the water as they mate, and the females lay eggs by dipping their rear ends below the water's surface. Some adult mayflies have such tiny mouths that they could not feed even if they had time!

Stoneflies

Stoneflies also have short lives as adults, usually just a week or two. Yet they also spend a year or more as water-dwelling larvae. Stonefly nymphs dwell in clear, rocky, fast-flowing streams. They grip the stony stream bed with their strong hooked legs, to prevent themselves being swept away in the current. Adult stoneflies resemble adult mayflies, but they have two tail filaments rather than three, and when at rest, they hold their thin, veined wings flat over their bodies.

Caddisflies

Adult caddisflies have slightly hairy wings and bodies, like some moths. They are seldom seen far from water, where their larvae live inside tube-shaped cases built from whatever is common in the pond or stream. Some caddis larvae even use tiny empty snail shells as mobile homes.

Like dragonflies, damselflies have thin, delicate wings strengthened by veins. These tubes contain blood as the new adult spreads its wings. But then they become hard, dry and empty.

Dragonflies and damselflies (Orthoptera)
- about 5,000 species
- two pairs of large, long, transparent, veined wings
- big eyes
- young (nymphs) live in water
- adults often fly near water

Mayflies (Ephemeroptera)
- about 2,000 species
- delicate veined wings, usually two pairs
- three thin or fan-shaped tail filaments
- young (nymphs) live in water
- adults very short-lived

Stoneflies (Plecoptera)
- about 3,000 species
- flattened body
- two thin or fan-shaped tail filaments
- young (nymphs) live in water
- adults live along river banks

Caddisflies (Trichoptera)
- about 6,000 species
- young (nymphs) live in water, often in protective cases
- adults hairy, with four wings
- live near fresh water

Bugs

THE WORD "BUG" IS OFTEN USED FOR ANY TYPE OF INSECT, or for a spider or any other kind of small, crawling creature. However, the bugs are really a distinct subgroup of insects, known as Hemipterans. There are some 70,000 different species of bug. They all share the usual insect features of six legs, a three-part body, and four flapping wings, but they also have a feature unique to the group. This is a beak-shaped or needle-like mouth, specialized for piercing and sucking liquids and juices. Some bugs are predators.

Many bugs, like these blackspot leaf bugs, are colored or camouflaged to match their surroundings.

Cicadas are large bugs that make loud, shrill chirping sounds.

Assassin bugs and bedbugs, and water bugs such as pondskaters and backswimmers, feed on the blood and body fluids of other animals. Other bugs are plant-feeders, such as leafbugs and shieldbugs, cicadas, leaf hoppers, and aphids.

After crawling from its old split skin, the cicada's crumpled wings soon expand.

The backswimmer's front four legs touch the water's surface, to detect tiny ripples that could mean prey.

Several kinds of bug live on or under the water. Pondskaters skim around on the surface, hunting for flies and other insects that have fallen in. The pondskater senses the ripples made by the struggling prey and speeds over to bite and suck out its body juices. Backswimmers and water boatmen row themselves through the water using their hairy legs. They have very strong mouthparts for catching tiny pond creatures and can even give a person a painful bite. The water scorpion is a large bug that captures prey with its pincers. The long tail is not a sting, but a snorkel—a tube through which the water scorpion breathes as it hangs just below the surface.

Calling to attract a mate

Some insects use sounds to attract mates. And some of the loudest insect sounds are made by male cicadas. Their piercing, high-pitched calls are heard in

Inside an insect's leg

The leg of an insect or other arthropod is like a long, slim tube made of several sections. The casing, or exoskeleton (page 72), is thin between the sections to allow the leg to bend, moved by several muscles inside.

coxa (joins to body)

trochanter

exoskeleton

femur

joint

tibia

leg-bending muscle

leg-straightening muscle

tarsus

claws

At certain seasons, usually summer, female aphids do not lay eggs. They give birth to fully formed babies, or nymphs. This allows them to reproduce very quickly when conditions are suitable.

Some bugs show parental behavior, which is rare among insects. This female shieldbug guards her eggs against predators.

many of the warmer parts of the world. The noise comes from the sides of the cicada's thorax or body, which flick in and out, like shaking a metal sheet to and fro very rapidly. Adult cicadas live and feed in trees. But their young, or nymphs, develop in the soil, feeding on the sap of plant roots. They are among the longest-lived of all insects. Some cicada nymphs stay underground for more than 20 years, before emerging and shedding their skins to become adults.

Leaf hoppers and frog hoppers are small bugs that suck sap from plant stems and buds. Their nymphs make bubbly froth around themselves, called "snake spit," for protection from the hot sun and predators.

They are among the toughest of all insects, and with their strong chewing mouthparts they can survive on almost any scraps of food. They also reproduce quickly and may become serious pests. Different types of cockroach live in almost all land habitats, from icy mountains to deep caves, to the dead leaves and soil of tropical forests.

the much larger, thinner, more delicate flying wings folded beneath them. The female earwig is a caring parent. She cleans her eggs and protects her newly hatched young too.

Aphids
The greenflies and blackflies that become pests in the garden during summer are bugs called aphids. They are mostly small, just fractions of an inch long. They suck sap from flowers such as roses, fruits like currants, vegetables such as cabbages and lima beans, and many other plants.

These tiny bugs have amazing powers of reproduction. They spend the winter as eggs. The first aphids to hatch in spring are females. They can produce young without having to mate with a male first. This method of breeding is found among a few other animal groups and is known as parthenogenesis. In this way aphids reproduce very fast and build up large swarms. In late summer, females produce some male babies as well. These mate with the females, which then lay eggs to live through the winter.

Earwigs
Earwigs look fierce, with their curved clawlike tails. But they are harmless to people. Old tales which tell of earwigs creeping into ears or under wigs are not strictly true—an earwig will hide in any

The earwig's tail pincers, or cerci, are used to capture prey, fend off enemies, and hold the partner when mating. They are curved in males (above) and straight in females.

Cockroaches
Flattened and quick-moving, cockroaches look like bugs but belong in their own insect subgroup.

dark hole or crevice. Most earwigs burrow in soil or crawl under tree bark. They eat a range of plant and animal food, including harmful grubs. The two front wings of both earwigs and cockroaches are small and hard. They protect

Green leaf bug

This tropical cockroach is camouflaged to resemble dead leaves on the forest floor. Cockroaches are very primitive insects. This means they were one of the first kinds of insect to appear on Earth, more than 300 million years ago.

True bugs
(Hemiptera)
- about 70,000 species
- beaklike mouthparts for piercing and sucking
- many have narrow or flattened bodies

Cockroaches
(Blattodea)
- 3,700 species
- long, low, flattened body
- long feelers
- hard front wings protect rear wings underneath
- fast-running

Earwigs
(Dermaptera)
- 1,200 species
- flattened body
- pincer-like tail

Crickets and grasshoppers

CRICKETS AND GRASSHOPPERS HAVE LONG, POWERFUL BACK LEGS FOR LEAPING AND JUMPING, USUALLY TO ESCAPE PREDATORS. They belong to the insect subgroup known as Orthopterans. Most have camouflaged bodies, colored and patterned to blend in with their surroundings. As they leap, they may spread their two rear wings in a flash of whirring color. The young or larvae of crickets and grasshoppers look like small versions of the adult, except that they do not have wings. The wings grow gradually, each time the larva sheds its skin. This type of development is known as incomplete metamorphosis and the larvae are called nymphs. There is no pupa or chrysalis stage (page 77). Other insects that grow like this include cockroaches, bugs, dragonflies, termites, mantids, earwigs, and stoneflies.

A grasshopper (left) has shorter antennae or feelers than a cricket (below).

Leaf insects (above, above right and below right) are extremely well camouflaged in both appearance and behaviour. They move and sway to mimic a leaf being blown by the wind.

Stick and leaf insects

The stick and leaf insects, or phasmids, live mainly in tropical regions. They avoid birds and other predators with their amazing camouflage. Their bodies look like thin sticks or twigs, or like flat leaves. Most are green or brown, to match the plants on which they feed.

The rasping and chirping of crickets and grasshoppers are familiar sounds in hot weather. The male insects "sing" to warn others off their territory or to attract a mate. Crickets and the similar katydids rub the comblike front wing veins together to make the noise. Grasshoppers and locusts rub their back legs against the front wing veins. Each leg has a row of hard pegs which make the wing vibrate.

A leaping desert locust straightens each leg section in turn.

One kind of cricket, the mole cricket, lives in a burrow rather than on grass stems and plants like most crickets and grasshoppers. He uses a special method to make his song even louder. He digs a mating burrow with the entrance shaped like a double funnel. This acts as a kind of megaphone or loudspeaker, making the chirping much louder. On a still night the mole-cricket's song can be heard more than a mile (1.6 km) away.

Some leaf insects even have V-shaped patterns on their bodies resembling the veins or ribs of a leaf. Others have brown edges, patches or blotches, so that they look like old or damaged leaves.

Stick insects hold out their legs at the same angles as the twigs around them.

Locusts (above) and grasshoppers sometimes breed so rapidly that they form huge swarms which devastate crops. Crickets, like the green bush cricket (left), and mantids (below) usually live singly.

Mantids

Mantids are fierce hunters. They catch and eat other small animals, such as large insects and spiders, grabbing them with their spiny, pincer-like front legs. The mantis has large eyes for excellent vision. It sits patiently on a plant or flower, waiting until a suitable victim

No males needed

Some kinds of female stick insect do not need to mate with a male before laying eggs. In some species males are hardly ever found. This kind of breeding is called parthenogenesis (page 85).

Longest

The longest insects are some kinds of stick insect. They grow to 14 inches (35 cm) from head to tail.

!

The praying mantis is named from its waiting-to-pounce posture, with front legs folded as if in prayer.

comes near. Then it strikes, too fast for us to see, and grabs the prey in its spiny "arms." When some kinds of mantid breed, the female eats the male just after they mate, or even while mating. In other species this cannot happen because

there are no males. The females reproduce by parthenogenesis.

Both stick insects (above) and grasshoppers (left) have large, fanlike rear wings. When these are not in use they are folded and protected by the smaller, harder front wings.

Crickets, locusts and grasshoppers (Orthoptera)	Stick and leaf insects (Phasmatoidea)	Mantids (Mantodea)
• 20,500 species	• 2,500 species	• 1,800 species
• long, strong hind legs for jumping	• live mainly in the tropics	• live mainly in warmer countries
• shieldlike covering behind the head	• resemble leaves, twigs or sticks	• triangular head with big eyes
• small, hard front wings	• even the eggs are camouflaged, to resemble plant seeds	• large front legs with pincerlike claws
• large, fanlike rear wings	• large, fanlike rear wings	• eat mainly other insects
• feed on plants	• eat plants	

Fleas, lice, and other insects

FLEAS AND LICE ARE TINY, WINGLESS INSECTS THAT ARE PARASITES. They feed on other animals, called their hosts, either by sucking their blood or by chewing their skin or feathers. Fleas have sideways-flattened bodies and can slip easily among fur or feathers. They pierce the flesh of the host using their sharp, needle-like mouthparts. Most fleas are parasites of mammals. Humans, rats, cats, dogs, rabbits, bears, porcupines, beavers and many others each have their own particular flea species. Other fleas are parasites of birds, especially those that live in burrows, such as puffins, where the flea larvae can develop in warm safety. A flea escapes danger by leaping with its long, powerful back legs. These have a special click mechanism that stores energy and then releases it suddenly, like a spring-loaded lever. The average flea measures just a few pinheads across, but it can jump more than 12 inches (30 cm)—about 100 times its own length. This means, for its size, the flea is the world's greatest animal athlete.

Thrips are tiny, fly-like insects with two pairs of hairy or feathery wings. They can breed fast to form huge swarms that ruin farm crops.

A human louse sucks the blood of its host. The blood gradually fills the front of the louse's abdomen, turning it dark red.

A louse clings onto its host using its sharp claws. Its flattened body lies close to the skin, making it very difficult to remove. Like fleas, there are different kinds of lice for different animals, including humans, dogs, guinea pigs, elephants, seals, warthogs, and hummingbirds! The human louse is about 0.1 inch (2 mm) long and its bite causes an itchy lump. The female glues her eggs to human hairs. The eggs look like tiny grains of salt and are called "nits."

The louse has hook-shaped, gripping legs with very strong claws. It clings to the skin or hair and resists being brushed off or washed away. In tropical regions, lice spread diseases such as typhus and relapsing fever.

Barklice and booklice
In addition to the lice described above, which are sometimes known as sucking or parasitic lice, there are two other

Silverfish

This is one of the simplest or most primitive of all insects. It has no wings, but very long antennae and a three-forked tail. It is found in kitchens and food stores, coming out at night to feed on scraps. The silverfish is named after its silvery color and its bendy, fishlike movements.

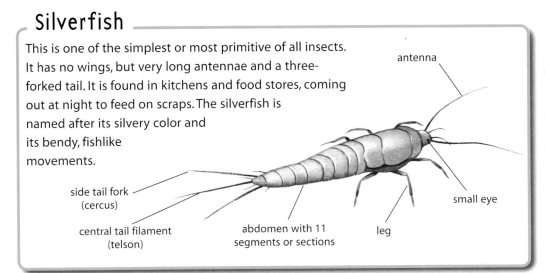

antenna

side tail fork (cercus)

central tail filament (telson)

abdomen with 11 segments or sections

leg

small eye

They can multiply quickly and eat the flowers of crops such as wheat and other cereals, onions, carrots, and fruits such as apples and oranges. In warm, thundery weather they may take to the air in great swarms, crawling on our skin and in our hair and eyes. They are sometimes known as thunderflies or thunderbugs.

Oldest

The first insects were probably springtails. Their fossils have been found in rocks about 400 million years old, formed during the Devonian Period. At this time most animals lived in the water of seas and rivers. Springtails were among the first creatures to venture onto land.

groups of lice. Barklice are small and active, living on the bark of trees, among leaves or in birds' nests. They feed mainly on tiny plants and molds. Booklice are similar and are sometimes found in old

Thrips

The thrips are among the smallest of all insects. They have feathery or fluffy wings and can fly quite well. Most feed on plants, and especially on the flowers.

Springy tail

Springtails are also very small insects, none being longer than a quarter of an inch (5 mm). They are named after the springlike structure on the tail. They flicks this down to jump away when disturbed. They are so different from other insects that they have their own major subgroup (subclass), Collembola.

Springtails are among the most abundant and widespread of all insects. They live in their millions in the soil, among dead leaves and moss, and in rotting wood. Some kinds are pests because they eat farm crops such as cereals and clover. Others live on sandy beaches, around rock pools on the shore, and even at the surface of the stagnant, polluted water in ditches.

houses and buildings. They usually feed on mold, but they also eat the starchy paste used in the glue that binds the pages of old books.

A flea's back legs are more than twice as long as its front and middle legs. The needle-like mouthparts are between the two front legs.

The springtail has a long, leverlike tail. This is normally hooked under the main body. When released, it springs downward and flicks the insect into the air.

Fleas (Siphonaptera)
- 1,800 species
- very small
- wingless
- body flattened sideways
- powerful jumpers
- blood-sucking parasites of mammals and birds

Lice (Phthiraptera)
- 3,500 species
- very small
- wingless
- parasites of other animals

Booklice and barklice (Psocoptera)
- 2,000 species
- resemble lice but more active
- some eat paper and book bindings

Thrips (Thysanoptera)
- 5,000 species
- tiny
- resemble flies with hairy wings

Bristletails and silverfish (Thysanura)
- 600 species
- wingless
- shiny flat body, long antennae
- bristly two- or three-pronged tail

Springtails (Collembola)
- 2,000 species
- very small
- wingless
- spring-lever mechanism on tail for leaping
- live in damp habitats, including surfaces of ponds and streams

Crabs, lobsters, and shrimps

INSECTS ARE THE MOST COMMON ANIMALS ON LAND. But they do not live in salty water. Instead, another group of arthropods occupies the oceans—the crustaceans. They include crabs, lobsters, shrimps, and barnacles. The shrimplike krill eaten by great whales are crustaceans. So are the small creatures called copepods, which teem in such vast swarms that they are the most numerous animals in the sea. Some crustaceans, such as water fleas and crayfish, live in fresh water. A few, like woodlice, live on land.

Common shore crab

Male ghost and fiddler crabs have one pincer larger than the other, to signal to rivals and mates.

Some crabs, like the robber crab, live partly on land. This powerful crustacean can even climb up trees near the shore.

For many people, the most familiar crustaceans are crabs. There are thousands of crab species, from giant spider crabs with pincers as long as your arm, to tiny porcelain and pea crabs that would fit in this o. A typical crab has a flattened body covered by the hard, shell-like carapace. The abdomen (rear part of the body) is small and tucked under the shell at the back. There are ten limbs—one pair of large pincers and four pairs of walking legs. Most crabs live in the sea, but a few dwell in rivers and lakes. The common shore crab is very hardy and can live in both salt and fresh water, and even out of water for a few hours.

Biggest

The Japanese giant spider crab is the largest crustacean and also the largest living arthropod. Its body is the size of a dinner plate, and it can measure 12 feet (3.5 m) across.

!

The hermit's home

The front end of a hermit crab has the typical hard crab carapace and pincers, and two pairs of large walking legs. But the rear of its body is soft and twisted. This is because a hermit crab lives in the abandoned shell of a sea snail, such as a whelk. It holds the shell from inside with its two pairs of smaller rear legs. When the hermit crab grows too big for its shell it has to "move house." It finds a larger shell, then quickly slides its body backward into the new home.

Krill live in cool oceans, in swarms several miles long, numbering many millions. They are cousins of shrimps and feed by filtering the tiny plants and animals of the plankton from seawater.

Crayfish and lobsters

Crayfish and lobsters are like elongated crabs with the rear body part, the abdomen, held out straight at the rear like tail, rather than tucked underneath. The middle body part, the thorax, has four pairs of walking legs with a pair of very large, strong pincers or claws at the front. In some types of lobster one pincer is bigger and designed for crushing, while the smaller one is sharper for cutting and snipping.

The lobster's head has two pairs of antennae or feelers. The larger pair curl out in front and may be longer than the whole body. The lobster uses these to feel among rocks and seaweed, searching for food such as worms and shellfish, which it crushes and cuts up with its pincers.

Like all crustaceans, the slipper lobster grows by shedding or molting its old carapace (shell). The new one underneath enlarges and then hardens.

Crustacean protection

A lobster is well protected. Its head and thorax are covered by a thick, rigid carapace. The abdomen has a series of jointed plates, one for each segment. This crustacean can also defend itself with its powerful pincers against predators such as seals and rays. Normally it walks along, but it can bend its abdomen and flattened tail suddenly and shoot backwards to escape.

Shrimps and prawns

Shrimps and prawns are like small, lightly built lobsters. Shrimps can crawl well but prawns usually swim by rowing with the five pairs of paddle-shaped limbs, or swimmerets, under the abdomen. The shrimp has a body flattened from top to bottom, while the prawn is flattened from side to side. Both these types of crustacean eat almost anything they find, including dead animals. When alive they are almost transparent and well camouflaged against rocks and sand. They only turn pink when cooked!

Shrimps are similar to prawns, but lack the long, beaklike, pointed snout or rostrum at the front of the head.

Prawns use their delicate pinchers to search through mud and sand for anything small and edible.

The red-banded cleaner shrimp lives on coral reefs. Its bright colors advertise the service it provides—picking tiny parasites and pests off larger animals such as fish. The shrimp gets a meal and the fish gets cleaned.

Crayfish are the largest freshwater crustaceans. Like their cousins, lobsters, they feed at night. By day they hide in a lair, in a hole or under a stone.

Barnacles and other crustaceans

WHEN THE TIDE IS OUT, AN ACORN BARNACLE HARDLY LOOKS LIKE AN ANIMAL AT ALL. Its pyramid-shaped shell, cemented firmly to a rock, has a tightly shut door at the top. But when the tide comes in, the door opens and the barnacle extends its long, feathery, fanlike limbs into the water. These beat regularly with a grasping motion to pull tiny bits of food towards the barnacle's mouth. Many other kinds of small crustaceans live along seashores and in the open oceans. The adults look very different, resembling shrimps, fleas, or mussels. But their young forms or larvae are all very similar. These billions of small crustaceans make up much of the ocean plankton.

Acorn barnacles coat rocks along the seashore and in shallow water. They are preyed on by whelks, starfish, and fish. Some species can survive above the high-tide level, with the occasional spray from waves.

Brine shrimps are food for crabs and flamingoes.

Living upside down

Fairy shrimps and brine shrimps have rows of feathery or brushlike limbs along each side of the body. They swim slowly—and upside down—by waving these limbs. These delicate-looking crustaceans rarely grow bigger than your finger, and most are much sorter. They have no defenses against predators, partly because they live in places where predators are uncommon. Fairy shrimps inhabit temporary pools, such as puddles of rainwater, where animals like fish cannot survive. When the pool dries out, the adult fairy shrimps die, but they leave very tough eggs in the mud. These hatch when the pool fills again. Brine shrimps can survive in the extremely warm and salty water of salt lakes and coastal lagoons.

A barnacle begins life as a tiny egg which hatches into a vaguely shrimplike larva. This drifts and swims as part of the plankton for a few days. In shallow water, it finds a firm place like a rock where the waves break at low tide. The larva sticks its head to the rock with its own natural glue and grows several hard, chalky plates around its body. Finally it changes into the adult barnacle, which feeds by kicking its feathery limbs to create water currents that draw food particles into its shell. Sometimes barnacles cause problems when they settle to live on a ship's hull, a buoy, or an undersea cable. They also attach to large sea animals such as whales, sharks, and turtles. They may live there for 20 years or more.

Most copepods (page 93) in the ocean plankton, like calanus, are smaller than a fingertip. But some deep-sea copepods reach a foot (30 cm).

Tough!

The eggs of brine and fairy shrimps are very hardy. They can survive being deep-frozen or even boiled. The adults can cope with great heat too. Some live in hot springs where the water is a scalding 160°F (71°C).

The most common crustaceans

The open seas and oceans are the main home of copepods and ostracods, although some kinds are found in ponds and lakes. Copepods resemble slim woodlice with very long feelers. They are among the most numerous creatures found in plankton, and many kinds of sea creatures depend upon them for food. Ostracods look like tiny versions of mussels or clams, or even like plant seeds such as bean seeds. They are sometimes called mussel shrimps or seed shrimps. They are more at home on the sea floor where they filter food from water or mud. The largest kinds are just a quarter-inch (5 mm) across.

Some ostracods release substances into the water which glow with an eerie greenish-yellow light. This may be a signal that breeding time has arrived. Or it may be a light version of a smokescreen, to confuse their many predators, such as worms and shrimps.

Water fleas and fish lice

Water fleas have large feathery antennae, which they use to row through the water. As they move, they both

Goose barnacles have shell-like plates around the body for protection, like their cousins the acorn barnacles. They also have a fleshy stalk, or peduncle, which attaches to a floating piece of debris such as a lump of driftwood (or a boat).

feed and breathe using their legs, which work as gills (page 102) to take in oxygen and as sieves to gather food. Fish lice are not true lice, but louse-shaped crustaceans. They are blood-sucking parasites on fish and other water-dwellers, sticking to their scales, skin, gills, or even their eyes.

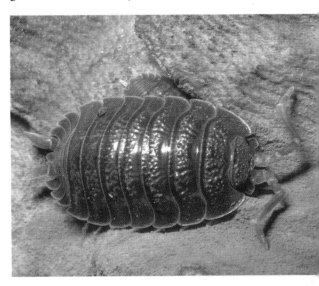

Woodlice (sowbugs) can only survive in damp places, such as among dead leaves or under tree bark. This is because the covering, or cuticle, over the jointed body shell is not waterproof. If a woodlouse is exposed to the hot sun it dries out and dies.

Pillbug

Oniscus woodlouse

The oniscus woodlouse is very common and lives in woods, parks, and gardens. The pillbug is a woodlouse that can roll up into a ball for protection.

Inside a water flea

The common water flea, daphnia, is about the size of this O. It swims jerkily by rowing with its long feelers (antennae), and feeds by filtering microscopic plants and animals from the water with its feathery legs. Although it is called a water "flea," it is not a true flea—it is a crustacean. There are thousands of daphnia in even the smallest pond. They are important food for small worms, fish and shellfish.

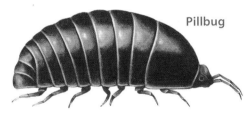

branched main antenna

eye

tiny secondary antenna

mouth

feathery legs

heart

gut

eggs in brood pouch

transparent shell (carapace)

More groups of crustaceans (continued from page 91)

Barnacles
- 1,000 species
- live in the sea
- featherlike legs
- some have shells and attach to rocks
- some are parasites

Ostracods
- 5,700 species
- most live in the sea
- very small
- oval body enclosed in hinged shell

Copepods
- 8,400 species
- most live in the sea
- shrimplike body

- long feelers
- largest are coin-sized
- swim jerkily

Water fleas
- 480 species
- mainly freshwater
- oval shell
- long branched feelers for rowing
- bob up and down

Fairy shrimps and brine shrimps
- 175 species
- fairy shrimps live in freshwater pools, brine shrimps in salty water
- long body
- feathery legs for swimming and feeding

Tadpole shrimps
- 15 species
- live in freshwater pools
- shell-like covering at front, long forked tail
- up to thumb-sized

Amphipods
- 3,600 species
- most live in the sea
- small and shrimp like
- narrow body
- includes freshwater shrimps, sandhoppers and beach fleas

Isopods
- 4,000 species
- most live in the sea
- flattened body
- seven pairs of legs
- includes woodlice

Spiders

SPIDERS ARE MEMBERS OF THE ARTHROPOD GROUP CALLED ARACHNIDS. The main feature of an arachnid is that it has eight legs, unlike an insect which has six, and a crustacean which has ten or more. Other arachnids include harvestmen, scorpions, ticks, and mites. With some 80,000 species, arachnids form the second largest group of arthropods, after insects. Like insects, they are mostly land-living, although a few kinds of spiders and mites inhabit fresh water. Unlike insects, arachnids lack wings and cannot fly. Most arachnids are predators or hunters, but some mites and ticks are parasites of other animals. Arachnids live all over the world, in a wide range of habitats, from woods and grasslands to mountains, deserts and swamps.

Spiders have one important ability that sets them apart from most other arthropods, including other arachnids. They make a kind of silk thread using special parts at the rear of the body, called spinnerets. Spider silk is used for various purposes—to spin protective cocoons around the eggs, to make a parachute for a baby spider so that it can blow in the wind to a new place, to act as a safety line in case the spider loses its footing and falls, to line a burrow or tunnel, to wrap up and subdue prey before it is eaten, and most obviously, to weave different kinds of webs, snares and traps for catching prey.

This yellow agriope orb-web spider has wrapped a moth in silk thread to eat later. If the spider has plenty of food, it may leave the victim tied up but alive, hidden in the fork of a nearby twig.

Spider silk is one of the strongest materials known. It can take more strain than a steel thread of the same thickness. Different sorts of silk are used for different purposes. Cocoon silk is thick and smooth, while web silk is like sticky, coiled elastic.

Huntsman spiders live in tropical forests. They are large and strong enough to catch prey by force and do not spin webs.

Hidden danger

Trapdoor spiders live in burrows, using their silk to make a hinged, doorlike covering to the entrance. The trapdoor spider detects vibrations in the ground as a suitable small creature passes by. Or it lays silk threads as tripwires that the creature touches. The spider then darts out of its burrow and bites the victim with its large

Bird-eating spiders have very large mouthparts, or chelicerae, with sharp fangs. They also have long palps which look like a front pair of legs. The palps are used for touching and tasting.

Spiders, like other arachnids, may lose a limb through injury. In a young spider which is still going through its molting stages, the leg will regrow at the next molt.

The net-casting spider spins a small web and holds it out with its three front pairs of legs. The web is a net ready to throw over the prey. This spider's huge eyes watch for victims and see where to cast the net.

Making a web

A common type of web is the orb web. It is roughly circular with radial threads like spokes in a wheel. The first stage is to choose a suitable place with twigs the correct distance apart. The spider sets out the top frame and makes a couple of radial threads (1). Next comes the rest of the frame and more radial threads (2), then the last of the spokelike radials (3). These are all made from a strong, tight, nonsticky type of silk. The spider then works around in a spiral from the outside toward the center, spinning a much looser, elastic, sticky silk to snare its prey (4).

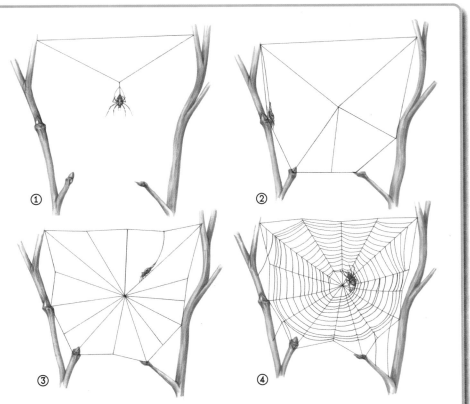

① ② ③ ④

Tarantula

fangs, which all spiders possess. It injects poison and drags its meal down into the burrow, closing the trapdoor behind.

Poisonous spiders

All spiders have poisonous bites. But only about 30 species have fangs strong enough, and poison powerful enough, to harm people. The most deadly are the black widows, *Latrodectus*, that live in many warm countries, the Australian funnel-web spiders, and the Brazilian huntsman.

Largest

The largest spider is the goliath bird-eating spider, *Theraphosa leblondi*, of South America. It measures 11 inches (28 cm) across its legs. It catches other spiders, and also lizards, birds, and small mammals like mice!

(!)

Webs galore

Web-spinning spiders make all shapes and sizes of webs. Some are woven in amazingly precise geometric patterns. Others are a tangle of threads in a dark corner. But when a victim hits the web, the silk threads quickly entangle it. If the web is badly damaged, the spider eats the silk and recycles it to spin another one.

Some spiders, like the Costa Rican orb-weaver, build an extra-visible zigzag area of silk in the middle of the web. This is called the stabilimentum.

Wolf spiders do not make webs. They run quickly across soil, rocks, and tree bark after their prey, using their extra-long legs. Since they have no home base, the female wolf spider carries her whitish silk egg cocoon under her body.

ARACHNIDS
- members of the arthropod group
- about 80,000 species
- adult has eight legs

Spiders
- 50,000 species
- worldwide, all habitats
- body has obvious waist
- make webs from silk

Scorpions and other arachnids

A SCORPION'S LONG BODY AND LARGE PINCERS MAKES IT LOOK LIKE A SMALL LOBSTER. But the scorpion's eight legs show that it is an arachnid, not a crustacean. The sting at the end of its long, arching tail is occasionally used to paralyze prey, but mainly for self-defense. Several kinds of scorpion can inflict very painful stings on larger animals and people, and a few are even fatal. So a scorpion should never be disturbed or handled! Although scorpions have from four to eight eyes, like spiders, their sight is poor. But this is not important since most scorpions hide by day, squeezed into a rocky crevice or wedged under a stone or log. At night they come out and detect prey mainly by feeling vibrations in the ground. A scorpion grabs its victim using its large pincers, or pedipalps. It may sting the prey to stop it struggling, before tearing it to pieces using its strong, clawlike mouthparts called chelicerae.

The giant red velvet mite, is one of the biggest mites, at about 0.6 inch (15 mm) long. It lives in the dry terrain of Africa. It hunts tiny worms and insects, and also scavenges on dead bits of plants and animals.

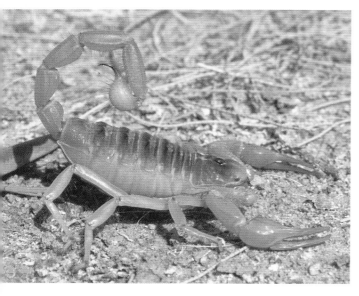

Desert scorpion

In addition to true scorpions, there are also false scorpions or pseudoscorpions. These tiny arachnids are only as long as this "I" and look like miniature scorpions. But they lack the stinging tail of their larger relatives and are quite harmless to humans. They walk backward as well as forward, and often wave their large claws in the air. False scorpions live among dead leaves and moss under bark and in compost heaps. They hunt tinier animals.

Ticks and mites

There are about 32,000 species of ticks and mites, which are the smallest arachnids. Some mites are less than one hundredth of an inch (0.2 mm). Both mites and ticks look like small, fat spiders. All ticks are parasites of larger animals such as mammals, birds, and reptiles. They bite into the skin and suck the host's blood. Some ticks spread diseases, such

A false scorpion uses its pincers in the same way as its larger relative, to grab prey.

as Rocky Mountain fever and Lyme disease (spread by deer ticks). Some mites are also parasites. They infest plants and animals, including humans, sucking their fluids. Other mites feed on tiny scraps of food and skin flakes in dust. Some people are allergic to dust mites, or rather, to their dry, powdery droppings. They may develop breathing problems such as asthma. Mite also infest food stores, especially dry foods such as grains, flour, or bran.

Parasitic mites have bladelike mouthparts that they drive into their host, to suck sap or blood.

The flour mite lives all over the world and causes immense damage in food stores. Yet other kinds of mites catch small insects and other prey.

Harvestmen

Harvestmen, sometimes called harvest spiders, are like very long-legged spiders. But they have a small, rounded, one-piece body, without the "waist" that divides the body of a true spider into two parts (the front cephalothorax and the rear abdomen). Harvestmen live in rotting leaves, old logs, damp grass, and similar places.

Some kinds of harvestmen can inflict a painful bite or even spray nasty-smelling liquid at an attacker. These arachnids eat a variety of food, from tiny animals to bits of plants and molds.

Deadly!
One of the most dangerous scorpions is the fat-tailed scorpion of North Africa. Its venom is as strong as a cobra's. The durango scorpion of Mexico and Central America is also deadly. It kills up to 1,000 people each year.

much like spiders. They have extremely strong fang-like pincers but lack a poisonous bite. They lurk under stones or in burrows and race after their prey of insects, worms, lizards, and even spiders and scorpions.

Heaviest

The heaviest and largest arachnids are tropical scorpions from India and West Africa. Some species grow up to 10 inches (25 cm) long. They look ferocious, but their stings are rarely more painful than a wasp's sting.

Scorpions are unusual among arthropods in that the female takes care of her young. She lays from one to 100 eggs, depending on the species. The eggs hatch into tiny baby scorpions, which clamber onto their mother's back. Behind her great pincers and below her poison sting, they are very safe. After a week or two they leave to fend for themselves.

Sun spiders

These desert-dwelling arachnids, also called wind spiders or solifuges, look very

The sun spider runs on its six rear legs, using the slimmer front pair and its very long palps to feel vibrations in the ground. It can outpace most prey, even lizards.

More groups of arachnids (continued from page 95)

Scorpions
- 1,200 species
- worldwide, but mainly in warm places
- large pincers
- slim curved tail with poisonous sting
- prey on smaller animals

Ticks and mites
- 32,000 species
- most mites are smaller than ticks
- resemble small, fat spiders
- ticks are parasites of mammals, birds, or reptiles
- some mites are parasites, others are free-living
- some mites are brightly colored

False scorpions
- 2,000 species
- tiny
- look like miniature scorpions, but without a stinging tail
- live in soil, decaying leaves, old wood

Harvestmen
- 4,500 species
- worldwide
- live in woodland, grassland, gardens
- resemble a spider but with a one-piece body and long, stiltlike legs

Sun spiders (Solifuges)
- 900 species
- live mainly in deserts
- huge but nonpoisonous pincer jaws
- run extremely fast

Centipedes and millipedes

CENTIPEDES LIVE AND HUNT UNDER LOGS AND STONES, IN SOIL AND AMONG DEAD LEAVES. They locate prey with their long, sensitive feelers on the head, and bite with the sharp, clawlike fangs on the first body segment, injecting a poison which stops the prey struggling. The centipede then tears it apart with its strong jaws. Many centipedes can run very fast on their numerous pairs of legs. The name *centipede* means "hundred legs" but most species have about 40, although some have more than 340.

Various kinds of pill millipedes (above and far left) roll into a ball when in danger. The curved plates, tergites, covering each body segment are jointed so that they overlap to form a smooth, rounded ball.

Millipedes look like centipedes but they have a more rounded, tube-shaped body, shorter feelers and move more slowly. The name *millipede* means "thousand legs,", but again this is an exaggeration, the maximum being about 750. Millipedes eat bits of plants, such as roots, buds, and flowers, and also old, moldy plant parts. Large centipedes can give an extremely painful bite, but millipedes cannot. Instead they ooze or spray a horrible-tasting fluid from small glands along the sides of the body, to defend themselves against attack.

A giant tropical centipede (above) has two long feelers or antennae on its head, and two long tail filaments. Its poison fangs on the first body segment are held alongside and just under the head. A millipede such as polydesmus (left) has short feelers and no tail filaments. Its hard body gives good protection against predators such as birds and spiders.

Most centipedes and millipedes are quite small, less than 4 inches (10 cm) long. But some tropical species grow much larger. The scolopendra centipede of Central and South America reaches 13 inches (33 cm) in length. It is strong and fast enough to catch lizards, mice, and small birds. Its bite is dangerous, even fatal, to people. The largest millipedes are found in Africa, and some of these grow to about 11 inches (28 cm) long. Millipedes have chewing or scraping mouthparts and some damage vegetables, fruits, and other crops. However, most millipedes live in woodland and help to recycle dead leaves and rotting wood.

Blind creepers

Two smaller groups of arthropods are related to millipedes and centipedes. These are symphylans and pauropods. They are like miniature centipedes, about the same size as ants. They have no eyes and creep about in leaf litter and moist soil. Symphylans eat tiny bits of plants while pauropods scavenge on anything edible.

Centipede or millipede?

These two types of multilegged arthropods look quite similar, but there are several differences, as shown here (the millipede is on the left). They also live very differently. Centipedes are fast, active carnivores. They do not mind bright light and sometimes hunt during the day. Millipedes are slow herbivores or detritivores (eating old, decaying bits of plants or molds). They hide from bright light and usually come out to feed only at night.

long antenna
short antenna
sharp poison fang
one pair of legs per segment
two pairs of legs per segment
rounded body
flattened body
poison glands along body
tail filament

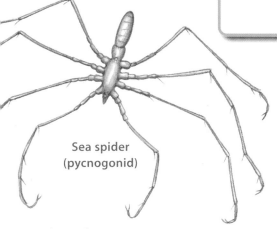

Sea spider (pycnogonid)

Seashore hunters

Sea spiders are well named because they look like spiders, with four pairs of long legs, and live in the sea. But they have their own arthropod group. Most are 1–2 inches (3–5 cm) across their outstretched legs. They clamber about on rocks and seaweeds on the lower shore, where they feed on sponges, corals, and anemones by piercing them with their sharp mouthparts. However, some deep-sea species grow to 30 inches (75 cm) across.

The two-headed centipede has only one head, on the left. Its tail is shaped and colored to look similar and confuse predators.

Velvet worms

These caterpillar-like creatures live in warm, damp forests. Their bodies are soft, squishy, and velvety, with stumpy clawed legs for walking. Like all arthropods, they grow by molting.

Velvet worms (onychophorans or peripatuses) seem like a combination of centipede and worm. They feed on small animals such as real worms and insects.

Other groups of arthropods include:

Centipedes
- 3,000 species
- worldwide, mainly in soil, under rocks and leaves, in old wood
- bendy, flattened body
- two legs per body segment
- long feelers
- sharp fangs and strong jaws
- prey on smaller animals

Millipedes
- 8,000 species
- worldwide, mainly in soil, old leaves, rotting wood
- tubular, rounded body
- four legs per body segment
- short feelers
- feed on plants, molds

Symphylans
- 160 species
- live in soil
- small, ant-sized
- look like small centipedes
- 12 pairs of legs

Pauropods
- 400 species
- live in soil
- tiny
- look like tiny centipedes
- nine pairs of legs

Sea spiders
- 1,000 species
- live in the sea
- resemble true spiders
- four pairs of long walking legs
- prey on other animals

Velvet worms
- 120 species
- live in tropical forests
- resemble large caterpillars
- 17 pairs of stumpy legs

FISH

Fish are easy to identify. They live in water, breathe through their gills, are covered by shiny scales, and swim by swishing their fins and tail. But there are exceptions. Lungfish can live out of water and breathe air. Some eels have no scales. Lampreys and hagfish, and some types of ray have no fins or tail. But fish, like all other vertebrates, have an inner skeleton with a backbone.

Fish make up a vast and varied group. Their habitats range from the deepest oceans to the clearest mountain streams, from sunlit tropical lagoons to dark, chilly underground lakes. They have a greater size range than almost any other animal group, from dwarf gobies that could fit onto your little fingernail, to massive whale sharks as big as a truck. Fish are almost every shape and color imaginable, from sharp-nosed, super-streamlined swordfish and marlin, to enormously bulky groupers, snakelike eels, and flatfish that are just that.

Fish obtain food in varied and imaginative ways. Some nibble at seaweed. Others filter tiny bits of food from the water. Sharks are the ultimate razor-toothed predators. Anglerfish use a "rod and line" made from their own bodies to catch their meals—of other fish!

What are fish?

FISH ARE VERTEBRATES (ANIMALS WITH BACKBONES) THAT ARE COLD-BLOODED, live in water, breathe by gills, swim with fins and a tail, and have a body covering of scales. At least, this is true of most fish (page 101). Fish make up by far the largest group of vertebrate animals. There are some 24,000 species, which is more than all other vertebrate animals—amphibians, reptiles, birds, and mammals—combined. The first fish to evolve on Earth, some 470 million years ago, were jawless fish. They had sucker-like mouths, rather than biting jaws with teeth. Two small groups, the lampreys and hagfish, survive today. A larger subgroup of fish is the sharks, rays, and chimeras. These are known as cartilaginous fish because they have a "backbone," or to give it the more accurate name, a vertebral column, made of tough, gristly cartilage rather than true bone. Easily the largest fish subgroup is the bony fish, with skeletons of true bone—as people know if they get the bones stuck when they eat fish. Fish are extremely important as food in many parts of the world.

The red-spotted hawkfish is an alert and agile fish of shallow tropical waters around coral reefs.

The monkfish, which is an unusual type of shark, has the flattened body shape typical of bottom-living fish.

This scene shows members from all the main fish subgroups. In the center is a large cartilaginous fish—a wobbegong or carpet shark. It lurks on the sea bed, disguised as a rock. On the lower left is a chimaera, another type of cartilaginous fish. The eel-like creature just above the "wobby" is a lamprey, a jawless fish with a sucker mouth. On the far right three hagfish, also jawless, suck rotting flesh from a carcass. The large silvery fish upper right is a tarpon, a type of bony fish. In the background is a school of cod, also bony fish.

All animals need oxygen to live (page 9). We breathe oxygen gas from the air into our lungs. A fish takes in oxygen dissolved in the water through the gills on either side of its head. Most fish have four sets of gills, which are red and feathery. They are made of rows of lamellae, thin, flat, delicate structures, filled with blood. Water flows into the fish's mouth and over the gills, where oxygen passes through the very thin gill coverings into the blood, to be carried around the body.

In sharks and other cartilaginous fish, the water then flows to the outside of the body through gill slits. In bony fish, the gills are covered by a bony flap, the operculum or gill cover, with a single slit along its rear edge.

The common spotted dogfish is one of the smallest sharks.

Jawless fish

Jawless fish have a skeleton made of cartilage, not bone. They also have no side fins, no scales on the long, thin body, round gill openings, and a sucking, disk- or funnel-shaped mouth. These creatures are survivors from a very early stage in the evolution of fish. They are mostly scavengers or parasites, sucking the blood of other water creatures. The hagfish is also called the slimehag, because it can produce a massive amount of slime from its body, which makes it far too slippery for a predator to hold.

Fish fins

Fish have two kinds of fins. These are paired fins, usually somewhere along the sides of the body, and unpaired fins, which are generally the dorsal fins on the top or back, and the anal fins on the underside or belly. The unpaired fins help the fish to swim straight or lean to one side. The tail or caudal fin is also unpaired and provides the main thrust for swimming. The paired fins are the pectoral fins just behind the head and the pelvic fins, usually lower and to the rear. They help the fish turn sideways, slow down and even swim backwards.

WORLD WATCH

Human activities are putting ever more fish species at risk. Some, such as cod, are victims of overfishing—we simply catch too many. Others suffer because we pollute their waters, divert or build dams across their rivers, or take to much water for our own use. We also take fish species to new areas, on purpose or by accident. The large, predatory Nile perch (page 122) was introduced into Africa's Lake Victoria in the early 1960s. It has now eaten many of the lake's own cichlid fish and completely upset the natural balance of life there.

Inside a fish

A typical fish like the salmon has a body that is mainly blocks of muscle, arranged in a zigzag pattern along either side of the backbone. These pull the backbone from side to side to swish the tail and make the fish swim.

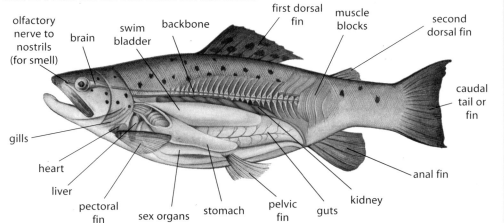

olfactory nerve to nostrils (for smell) · brain · swim bladder · backbone · first dorsal fin · muscle blocks · second dorsal fin · caudal tail or fin · anal fin · kidney · guts · pelvic fin · stomach · sex organs · pectoral fin · liver · heart · gills

FISH (PISCES)
- 24,000 species
- most have gills, fins, a tail and a body covered with scales

Hagfish (Myxini)
- about 50 species
- eel-like body
- sucker-like mouth (no jaws)
- live in the sea

Lampreys (Cephalaspidomorphi)
- about 38 species
- eel-like body
- sucker-like mouth (no jaws)
- live in the sea and fresh water

Sharks and rays (Chondrichthyes)
- about 900 species
- skeleton of cartilage
- no gill flap over gill slits
- most live in the sea
- includes sharks, dogfish, sawfish, rays, skates

Bony fish (Osteichthyes)
- over 23,000 species
- skeleton of bone
- gill slits covered by gill flap
- live in the sea and fresh water
- includes vast majority of fish

Sharks and rays

SHARKS AND RAYS, AND THE CREATURES CALLED RATFISH OR CHIMAERAS, make up the group called cartilaginous fish. This means their skeletons are not made of bone, as in other fish, but of cartilage. This is a gristly substance that is tough, yet light and bendy. The typical shark has a long, streamlined body designed to slip through the water with least effort. It is propelled by a tail with an upper lobe that is usually larger than the lower lobe. The shark's mouth is set back from the snout tip and is full of sharp teeth. The skin is not covered with the usual fish scales, but with tiny pointed structures called dermal denticles. In fact, these are much smaller versions of the teeth in the mouth. If you stroke shark skin the wrong way, from tail to head, the dermal denticles make the skin feel so rough that it could cause your hand to bleed.

The "mermaid's purse" washed up on the shore is the empty case in which a baby shark or ray developed. It was attached to rocks or weeds by the long, stringy tendrils.

The largest predatory or hunting shark is the great white or white pointer, feared in all warmer oceans of the world. It can grow more than 20 feet (6 m) long.

Unlike other fish, sharks and rays do not have a swim bladder for buoyancy control. As a shark swims, its upward-sloping snout and front side (pectoral) fins work like hydrofoils to provide a lifting force. Along with the shark's large, oily, lightweight liver, this keeps the shark off the seabed.

Most sharks are fast-moving, torpedo-shaped hunters of the open ocean. But others, such as the carpet sharks or wobbegongs, have a flattened body shape. They also have fringes and tassels of skin to camouflage their bodies as seaweed-covered rocks. They spend much of their lives lying on the seabed, waiting to ambush and gulp down any prey that comes near.

A typical ratfish has a large head, big eyes, fleshy lips, sharp teeth, a long, tapering body, and a "rat's tail" instead of the usual tail fins.

Flying through the water

Most rays also have a body flattened from top to bottom. Their wide, flaplike pectoral fins look and work like a bird's wings. The ray flaps or undulates them to "fly" through the water. The majority of rays have wide, flattened, crunching teeth and feed on shellfish and worms that they uncover on the seabed.

Poison for defense

Chimeras, the fish group also known as ratfish, usually live on or near the sea bed. They can live at great depths, more than 6,600 feet (2,000 m). Most chimeras have long, scaleless bodies. The ratfish (short-nose and long-nose chimeras) have stringy, ratlike tails. Plownose chimaeras have a tail similar to that of a shark. All chimaeras have a long spine at the front of the dorsal (back) fin. This is linked to a venom gland. The poison in the spine can cause a painful wound to an attacker. Most chimaeras eat small sea-bottom creatures such as crabs, clams, and shrimps, as well as other fish.

Making baby sharks

Different sharks and rays have different ways of producing young. Some, such as the horned or Port Jackson sharks and the dogfish, lay eggs protected by tough, leathery cases. The mother hides these

The Caribbean reef shark, or black-tip (above), cruises along the edges of coral reefs in its search for sick or injured fish, seals, seabirds, and other likely victims.

Biggest

The largest fish in the world is the whale shark, at more than 40 feet (13 m) long. It is not a fierce hunter. It feeds by filtering the tiny plants and animals of the plankton from sea water. !

in seaweed or rocks. The youngster develops inside for several weeks, nourished by its large yolk sac, until it is ready to hatch and fend for itself. Others, such as the tiger sharks, produce eggs with thin shells that are kept inside the mother's body. The young feed from their yolk sacs, hatch from the thin shells and are then born. More extraordinary still are the hammerheads, blues, white-tips, and bull sharks. The young grow

Most rays, like this southern ray, stay near the seabed. Like sharks, they have dozens of tiny electricity-sensing pits on the head. These detect weak pulses of electricity from the muscles of buried prey animals, which the ray then digs out. To hide from predators, the ray buries itself in the sand.

inside the mother, but not inside egg shells. When their yolk is used up, they are nourished directly from the mother's blood. Finally they are born as well-formed young.

WORLD WATCH

Every year around the world, 30–50 people are reported as killed by sharks. Also every year, about 100 million sharks are killed by people. They are caught for many reasons—for food, for sport by anglers, because their body parts are thought to have healing powers, and because they might menace tourist areas. Several kinds, including the great white, are now very rare. Some are protected by world wildlife laws.

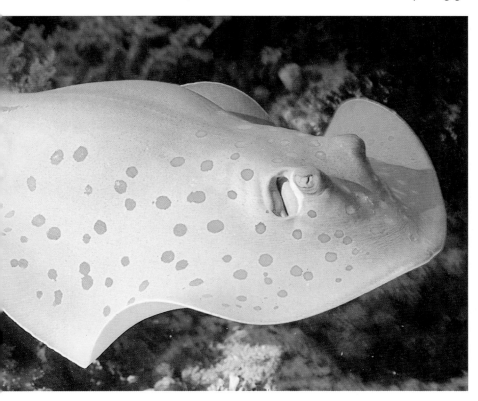

This spotted eagle ray has large eyes and, just behind each one, a flap-covered opening or spiracle. This lets in water which flows over the gills, so that the ray can breathe (take in oxygen from the water). The water then leaves through gill slits on the ray's underside.

Sharks (Elasmobranchii)
- about 375 species
- all but a couple live in the sea
- includes hammerhead, dogfish, carpet shark, mako, great white

Rays (Rajiformes)
- about 450 species
- most live in the sea
- includes electric ray, stingray, skate, manta

Chimeras (Chimaeriformes)
- about 30 species
- live in the sea
- includes ratfish, chimera

Sturgeons and gars

THE GROUPS OF FISH THAT INCLUDE
STURGEONS, PADDLEFISH, AND GARS
were very common and widespread many millions of years ago
when dinosaurs walked the land. Today there are far fewer species.
A typical sturgeon has a long, heavy body with five rows of bony plates. Its
mouth has fleshy "whiskers," which are known as barbels. These feel and taste
for prey on the bottom of a lake, river, or sea. Some types of sturgeon live in rivers and
lakes in North America, Europe, and Asia. Others grow up in fresh water, then swim out
to sea for several years, returning to their rivers to breed.
Paddlefish live only in the Mississippi River in North America and the Chang Jiang (Yangtze
River) in China. They grow to six feet (1.8 m) long and have a flat, spoon-shaped snout. The paddlefish swims along with its mouth wide open, filtering tiny animals from the plankton. The gars or gar pikes of North America are also long, slim fish, with a covering of especially thick, hard scales to protect against attackers. The very long, slender jaws are studded with small teeth. Gars lurk in water weeds, waiting to grab prey.

Gars have very thick, diamond-shaped scales. They seize prey such as small fish in their long, slim jaws. The common gar pike grows to about 3 feet (90 cm) in length.

The thick plates along a sturgeon's body are not scales but bony slabs called scutes.

A young sturgeon has smaller bony scutes. They will enlarge and thicken with age.

Most kinds of sturgeon spend part of their lives in the sea, where they feed on bottom-living creatures such as worms, shrimps, and flatfish. When they become fully grown, they swim into rivers in spring to breed. The female lays her sticky black eggs among gravel on the riverbed. A large female normally produces more than two million eggs. A female of the largest type of sturgeon, the beluga or white sturgeon, produces up to seven million eggs. After about one week the tiny young sturgeons hatch out. They stay in the river for up to three years, feeding on small creatures such as water insects, shrimps, and worms which they detect in the mud with their whiskery barbels. Then they travel or migrate out to sea, to continue their growth.

Endangered!
Sturgeons are well known for their shiny black eggs, which are called caviar. These are gathered as an expensive food for people to eat. The female sturgeon may be killed in order to take her eggs. Or the eggs can be "milked" from her while she is alive, and then she is put back in the water. Taking eggs for caviar has made most kinds of sturgeon very rare.

The beluga of Central Asian lakes and rivers is one of the world's largest fish. The biggest specimens once grew to 26 feet (8 m) long and weighed well over 1.5 tons. However, few belugas today live long enough to reach 15 feet (4.5 m). This is due to overfishing and water pollution, and also dams across rivers that interfere with their migration to the sea.

The alligator gar (below), at 10 feet (3 m) long, is one of the biggest freshwater fish in North America. Like other gars, it is a fierce hunter. It eats smaller fish and shellfish such as crayfish.

Bonytongues

The bonytongue fish group includes the goldeye, mooneye, pirarucu, aruana, butterflyfish, and knifefish. They all live in fresh water. The name of the group comes from the structure of the tongue. It has large, stiff bones in it, and also has teeth that bite against the teeth in the upper jaw.

A giant of fresh water

The pirarucu or arapaima is a huge bonytongue fish that lives in the Amazon region of South America. It grows to more than 10 feet (3 m) long and 440 pounds (200 kg) in weight, making it one of the biggest freshwater fish in the world. (Some sturgeons grow larger but they live partly in the sea.) The pirarucu inhabits stagnant, swampy places where the water has little dissolved oxygen. However, it can gulp air into its swim bladder, which works as a simple lung to absorb the oxygen from the air.

Unlike most fish, the female pirarucu takes good care of her young. She lays her eggs in a sheltered part of the river, hidden among plants. She guards the eggs against hungry predators, and she also protects the babies or fry when they hatch.

There are about 100 species of elephant-nose or elephant-snout fish. They live mainly in rivers and swamps in Africa. The long, flexible snout looks like an elephant's trunk. The fish uses it to probe in the mud and gravel for small animals to eat.

Electric fish

Elephant-nose fish are mostly less than 3 feet (90 cm) long. They use the long, flexible snout to dig in the mud for food. These fish are electric! Special muscles at the rear of the body produce weak pulses of electricity, which pass through the water around the fish. The pulses are detected by tiny sensors over the head. The electricity is too weak to stun prey. But another animal nearby disturbs the pattern of pulses and so the elephant-nose fish can detect it. This helps the elephant-nose to avoid enemies and also to find its prey— even in very muddy, murky water and at night.

Oldest

Fossils show that coelacanths lived more than 300 million years ago. They were thought to have died out with the dinosaurs, 65 million years ago. Then they were discovered still living in the Indian Ocean near Africa in the 1930s. The fins have fleshy lobes at the base. The legs of the early land animals may have evolved from fins like these.

!

Sturgeons (Acipenseriformes)
- about 25 species
- most live in fresh water and may travel into the sea
- includes sturgeon, beluga, paddlefish

Bonytongues (Osteoglossiformes)
- about 215 species
- live in fresh water
- includes pirarucu, elephant fish

Gars (Lepisosteiformes)
- about 7 species
- live in fresh water
- includes longnose gar, alligator gar

Elephant-nose fish (Mormyriformes)
- about 100 species
- live in fresh water in Africa
- can make and detect electrical pulses
- some types are caught or farmed for food

Eels and herrings

MOST EELS ARE LONG, SLIM, SNAKELIKE FISH WITH TINY SCALES OR NONE AT ALL, AND NO PELVIC (REAR SIDE) FINS. MOST HERRINGS ARE SMALL, SILVERY OCEAN FISH AND SWIM IN HUGE GROUPS OR SCHOOLS.

Both these kinds of fish are extremely numerous and are caught by people for food. The largest type of herring is the huge wolf herring, a fierce hunter that can grow more than ten feet (3 m) long. But most herrings, including sardines or pilchards, sprats and anchovies, are less than three feet (90 cm) long. They feed on tiny animals in the plankton, which they filter from the water using the comblike rakers on their gills. Herrings are, in turn, important food for many larger creatures, including predatory fish, dolphins, and seabirds. Most types of herring live in the sea, but some live in fresh water in North and South America, parts of Africa, and Australia. Most eels also live in the sea. However, some kinds spend much of their lives in rivers and lakes, and then travel to the sea to lay their eggs. The eggs hatch into thin, see-through, leaf-shaped young, or larvae. The eel larvae drift in ocean currents for years before developing into young eels and swimming into rivers. Other eels, such as the snipe eel with large fangs in beaklike jaws, live in the deepest ocean.

The gulper eel can swallow prey larger than itself, into its stretchy stomach.

The wolf herring has a long body and large, sharp teeth. It lives in the warm, shallow waters of the Indian and West Pacific Oceans.

The eel's journey

Freshwater eels live in rivers and lakes, but travel to the sea to spawn (lay their eggs and breed). American and European eels migrate to the weed-rich Sargasso Sea, in the western North Atlantic. Here, ocean currents swirl warm water down to great depths. The adult eels dive down many hundreds of feet, breed, and then die. The eggs hatch into leaf-shaped larvae as long as a thumbnail. European eel larvae drift across the Atlantic in the current known as the Gulf Stream for three or four years, altering their shape as they go. Near European coasts they change, or metamorphose, into young eels, called elvers. These swim into rivers, where they live for several years until they are 20–40 inches (50–100 cm) long and ready to breed. American eel larvae drift west and their journey takes only a year or two.

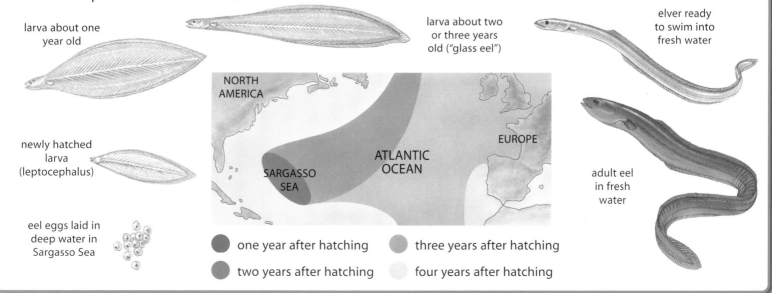

larva about one year old

larva about two or three years old ("glass eel")

elver ready to swim into fresh water

newly hatched larva (leptocephalus)

NORTH AMERICA

EUROPE

ATLANTIC OCEAN

SARGASSO SEA

adult eel in fresh water

eel eggs laid in deep water in Sargasso Sea

● one year after hatching   ● three years after hatching
● two years after hatching   ○ four years after hatching

A spotted moray eel peers from its lair, ready to snap at prey or bite enemies. There are about 100 different species of moray.

Lurking danger

Moray eels live in tropical and subtropical waters, often around coral reefs. Most have scaleless bodies, boldly patterned with bright colors, and strong, sharp teeth. Morays are powerful hunters and tend to hide in crevices in rocks, watching for prey such as fish and squid. The largest morays measure more than 12 feet (3.5 m) long.

Deep-sea eels

Gulper eels live in the darkness of the deep ocean, where prey is hard to find. They swim with their enormous mouths wide open, ready to engulf any creature that will fit through the jaws. These eels have tiny eyes or none at all, since they live in permanent blackness more than 3,000 feet (900 m) below the surface. They grow to about 2 feet (60 cm) long.

Breeding herrings

Most members of the herring group, including the Atlantic herring, lay their eggs close to the seabed. The eggs stay

The herring grows to about 16 inches (40 cm) long, while the sardine is 10 inches (25 cm). The various kinds of anchovies are about 8 inches (20 cm) long.

Thousands of sardines shoal in the shallow waters near the Galapagos Islands in the Pacific Ocean.

A garden of eels

Garden eels live in colonies on the sea bed, usually in a shallow, sunlit area where water currents bring plenty of plankton. Each eel digs a burrow with its tail and spends much of its time with its rear half anchored inside. Its top half extends upward so it can feed on the plankton. Lots of these eels close together sway in the current like tall flowers in a garden. If danger comes near, such as a predatory fish, the eels quickly whisk themselves into their burrows and the entire "garden" disappears.

there until they hatch into tiny larvae one-quarter inch (5 mm) long. These drift in the plankton until they are able to swim in schools.

The Atlantic herring is a slender fish with large, silvery, easily damaged scales.

The conger, like all eels, has long dorsal and anal fins on the top and underside of the body.

Eels (Anguilliformes)
- about 690 species
- mostly live in the sea, a few are freshwater
- includes moray, conger, garden, snipe and gulper eels

Herrings (Clupeiformes)
- about 360 species
- live in the sea, filtering plankton
- silvery bodies
- includes sardine or pilchard, anchovy, shad, menhaden

Salmon, pike, and hatchetfish

SALMON AND THEIR COUSINS—TROUT, CHARR, WHITEFISH, SMELT, AND GRAYLING—live mainly in rivers and lakes in northern continents. They are mostly sleek fish with slender, tapering bodies and forked tails. Their small sharp teeth show that they hunt animals for food. The various types of salmon make regular journeys or migrations between salt and fresh water. The young are born in rivers, but after a few years' feeding and growing, they swim into the sea, where they spend the next few years. Then they return to the rivers where they grew up, to spawn. Pike and pickerels spend all their lives in fresh water. The northern pike is a large, widespread predatory fish with a big mouth, strong jaws and sharp teeth. Hatchetfish and viperfish belong to the bristlemouth group, named after their long thin hinged teeth that look like brush bristles. They live in deep oceans. Many have special light-producing parts on their bodies. The eerie glow from these lights helps to camouflage the fish, lure prey, attract a mate, and confuse an enemy.

The female salmon hides her eggs in the gravel on the riverbed. The eggs contain reddish-yellow yolk, which nourishes the baby fish.

How Atlantic and Pacific salmon return from the middle of the ocean to the exact stream where they hatched from eggs is one of the marvels of the animal world. It is known that they can detect the "smell" of their home river, from dissolved minerals and other substances, but how they navigate from far out at sea is not fully understood.

The journey upstream is dangerous and tiring. Pacific salmon, in particular, must leap many waterfalls on the way. The males change in color and the lower jaw grows a hooked tip as they reach their home. In the spawning stream, male and female court briefly. Then she sheds her eggs (spawn) on the gravel bed and he fertilizes them with his sperm (milt). By this time many of the salmon are so exhausted that they are easy prey for eagles, bears, wolves, and other animals. Most Pacific salmon die after spawning. Atlantic salmon may survive, return to the sea and make the journey again two or three times. Large salmon grow to 4 feet (1.2 m) in length and weigh 60 pounds (27 kg).

Salmon leap up rapids and waterfalls with powerful thrusts of the tail. They can swim 60 miles (100 km) upstream each day.

The variable trout

There are two forms of the common trout. These are the silvery sea trout, which migrates between river and sea like the salmon, and the smaller, darker-spotted brown trout, which stays in fresh water. Most trout eat baby fish, worms and other small prey. Some types are farmed as food for people.

The rainbow trout has pink-tinged sides and spots on its tail. It has escaped from fish farms into rivers around the world.

Salmon gather below a waterfall, ready to surge upward and leap the obstacle.

Copper sweepers (left) are reddy-gold members of the hatchetfish group, the bristlemouths. This shoal is sheltering from danger below a deep rock overhang.

Hidden danger

The largest member of the pike group is the muskellunge or muskie of North America, up to 5 feet (1.5 m) long and 65 pounds (30 kg) in weight. The northern pike looks similar but shorter. It lives in rivers and lakes in northern regions around the world. This huge-mouthed predator lies hidden among water plants, watching for prey. When it spots a victim, the pike lunges like lightning from the weed and seizes the prey with its sharp teeth.

Pop-eyed!

The baby black dragonfish looks pop-eyed. Its eyes are on long stalks, almost like a garden snail. As the dragonfish grows, the stalks shrink back into the head. The eyes finally settle and slot into the normal sockets in the skull.

Swimming hatchets

Common hatchetfish are indeed very numerous in warmer seas, at depths of about 600–2,500 feet (180–750 m). They are only 3 inches (8 cm) long and preyed on by many larger sea hunters. The common hatchetfish has a deep, flattened body, a large mouth,

Deep-sea hatchetfish (right) are named from their silvery, narrow, deep-chested body shape, which resembles an ax or hatchet.

bulging eyes and rows of light-producing organs along the belly. Other types of hatchetfish live even deeper—below 6,000 feet (1,800 m). The particular pattern of lights along the body helps each type of hatchetfish to recognize its own species at mating time in the darkness.

Deep-sea viperfish are also members of the bristlemouth group. Their long, backward-pointing teeth grab prey lured by the long fin spine tipped with a light-producing organ.

A viperfish dangles a glowing bait in front of its mouth (above). Its "fishing rod" is made from the greatly lengthened first or second ray (spine) of its dorsal (back) fin. A close-up of the viperfish's mouth (left) shows its long, needle-shaped teeth, at the front of the lower jaw. Viperfish grow to about 12 inches (30 cm) in length.

Salmon (Salmoniformes)
- about 140 species
- freshwater and sea-dwelling
- includes salmon, trout, smelt, charr, grayling

Pike (Esociformes)
- about 12 species
- freshwater
- includes pike, pickerel, muskellunge (muskie)

Bristlemouths (Stomiiformes)
- about 250 species
- live only in the sea
- includes hatchetfish, dragonfish, viperfish, snaggletooth, loosejaw

Characins, carp, and catfish

THESE THREE GROUPS INCLUDE NEARLY A THIRD OF ALL FISH— MORE THAN 6,000 SPECIES. They vary widely in appearance, but most live in fresh water. The majority can detect sounds in water, by picking up sound waves in the swim bladder, which other fish cannot do so well. In addition, these fish have special alarm substances in the skin which are released into the water if the skin is damaged. When a fish is seized by a predator, the substance passes into the water. This may not

The neon tetra's colors are so bright, they seem to glow like electric neon lights.

help the victim, but other members of its species can quickly escape, so the whole species benefits.

The many colors and shapes of goldfish have been bred over centuries from wild carp.

Members of the carp group live across North America, Europe, northern Asia, and Africa. They lack teeth in their jaws. Instead, they have a pair of toothed bones in the lower throat to crush and grind food against a hardened pad at the base of the skull. Most carp tackle a wide range of foods, including plants, fish, and shellfish.

Some types of carp, including the roach, bream, common and crucian carp, have

been introduced to lakes and slow rivers around the world. They are caught by anglers and are popular as food. These types of carp are bottom feeders. They grub in the mud, using their sensitive whiskerlike barbels to find worms, insect larvae, snails, and shrimps.

An unusual nursery

Most members of the carp group simply scatter their eggs in water and leave the young to hatch and fend for themselves. But the small carp known as the bitterling has a more unusual method. At the start of the breeding season the female develops a long egg-laying tube, the ovipositor. She uses this to place her eggs inside the shell of a freshwater mussel. The male bitterling releases his sperm near the mussel. As the mussel filter-feeds, the sperm are sucked in to fertilize the eggs.

Glassfish, types of small carp, form large schools. Like most carp, they feed at night.

The European catfish, or wels, is one of several kinds of catfish that grow to massive size, more than 6 feet (1.8 m) long.

Characins

The characins live in rivers and lakes in Central and South America and Africa. They include the piranhas of South America, and the tetras that have been bred in many colors as popular aquarium fish. Some characins eat plants, others eat small creatures such as

The mirror carp has shiny, extra-large scales.

insects and worms, and still others are hunters of larger animals such as fish and frogs. One group, the toothless characins, survive by sucking up the slime that covers leaves, stones, and other underwater objects.

A female bitterling lays her eggs into a mussel, as the male waits to fertilize them. The baby fish emerge about 2–3 weeks later.

Not all so fierce

The piranhas of South America have a fearsome reputation as bloodthirsty hunters. But some types of piranha, such as the pacu, feed on plants. The flesh-eating types include the red piranha. They are only about 12 inches (30 cm) long, but they have strong jaws and thin, razor-blade teeth for slicing chunks of flesh out of their victims. One piranha cannot do much harm.

Various kinds of characin tigerfish are named after their tigerlike stripes and the way they stalk and eat other fish.

But a large school of them can strip the flesh from a large animal like a horse in minutes. Piranhas are attracted by blood in the water. So a wounded animal that comes to drink at the river bank is in real danger.

Cat's whiskers

Catfish are named after the very long, whiskerlike barbels around the mouth. The fleshy barbels taste the water to find food. Most catfish also have stiff spines at the front of the dorsal and pectoral fins. These can be "locked" in position, sticking outward, so the fish is very hard to swallow.

Glass catfish live in Africa and Southeast Asia. Their almost see-through bodies, apart from the heart and guts, help with camouflage.

Shocking fish

Knifefish are close relatives of catfish. They have special muscles that can produce pulses of electricity in the surrounding water. These pulses help them to find their way in muddy, dark lakes and rivers (like the elephant-nose fish, page 107). The knifefish that produces the most powerful

Bream

Blue piranha

The electric eel is shaped like an eel, but it is really a type of knifefish. It grows to 7 feet (2.1 m) long and can give 550-volt electric shocks.

electrical pulses is the electric eel of northern South America. The electricity is so strong, it can stun prey fish. Another amazing catfish is the walking catfish. It can crawl on land, using its strong pectoral fins, and breathe air while it does so. It usually lives in ponds or rivers. If these dry up in a drought, the catfish can move overland to another area of water.

Carp (Cypriniformes)
- about 2,050 species
- almost all live in fresh water
- includes goldfish, loach, minnow, tench, barbel, mahseer

Characins (Charciformes)
- about 1,400 species
- live in fresh water
- includes pike characin, tetra, piranha, pacu, giant tigerfish

Catfish and knifefish (Siluriformes)
- about 2,415 species
- most live in fresh water
- includes wels, walking catfish, knifefish, butterfly, electric eel

Cod, anglerfish, and toadfish

THE VARIOUS TYPES OF COD INCLUDE HAKE, HADDOCK, AND WHITING. They are mostly long, fast-swimming fish with large fins and live in cool seas around the world, some at great depths. They are extremely valuable as food and in the past millions of tonnes were caught every year. But overfishing has greatly reduced their numbers in some areas. Anglerfish, batfish, and frogfish live in warmer seas and they are much more squat in shape, with a short body, large head and gaping mouth. They are not built for speed and prefer to lie in wait for prey. The front spine of the anglerfish's dorsal (back) fin is separate from the rest of the fin. It forms a long "fishing rod" with its fleshy tip as a bait to attract other fish. Once a victim is near enough, the angler opens its huge mouth and the rush of water sucks in the prey.

Atlantic cod can be recognized by their three dorsal fins.

The rosy-lipped batfish crawls well on its strong, leglike fins. It spends more time walking than swimming.

Toadfish live in warm coastal waters. They have excellent camouflage with lots of fleshy fringes, flaps and whiskery barbels around the big head and wide mouth, so they look like seaweed.

the water, where they float near the surface. When the young fish hatch they stay in surface waters until they are about 2 inches (5 cm) long, then they move closer to the ocean floor.

Rattails
The cod group also includes the grenadiers or rattails, which live in water 600–6,000 feet (150–1,800 m) in depth. With a large head, short body and long, ratlike tail, the grenadier resembles the ratfish (page 104). The male makes loud sounds using muscles linked to his swimbladder, probably to attract a mate.

The Atlantic cod grows to about 4 feet (1.2 m) long and is the best-known fish of the cod group. This group includes many other fish eaten as food, such as ling, pollock, rockling, and pout. Like many of these, the haddock has a fleshy, sensitive barbel on its chin to help it find food such as worms and shellfish on the sea bed. Haddock usually spawn in spring, shedding large numbers of eggs into

A toadfish's face, with its broad mouth and big eyes, looks like the face of a toad.

Toadfish
Toadfish look like toads, and they also make toadlike croaks. The male makes a nest hole in weed and mud near a rock. He croaks by vibrating his swimbladder muscles to encourage a female to lay her eggs in the nest. She glues each egg into the nest by a sticky disc on its underside. The male guards the nest until the baby fish hatch. They remain glued to the nest for a few days. Even when they break free, he continues to guard them.

A flagtail rock cod shows off its small, sharp teeth and its gills in the cheek region.

Among the sponges and corals of the Caribbean a long-lure frogfish, dark grey in color, peers to its right. To its left a smaller, pale frogfish looks almost straight at the camera.

Anglers and frogfish

Anglerfish are so named because they do what human anglers do—use a "rod and bait" to catch other fish. There are coastal and deep-sea kinds. The lure or bait of the female deep-sea anglerfish glows in the darkness, to attract curious fish. The male deep-sea angler is one tenth the size of the female. He has no lure, and no teeth either, so he cannot feed. But he does have an excellent sense of smell, to find the female. Once he locates a mate, he attaches himself to her and fertilizes her eggs. He may then merge partly into her body and live as a parasite on her. This saves both partners a long search, since mates are difficult to find in the vast, deep ocean!

The frogfish lies on the sea bed, watching for prey. Its lumpy, frilly body gives amazing camouflage among seaweeds, corals and sponges. It can even change color to match the surroundings. Frogfish grow up to 8 inches (20 cm) long and eat small fish, shellfish and worms.

This deep-sea anglerfish has a glowing lure above its head. Its long, frilly chin barbel resembles a frond of seaweed.

The football-fish is a type of anglerfish. It is about 2 feet (60 cm) long and has studlike bony plates scattered over its body. Like all anglerfish, it lures its prey.

Cod (Gadiformes)
· about 500 species
· nearly all live in the sea
· includes cod, grenadier, hake, ling

Anglerfish (Lophiiformes)
· about 300 species
· all live in the sea, often at great depths
· includes frogfish, batfish, football-fish, sargassumfish

Toadfish (Batrachoidiformes)
· about 69 species
· most live on the sea bed
· includes midshipman

Scorpionfish and seahorses

SCORPIONFISH RANGE IN SHAPE FROM LONG AND SLENDER TO ALMOST AS ROUND AS BALLOONS. Most have spines, especially on the head and fins. Some, including the lionfish and stonefish, are extremely dangerous because the venom from their spines can kill people. Scorpionfish are all predators, catching other fish and shellfish. The pipefish and seahorse group is also extremely varied in shape, but most of the members have long, tube-shaped snouts. They live in warm, shallow waters near the coast. This group includes seadragons, shrimpfish, sea moths, and trumpetfish.

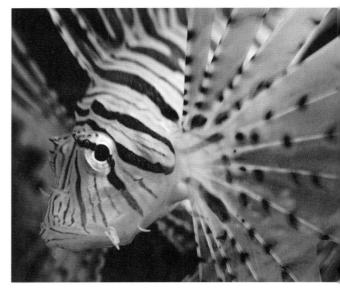

The lionfish has lacy, fan-shaped fins. These look delicate, but their spines can jab deadly poison.

There is also fish called the tubesnout, with a tubular snout, but it is in yet another fish group— the sticklebacks. They are found in rivers and lakes in northern continents and in the Atlantic and Pacific Oceans. Sticklebacks get their name from the strong, prickle-like spines on their backs.

The stonefish lies in shallow water, among weed and rocks, or part-buried in sand. People sometimes accidentally step on it when wading along the beach. The small spines on its back contain one of the most powerful venoms in the whole animal kingdom.

Caring parent

The male three-spined stickleback takes good care of his young. He builds a nest from bits of water plants stuck together with sticky substances from his own body. He then "dances" to attract a female, swimming to show off his brightly colored throat and underside. These have turned bright red for the breeding season. The female comes to the nest and lays her eggs, then the male fertilizes them.

nest

male in breeding colors

female

He stays at the nest and chases off intruders. When the fry (baby fish) hatch, he guards them for a few weeks, until they fend for themselves.

The scorpionfish's lumpy, mottled body is difficult to see as it lies among stones on the seabed, watching for prey. Sharp spines in its dorsal and pelvic fins are linked to venom glands and can cause serious wounds. Its close relative the lionfish is far easier to see, with its bright colors, fanlike fins, and lazy swimming. These features warn other creatures that the lionfish has deadly poison in its fin spines.

Suckered to the rocks

The lumpsucker, a relative of the scorpionfish, has a sucking disk on its throat formed from its pelvic fins. With this disk, the fish clings onto rocks in the shallows, to avoid being battered by waves. The small dark eggs of lumpsuckers are sold as a type of caviar.

Father gives birth

The seahorse does not lay eggs, but seems to give birth to its baby fish—and it is not the female that does this, but the male! The female seahorse lays her eggs into a special pouch on the male's front. He keeps the eggs safe here while they hatch and grow. He even nourishes the tiny babies with a special substance from his own body. When the young are ready for the outside world, they shoot out through the opening of the pouch.

The flying gurnard of the Atlantic Ocean has enormous pectoral fins, like wide wings. But this fish cannot fly, or even glide like the flyingfish.

Seahorses use their curly tails to hang onto coral branches or seaweed fronds. They swim slowly by rapidly flapping the dorsal fin on the back.

WORLD WATCH

Every year, millions of seahorses are killed. Their bodies are dried and ground up to make powders which are supposed to have medical uses, such as relieving asthma. Other seahorses are dried and used to make souvenirs such as fobs for key rings. In some years an estimated 8 million seahorses are killed in Southeast Asia. These little fish have become extremely rare in some places. One idea is that seahorses should be caught only in certain areas, and left to breed and keep up their numbers in nearby areas.

Pipefish (right) curve themselves into the shape of seaweed, for better camouflage.

They quickly attach themselves to floating weed or other objects and, like their parents, feed on tiny animal plankton.

Pipefish

The pipefish has a pencil-sized body encased in bony armor plates. Like its cousin the seahorse, it has a long snout but no teeth, and feeds by sucking in tiny animals from the plankton. Also like the seahorse, the male pipefish keeps or incubates the female's eggs in a pouch on his own body. The largest pipefish grow to about 20 inches (50 cm) long.

A pipefish (seen from above) swims over red coral.

Scorpionfish (Scorpaeniformes)
- about 1,200 species
- most live in the sea, some in fresh water
- includes stonefish, sea robin, sculpin, lionfish, lumpsucker, tub gurnard, sablefish

Seahorses and pipefish (Sygnathiformes)
- about 275 species
- live in the sea and fresh water
- thin, tubular snout for sucking in food

Sticklebacks (Gasterosteiformes)
- about 10 species
- live in the sea and fresh water
- includes three-, four-, nine- and 15-spined sticklebacks

Flyingfish, silversides, and killifish

THE FLYINGFISH GROUP INCLUDES NEEDLEFISH, LONGTOMS, AND HALFBEAKS. They are mostly very silvery, slim and streamlined, with spear-like pointed snouts, and dorsal and anal fins near the tail. Flyingfish themselves should really be called glidingfish. They swoop above the surface for a few seconds using their winglike pectoral fins. Silversides are small, shoal-dwelling fish of tropical and temperate seas and fresh water. Most have large eyes, extremely shiny and silvery scales, and two dorsal fins. Some, such as the rainbowfish, are popular in aquariums. Killifish are mostly small and hardy, and live in fresh water—even in the stagnant or brackish (slightly salty) water of ditches, canals, salt marshes, and estuaries. Most types live near the surface, feeding on insects and bits of plants. One of the most common is the mosquitofish, named because it feeds on mosquito larvae. It has been introduced to most parts of the world. Without it, there would be many more mosquitoes!

Guppies (above) belong to the killifish group. They are bred in many colors for aquariums.

The Atlantic flyingfish (below), about 16 inches (40 cm) long, is "four-winged." Its large pelvic fins lie behind and below the main pectoral fins.

All flyingfish have large, winglike pectoral fins just behind the head. Some "four-winged" types also have large pelvic fins, to help them glide. If danger threatens the flyingfish builds up speed just under the water's surface, thrashing its tail powerfully and holding its fins against its body. Then it leaps into the air and stretches its fins out sideways to soar along. A long glide may last 20–30 seconds and cover 600 feet (180 m) at 3-6 feet (90–180 cm) high. Flyingfish feed on plankton and small animals. They, in turn, are eaten by many larger fast-swimming fish, such as tuna and marlin.

Half a beak

The slender-bodied halfbeak is named from its half-a-beak—its long, sharp snout is made of its lower jaw only. The upper jaw is much shorter. Many halfbeaks feed on the seaweed called sea grass, which they gather with the lower jaw. Others feed on smaller fish or floating insects.

The silver needlefish (below) is typical of the 25 or so kinds of needlefish and garfish. Some needlefish in the Amazon region grow to only 2 inches (5 cm) long.

The four-eyed fish (above) has only two eyes, but each is divided into two by a dark band. The lower part is curved to see clearly in water, while the curvature of the upper part is suited to air. Floating at the surface, this fish can look out for prey and enemies, both above and below the water.

Grunions on the beach

The grunion is a silverside about 8 inches (20 cm) long that lives along North American Pacific coasts. Its breeding times are linked to the cycle of the moon and tides. At a full moon and spring (extra-high) tide, huge numbers of grunions "surf" ashore on the incoming breakers. They mate on the beach, lay their eggs in the sand, and return to the sea on receding waves. Two weeks later, at the new moon and next spring tide, the eggs hatch and the young grunions are swept away into the sea.

Marbled guppy

Guppies galore

Guppies come from tropical South America, but have now been introduced to most other parts of the world. Like mosquitofish, they eat the water-dwelling larvae and pupae of mosquitoes and similar insects. Also, like many other killifish, the babies develop inside the female. So she gives birth to tiny young, rather than laying eggs. The babies grow fast and are ready to breed at only ten weeks old.

Mosquitofish have been put into streams and ditches around the world, to control mosquito pests.

WORLD WATCH

Among the rarest fish in the world are Devil's Hole pupfish, small killifish less than an inch (2.5 cm) long. They live in an underground pool in the flooded cave system under Death Valley, California—and nowhere else. Water was pumped out of the cave network for use by people and farms. But the water level in the pupfish pool fell so much that the species was in danger of extinction. The US Supreme Court ordered that enough water must remain in the pool for the pupfish to survive.

The small, pointed teeth of longtoms grab small, wriggling prey.

Flyingfish (Beloniiformes)
- about 160 species
- live in the sea and fresh water
- includes two- and four-winged flyingfish, halfbeak, garfish, saury, houndfish, ricefish, needlefish

Silversides (Atheriniformes)
- about 250 species
- live in the sea and fresh water
- includes grunion, silversides, rainbowfish, swordtail

Killifish (Cyprinodontiformes)
- about 600 species
- live mainly in fresh water
- includes guppy, mosquito fish, four-eyed fish, mummichog or common killifish, toothcarps

Flatfish and triggerfish

FLATFISH LIVE IN ALL THE WORLD'S OCEANS, EXCEPT IN POLAR REGIONS. There are a few species in fresh water. The body of a flatfish is extremely flattened from one side to the other. (Rays look similar but their bodies are flattened from top to bottom.) The flatfish spends much of its life swimming or lying on one side on the seabed. Both its eyes are on the other side, facing upward, so it can watch for prey and predators. Some flatfish have both eyes on the right side; others have them on the left. Many flatfish are also masters of camouflage. They change their coloration and pattern to match the surroundings, making them very hard to see. All flatfish are predators and feed on shellfish, worms and similar sea-bottom animals. The triggerfish group includes poisonous pufferfish, spiny porcupinefish that can puff up their bodies like balloons, and the giant ocean sunfish. In most of these fish the mouth and a few teeth form a structure shaped like a bird's beak. Most live near the sea bed of tropical coasts.

The cowfish is a type of triggerfish named after the two spines above its eyes, which look like a cow's horns.

Ocean sunfish

When a baby flatfish first hatches from its egg, it has a normal fishlike body shape, with an eye on each side of its head. As it grows, over the next few weeks, one eye moves across the top of its head to the other side, so it is close to the other eye. At the same time the body becomes thin or flat and the mouth twists so that it lies on the same side as the two eyes. Turbots, some flounders, topknots, brill, and the windowpane (an exceptionally flat flatfish) usually have both eyes on the left side, and so lie on the right or blind underside. Halibut, plaice, dab, other flounders and most soles are right-eyed, so the left eye moves to the right, upper side. A resting flatfish usually flicks a little sand or gravel over its body, to conceal its fins and blur its outline for even better camouflage.

Plaice, like most flatfish, have a pale or white underside. This is because it is rarely seen.

The peacock flounder has both eyes on the left body side. It also has a large spiny dorsal fin that begins just below its mouth.

Different types of pufferfish have vivid colors and patterns. They "puff" up by swallowing water, so becoming too big to be swallowed.

Biggest flatfish

The Atlantic halibut is one of the biggest flatfish, at 8 feet (2.5 m) long and 650 pounds (295 kg) weight. However, due to overfishing, halibut of this size are now rare. They are more active than most flatfish, and chase prey rather than just lying in wait on the sea floor. Halibut feed on other fish, also on squid and crustaceans such as shrimps.

Triggerfish

Most triggerfish are brightly colored and live around coral reefs. They are named for the special tilting spines of the first dorsal fin. The front, larger spine can be "locked" upright by the second spine just behind it, like cocking the trigger of a gun. When in danger, the triggerfish takes shelter in a crevice among the rocks and locks its strong spine in the upright position. It is then very difficult for a predator to attack and remove the triggerfish.

Puffers and porcupine spines

The slow-swimming porcupinefish grows to about 3 feet (90 cm) long and lives in warm coastal waters, where it feeds on prey such as sea urchins, starfish and shellfish. It has extraordinary protection against enemies. It is covered with large, sharp spines. Normally these lie flat against the body. If threatened, the porcupinefish gulps in water to

The porcupinefish can puff itself up and has the added deterrent of sharp spines. Its hard, beaklike mouth crushes shellfish, urchins, and crabs.

make its body swell in size, until it is almost round. This forces the spines to stand out, making the fish like a prickly beach ball and almost impossible to attack.

The common flounder grows to about 20 inches (50 cm) long. It lies on its left side, unlike the summer, starry and peacock flounders.

Sunbathing fish

The amazing ocean sunfish is shaped like a huge pancake. It has tall, thin dorsal and anal fins, and a fleshy frill for a tail. This massive fish grows to 13 feet (4 m) long and weighs up to 2 tons. Ocean sunfish

Ocean sunfish

are rare and live far out at sea, eating jellyfish, comb-jellies, and other soft-bodied creatures. The name comes from this fish's habit of lying on the sea's surface, as though sunbathing.

Flatfish (Pleuronectiformes)
- about 540 species
- nearly all live in the sea
- includes sole, plaice, turbot, brill, tonguefish, adalah

Triggerfish (Tetraodontiformes)
- about 350 species
- mostly sea-dwelling, some freshwater species
- includes boxfish, pufferfish, burrfish, cowfish, filefish

Perch, groupers, and drums

THE HUGE GROUP OF PERCHLIKE FISH, THE PERCIFORMS, contains more than 9,000 species—almost half of all kinds of fish. They range from tiny gobies smaller than this word "goby," to huge, strong, superfast, open-ocean predators such as marlin and barracudas, to ponderous, massive, vast-mouthed, heavy-bodied groupers. Perchlike fish live in all aquatic (watery) habitats, from rushing mountain streams to tropical coral reefs, icy polar seas, and the ocean depths. Most have a front dorsal fin with spiny fin rays (the "rods" that hold up the soft fin parts). Some have a second dorsal fin too, but this has soft, bendy fin rays. There is also a spine at the front of each pelvic fin, and the pelvic fins are quite far forward on the body, below the pectoral fins.

The Nile perch, 6 feet (1.8 m) long, lives in rivers across Africa.

Groupers and seabass make up one of the biggest sea-dwelling families of perchlike fish. Most have robust, powerful bodies and two or three spines on the gill flap. Some seabasses and groupers, such as the striped bass and Nassau grouper, are important food fish and are caught in large numbers. The giant seabass of the Pacific North American coast grows to 6 feet (1.8 m) long.

The jewfish is the largest member of the family. It can grow to more than 7 feet (2.4 m) long and weigh as much as 650 pounds (295 kg). It usually lives in shallow water close to the shore, where it preys on fish, squid, crabs, and shellfish.

Archerfish (right) are small perchlike fish of tropical rivers, swamps, bays, and estuaries. The archer gulps in a mouthful of water and squirts it hard from just under the surface at a small insect or similar target on a plant above. The victim is knocked into the water and gobbled up.

hunting time. There are tales of curious groupers following human divers, although very few accounts of real attacks.

Noisy fish
Another large group of perchlike fish is the drum and croaker family. Most live in

Aggressive groupers
Groupers are fierce hunters and usually ambush their prey. They hide among rocks and seize anything that comes near in their huge mouths. Dusk is the favorite

The Murray cod is a type of seabass, but it lives in lakes and rivers in eastern Australia. It may reach a length of 6 feet (1.8 m).

shallow tropical seas. As their names suggest, these fish make a variety of sounds using special muscles to vibrate the swim bladder. The black drum of the western Atlantic Ocean grows to 6 feet (1.8 m) long and 140 pounds (65 kg) in weight. The white seabass, despite its name, is also a type of drum, and about the same size.

Fast-moving darters

The largest freshwater group of perchlike fish is the perch family itself, with more than 160 species living in North America, Europe, and Asia. The perch, with its spiny dorsal fin and

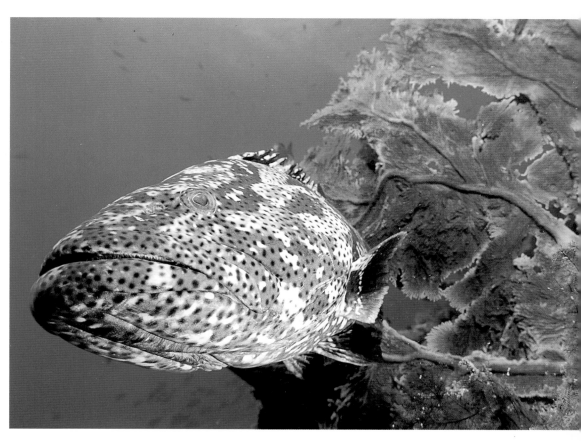

The brown marbled grouper is one of several groupers that grows larger than an adult human. It can easily swallow prey up to 3 feet (90 cm) long, into its cavernous mouth.

they dart quickly from place to place. The males are especially brightly colored during the breeding season, when they swim and dart to attract females. Once a male darter has a mate, he finds a nesting area among gravel on the stream bed where the female lays her eggs. He fertilizes the eggs and guards the nest until they hatch.

The walleye is one of the largest in the perch family, at 3 feet (90 cm) long. It lives deep in large rivers and lakes, eating fish, frogs, insects, and other water creatures. Walleyes breed in clear waters with a gravel bed. Newly hatched fry (babies) are just half an inch

(1 cm) long and spend a few days drifting near the surface, nourished by their yolk sacs. Then they feed on animal plankton until big enough to catch other fish.

Jack-knife drum fish

greenish dark-barred body, has been introduced to lakes and slow-flowing rivers in many parts of the world. Some members of this family are small colorful fish called darters, which live along the beds of fast-moving streams in North America. Most are less than 4 inches (10 cm) long and

A coney grouper, 12 inches (30 cm) long, watches from near its lair, a cave in a coral reef.

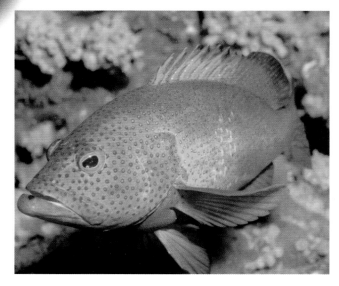

Some perchlike fish groups:

Perches (Percidae)
- about 160 species
- live in fresh water
- includes darters, ruffe, zander

Groupers and seabass (Serranidae)
- about 400 species
- most live in the sea
- includes jewfish, coney

Drums and croakers (Sciaenidae)
- about 270 species
- most live in the sea
- includes Atlantic croaker, jack-knife fish, red drum, black drum, red mullet, spotted seatrout

Tunas and marlins

FEW FISH ARE SLEEKER AND FASTER THAN THESE SUPER-STREAMLINED MEMBERS of the perchlike group (page 122). Tunas and their smaller cousins, bonitos and mackerels, are known as scombrids and have torpedo-shaped bodies. The crescent tail gives maximum power as it thrashes from side to side, to thrust the fish through the water. These types of fish live around the world, especially in warm waters, and are caught in huge numbers as food for people. The marlins and sailfish, called billfish, are also high-speed swimmers. They cruise long distances across oceans in their hunt for prey. Barracudas are another type of fierce fish predator. They usually prefer tropical waters, especially around coral reefs. Smaller barracudas tend to hunt in schools (groups). Larger barracudas travel alone and may threaten human divers. Some attacks on people which are assumed to be the work of sharks, may well be carried out by large barracudas.

The swordfish has the crescent-shaped tail of a very fast swimmer. Unlike marlins and sailfish, it has a flattened snout and lacks pelvic fins.

The bluefin tuna is the biggest of the tuna family. It can be up to 10 feet (3 m) long and more than 1,400 pounds (635 kg) in weight.

Most kinds of tuna, such as the bluefin and yellowfin, are large, powerful fish. They prey on smaller fish and squid, and in turn are eaten by large sharks and toothed whales such as the killer whale. The skipjack tuna is smaller, only 3 feet (90 cm) long. It swims in vast shoals of tens of thousands of fish, and is caught as a food for people, especially in the Pacific Ocean.

Fastest

The sailfish is probably the fastest fish. It has been timed swimming at more than 65 mph (110 km/h) over short distances. Another very speedy fish is its close relative, the wahoo. !

Mackerel

Large schools of mackerel are common in the Atlantic Ocean. In spring, summer, and autumn they usually stay near the surface and the shore, where they feed on small fish and crustaceans. In winter, they move into deeper water and appear to eat little. Mackerel usually breed in late spring or early summer, when females shed as many as half a million eggs into the water. The pinhead-sized eggs float

A hooked black marlin leaps in a fight for its life. Thoughtless "sport" fishing has reduced the numbers of these and similar billfish.

until they hatch about five days later, although most are eaten by small plankton-feeders. The tiny young mackerel grow fast and reach a length of 14 inches (35 cm) at only two years old. When fully grown they may reach 26 inches (65 cm) long.

Tiger of the sea

There are some 18 species of barracuda living in warm oceans around the world. The largest is the great barracuda, a slender fish found worldwide, especially well known in the Caribbean Sea. It grows to 6 feet (1.8 m) long and about 90 pounds (41 kg) in weight. It is an aggressive

The blue marlin has a long, pointed nose like a bird's beak or bill, hence the name "billfish."

hunter, known as the "tiger of the sea." It charges at its prey and bites off mouthfuls of flesh with its sharp teeth. Some barracudas are believed to cooperate in groups, herding their fish prey into a shoal before racing in for the attack.

Swords and spears

The mighty swordfish may weigh more than 1,100 pounds (500 kg) and be more than 13 feet (4 m) in length. Almost one third of this is the long upper jaw or "sword." A young swordfish has jaws of equal length. The upper jaw lengthens as the animal grows. The spearfish is very similar to the swordfish, but slightly smaller. The sailfish is another large, fast predator.

The sailfish (right) is named after its dorsal fin, which sticks up like the sail of a boat. It lives in cooler seas in summer but migrates back to tropical areas for winter.

Small barracuda (left), each about 3 feet (90 cm) long, form a hunting group. They may circle prey fish, to round them into a school that is easier to attack.

It grows to more than 12 feet (3.5 m) long and stays closer to coasts than the swordfish and spearfish. It has a huge sail-like fin on its back and long pelvic fins. The upper jaw comes to a point at the front, but it is rounded like a long rod, rather than flattened as in the swordfish.

Sharp!

A swordfish's "sword" is so strong that it has been known to pierce the sides of wooden boats to a depth of 12 inches (30 cm). It is slightly flattened from top to bottom and covered in sharp scales. Exactly what the fish uses it for is not clear. It may be for extra streamlining. It could be to attack enemies. It might be a hunting weapon to lash out at prey, to slice or impale them.

Tuna and mackerel (Scombridae)
- about 160 species
- all live in the sea
- includes bonito, wahoo

Swordfish (Xiphiidae)
- 1 species
- lives in the sea
- long, flattened snout

Sailfish and marlin (Istiophoridae)
- about 11 species known as billfish
- all live in the sea
- long, rounded snout
- includes sailfish, blue marlin, black marlin, striped marlin, spearfish

Barracuda (Sphyraenidae)
- about 20 species
- all live in the sea
- includes sennet

Cichlids, damsels, and parrotfish

THE CICHLIDS, DAMSELFISH, AND PARROTFISH ARE YET MORE TYPES OF PERCHLIKE FISH (page 122).
Cichlids are one of the largest groups of fish that live entirely in fresh water. Most dwell in tropical and subtropical lakes and rivers, mainly in Africa and also in South America. They vary in size and shape, although most are less than 20 inches (50 cm) long and generally silver in color. They all share the feature of a set of teeth in the throat, called pharyngeal teeth, as well as the normal teeth in the jaws. The throat teeth are used to slice and grind up the food grabbed by the jaw teeth to make swallowing and digestion easier. Their shape varies according to the type of food that the species of cichlid prefers. The throat teeth are large and flat in shellfish eaters, and sharp for cutting through flesh in fish eaters. Damselfish are brightly colored and common around coral reefs. Some species eat the little coral polyps (animals), others rasp at seaweeds, while still others feed on the tiny plants and animals of the plankton. Parrotfish also live on coral reefs and, like cichlids, they have throat teeth as well as jaw teeth. The jaw teeth are fused or joined into a sharp parrotlike beak for scraping and chopping food.

Various types of damselfish have become popular as aquarium fish. However, their colors tend to fade as they grow older. Also they can be aggressive to other fish in the tank. This is because, in their natural home, they have to battle for their patch of territory on the crowded coral reef.

A clown fish peeps from its safe home among the stinging, paralyzing tentacles of a sea anemone (page 34).

Mouthbrooders are named because they care for, or brood, their eggs and young in the mouth. There are many mouthbrooders in the cichlid group, such as this Nigerian mouthbrooder.

Male cichlids are usually more brightly colored than females. They perform courtship displays, swimming to and fro and waving their fins to show off their patterns and attract a mate. The firemouth cichlid has a red patch on its chin that becomes even brighter and more glowing during the breeding season. Some male cichlids even build a special structure to attract a female and serve as a nest for the eggs. This may be a deep pit in the mud on the bottom of the river or lake, or a mound of sand up to 3 feet (90 cm) high.

Most fish take no care of their offspring. But all members of the cichlid group look after their eggs or babies in some way. Some simply guard the eggs in their

The male garibaldi, a type of damselfish, collects only red seaweeds to make his nest. Here, he guards his mate's eggs.

nest on the river or lake bed, until the baby fish hatch. Others take the eggs into their mouths and carefully hold them until they hatch. When the eggs hatch, some cichlids even care for the baby fish in the same way. This is called mouthbrooding.

Usually the female does the mouthbrooding, but in a few species, it is the male. The parent is surrounded by a cloud of tiny babies, or fry, who dart after even tinier bits of food. If danger threatens, the fry dash back to the parent's mouth and disappear. It looks as if the adult has sucked them in and swallowed them! But after a minute or two, the babies slowly begin to emerge again. The young fish may also hide in their parent's mouth at night.

Helpful partners

Damselfish are mostly small, less than 8 inches (20 cm) long. Several types, known as clown fish, have partnerships with sea anemones. The clown fish lives among the anemone's stinging tentacles, where it is protected from attack by predators. It survives mainly because it has a special coating of slime that resists

Sandy!

Sand grains on a beach are usually worn-down chips cracked off larger boulders. But around a coral reef many of the fine, white grains have been made by parrotfish. These fish scrape food off the rocks with their very strong "beaks." Some stony fragments fall away as they feed. Others are swallowed, to emerge from the fish's other end as a shower of silvery sand.

anemone's stings or prevents them being fired (page 34–35). In return for this protection, the clown fish cleans any dirt or scraps of food from the anemone. Its presence may even lure predators to the anemone, which can then sting and eat them. Both partners gain in this relationship, which is called symbiosis. However, the anemone can survive without the clown fish, but a clown fish without an anemone is usually snapped up by a predator.

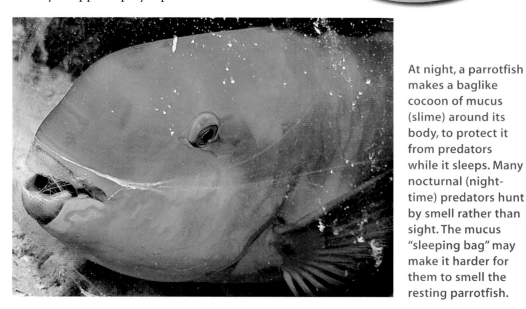

Sex change

Parrotfish, like wrasses (page 128), are able to change sex. Most parrotfish start life as females. As they grow older they become males. Some species also change color when they change sex. For example, the female stoplight parrotfish of Caribbean coral reefs is brownish-red. Males are blue and green, especially on their fins. Old males of the blue parrotfish even change shape too. They develop a large bump on

Sea-living angelfish like the emperor angelfish are mostly tall, thin and colourful. They are related to the butterflyfish group and popular as aquarium fish.

The great lakes of Africa include Victoria, Malawi and Tanganyika. They contain more different species of fish than any other lakes in the world. And most of these fish are cichlids. For the great majority, each species is found in one lake—and nowhere else. Sadly, many of these cichlid species are in grave danger of extinction. This is due to overfishing, pollution, and especially the introduction of predatory fish such as the Nile perch (page 103).

At night, a parrotfish makes a baglike cocoon of mucus (slime) around its body, to protect it from predators while it sleeps. Many nocturnal (night-time) predators hunt by smell rather than sight. The mucus "sleeping bag" may make it harder for them to smell the resting parrotfish.

the upper snout that looks like the beginning of a nose-horn! The blue parrotfish, a strong fish with a deep and muscular body, is one of the largest in its group, growing to about 4 feet (1.2 m) long. It lives along shores of the western Atlantic Ocean, from the Carolinas, through the Caribbean and south to Brazil. Another common species is the rainbow parrotfish, which inhabits the same region. The feeding activities of parrotfish keep the life of the reef turning over, since they clear areas of rock for new growths of sponges, corals, sea mats, barnacles, and similar animals, as well as seaweeds.

Cichlids (Cichlidae)	Damselfish (Pomacentridae)	Parrotfish (Scaridae)
• at least 1,200 species (may be many more to discover)	• about 300 species	• about 70 species
• live in fresh water	• live in warm seas	• live in warm seas
• includes zebra cichlid, discus fish, freshwater angelfish	• includes clown fish (anemone fish), sergeant major, garibaldi, beau-gregory	• includes blue parrotfish, stoplight parrotfish, rainbow parrotfish

Blennies, gobies, and wrasses

MOSTLY SMALL AND FOUND IN SHALLOW WATER, THE BLENNIES, GOBIES AND WRASSES are three large families of fish, each with hundreds of species. They belong to the main perch group (page 122). Most blennies have a tall dorsal fin, and small pelvic fins that are in front of the pectoral fins (rather than behind them as in other fish). They also have a hairlike covering, cirri, on the nostrils or eyes—which are on stalks in some species. Gobies are found all over the world, except in polar waters. Most are less than 4 inches (10 cm) long and have two dorsal fins. The two pelvic fins are joined to make a sucker on the underside. This enables the fish to cling to rocks or seaweed, since many types of goby live on the shore or the seabed. They feed mainly on small shrimps and other crustaceans. Wrasses are mostly less than 6 inches (15 cm) long, slim, and very brightly colored. They have two sharp teeth at the front of the mouth. Wrasses live singly, not in schools, along coral reefs and rocky shores in all warmer seas.

Like most shore fish, the mudskipper has a tough, rubbery body, as protection against crashing waves and rolling pebbles on the shore.

The largest blenny is the giant kelpfish (page 129), at 2 feet (60 cm) long. Like all the kelp blennies, it lives among seaweed. Its colouring varies from red to yellowish-green or brown, to match the particular type of kelp or other weed in its surroundings.

Stargazer blennies, like many other blennies, have eyes on stalks. The stargazer buries itself in the sand or mud of the seabed, but its eyes stick out above the surface, like periscopes, so it can still watch for danger or food.

Useful service

Many kinds of wrasse carry out a useful service for other creatures on the reef. They are called cleaner fish. A large "customer" fish, such as a grouper, swims to a certain place, the cleaning station, and stays still, with mouth and gill covers open. The cleaner wrasse approaches. The customer recognizes its bright colours and zigzag way of swimming, and allows the cleaner wrasse to use its sharp, ratlike front teeth to nip off fish lice and other pests and parasites from around its head, mouth, gills, and scales. The wrasse eats the parasites as food and the customer is cleaned of its pests.

A nasty trick

This helpful partnership between different kinds of animals is known as symbiosis. But it is open to trickery. The saber-toothed blenny looks so like a

Montagu's blenny (above) is typical of its group. It is a hardy fish of rock pools that grows to 3 inches (8 cm) long and eats a wide variety of food.

A cleaner wrasse picks dirt and pests from the huge mouth of a coral hind, which does not try to eat the cleaner.

Snappers, like this school of blue-striped snappers, are yet another group of perch-like fish. There are about 230 species. Most are brightly colored fish of warm seas.

particular cleaner wrasse that it is very hard to tell one from the other. This resemblance is known as mimicry. A customer fish allows the saber-tooth blenny to swim near. But the blenny does not clean—it takes a bite out of the customer with its sharp teeth. If the customer reacts and tries to eat the blenny, the saber-tooth bites the inside of its mouth and is quickly spat out.

Fish out of water

Mudskippers are small types of goby that can live out of water for minutes,

Like most blennies and gobies, the male giant kelpfish watches over the female's eggs and also guards the newly hatched young.

Smallest

The smallest fish are dwarf gobies in the Philippine Islands. They are 0.3 inch (8 mm) long.

!

Mudskippers (below) live among the tangled roots of mangrove, especially on the shores of the Indian and Pacific Oceans. Their pectoral fins are almost like walking legs.

even hours. They take in oxygen from small pools of water trapped in their large, cheeklike gill chambers. Every few minutes the mudskipper dips its head into a puddle to refresh this water. Mudskippers live in coastal mangrove swamps in tropical areas. At low tide they come out of their burrows to feed on insects and other small animals. They skitter across the mud on their strong pectoral fins, and watch for danger with their "popeyes" on stalks.

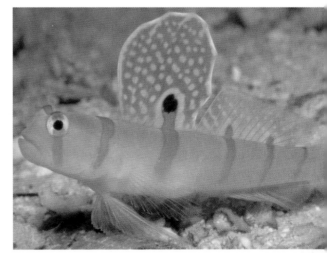

The sailfin goby (above) erects its flaglike dorsal fin. To rivals of the same species, this means: "Stay off my patch of shore!"

Blennies
(Blenniidae)
- about 275 species
- nearly all sea-living
- includes shanny, redlip, rock, and boss and butterfly blennies

Gobies (Gobiidae)
- about 2,120 species
- most live in the sea

- a few are cave fish
- includes mudskippers, guavina, bunaka

Wrasses (Labridae)
- about 600 species
- live in the sea
- includes bluehead, ballan, and cuckoo wrasse, corkwing, hogfish, razorfish

AMPHIBIANS & REPTILES

Amphibians live a strange double life. Most begin as tiny black dots in little balls of jelly floating in water. These eggs, or spawn, hatch into tadpoles that breathe by gills and swim with their tails. But as they grow, tadpoles undergo an amazing change called metamorphosis. They lose their gills and tails, and develop lungs for breathing air and legs for hopping on land. They develop into adult frogs, toads, salamanders, and newts.

Most amphibians have soft, moist skin. Reptiles do not. They can be recognized by their tough, scaly skin. The reptile group includes some of the most dangerous animals. There are poisonous snakes with deadly venom, such as cobras, rattlers, and vipers. Constrictor snakes, like pythons and boas, squeeze the life from their victims. Crocodiles and alligators threaten enemies with their hissing, gaping mouths, equipped with rows of pointed teeth.

Turtles, tortoises, and terrapins live a slow-paced life, safe in their domed protective shells. Much speedier are the lizards, another reptile subgroup. Some dart about so fast that we can hardly follow their movements. Lizards range in size from little geckoes that make a big meal of a fly, to monitors, such as the Komodo dragon, that can swallow a goat in one gulp.

What are amphibians?

AMPHIBIANS ARE COLD-BLOODED ANIMALS that have a "double life." They begin in water, as jelly-covered eggs which hatch into tadpoles that breathe by gills and swim with their tails. The tadpoles change shape or metamorphose as they grow, into adults that breathe by lungs and walk on land on four legs. There are about 4,000 species of amphibians, all over the world except Antarctica and the far north.

The spring peeper frog is named after its "teep-teep" call.

Like fish and reptiles, amphibians are cold-blooded. Unlike birds and mammals, they cannot make body heat to keep themselves at a constant warm temperature. Their bodies are usually at about the same temperature as the air or water around them. When they are warm, they can move actively. But in cold conditions, they cannot. They become still and their body processes slow down. This is called torpor. In temperate regions, many amphibians are torpid or "asleep" in winter.

Amphibian eggs
An amphibian begins life as a small, dark, dotlike egg. This contains yolk for nourishment and is surrounded by several layers of jelly. It does not have a protective outer shell like a reptile egg, so it must be laid in water or moist surroundings, to prevent it drying out. Lots of jelly-covered eggs clustered together are known as spawn.

Breathing in water
The eggs grow and become comma-shaped, then hatch into larval amphibians—tadpoles. These have feathery gills on the sides of the head (external gills) for absorbing oxygen from the water. Most amphibians lose their gills when they become adults, and take in oxygen through their lungs and moist skin. But some, such as the mudpuppy, keep their gills through life.

Groups of amphibians
More species of amphibians are being discovered every year, especially in their main habitats, the tropical rain forests. There are three main kinds of amphibians. They are newts and salamanders, frogs and toads, and caecilians.

Tailed and tailless amphibians
A typical newt or salamander has a long lizardlike body, a long tail, four usually small, sprawling legs at its sides, and smooth, scaleless skin. Most are active in the evening or at night, when they hunt for small creatures such as insects, spiders, and worms. In fact, all

Life of change
The lives of most amphibians start in water and move onto land. The drastic change in shape from legless tadpole to four-legged adult is known as metamorphosis. It takes about 3–4 months in the common frog.

spawn (jelly-covered eggs)

tadpole (larva)

legs grow and tail shrinks in young adult

adult frog is tailless

Bullfrogs are large, powerful frogs that eat a range of fish, insects, lizards, snakes, small mammals such as mice, and other prey—including smaller frogs. There are bullfrog species in North America, **South America**, and Africa.

Many frogs have brightly colored skin, like the tomato frog. Usually, the brighter they are, the more horrible-tasting the frog's flesh. The colors warn predators to leave the frog alone.

Frozen!

The spring peeper frog of North America can survive for as long as three days in icy temperatures, with almost half of the blood and other fluids in its body frozen solid. The frog produces extra glucose sugar, which concentrates its body fluids and reduces the amount of ice that forms, especially around its heart and brain.

The axolotl is a strange salamander that keeps its feathery gills even when adult (page 134).

Some newts have frilly crests of skin along the back. At breeding time, the male's crest becomes larger and his body develops brighter colors.

Male great crested newt

amphibians are predators. They cannot chew so they gulp down their victims whole, often still alive and struggling.

A typical frog or toad is in many ways the opposite of a salamander. It has a short, compact body, very long back legs for jumping, and no tail. The third amphibian group is the caecilians. These have no limbs at all and resemble overgrown earthworms. They burrow in the earth and dead leaves of tropical forests, searching for and devouring any small soil creatures.

Biggest

The largest amphibians are the giant salamanders of Eastern Asia, especially China and Japan. They grow up to 5 feet (1.5 m) in total length.

!

Caecilians, also called apodans, have no legs (page 134). They live underground, feeding on grubs and worms, although a few dwell in ponds and streams. They are eyeless and find their prey by touch and smell. They also have small scales in their skin, like reptiles.

A frog leaps using its powerful back legs. Each section of the leg is larger than the one above it. So the thigh is shortest, then the shin, and the foot is the longest. The hip, knee, and ankle joints straighten to fling the frog into the air.

AMPHIBIANS
- about 4,000 species
- vertebrates (animals with backbones)
- larvae or tadpoles live in water
- adults mostly live on land
- worldwide except coldest regions

Newts and salamanders (Caudata)
- about 360 species
- long body and tail, most four-legged

Frogs and toads (Anura)
- about 3,400 species
- no tail in adult
- long back legs for leaping

Caecilians (Apoda)
- about 160 species
- long wormlike body, no legs
- tropical and warm forests

Newts and salamanders

NEWTS AND SALAMANDERS ARE SHY, RARELY SEEN CREATURES. Most live in the northern half of the world, although there are some species of salamanders in South America. They usually stay hidden in cool, damp places during the day and come out at night to catch small creatures such as insects, snails, and worms. Some are typical amphibians in that they spend time both on land and in water. Others live entirely on land, or wholly in the water. The name "newt" is usually given to the types that are mainly aquatic (water-dwelling). Some salamanders have bright warning colors on their bodies. These signal to predators that their flesh is foul-tasting. Some can also ooze poisonous or horrible-tasting fluids from their skin.

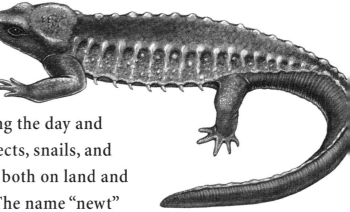

Spiny salamanders like the Chinese spiny newt have sharp ribs that almost poke out of the skin. They are too prickly for most predators to eat.

The yellow-eyed salamander is one of many species that lives on the damp forest floor. Its large eyes show that it is nocturnal, or active at night.

Many newts have long flaps of finlike skin along the upper and lower surfaces of the tail, which they keep from their tadpole stage. The fishlike tail is swished from side to side and helps the newt to swim faster.

Hot!
Legend says that the fire salamander walks through flames. Of course, it does not. But it does tend to hide away during winter in an old fallen log—which may be collected as firewood. When the log is thrown on the flames, the heat wakes the salamander, which quickly tries to escape!

or fertilize her eggs straight away, or they may be stored until she finds a more suitable time or place for her eggs.

Few eggs or many?
Some salamanders lay their eggs in damp places on land, such as under stones or old logs, or in moss. Others attach them to rocks or logs under the water. The number of eggs varies from only four or five to more than 5,000, depending on the species. If eggs are

Salamanders and newts are hunted by many other creatures, including birds and snakes. So apart from their nasty-tasting flesh, they have various ways of defending themselves. If the Chinese spiny newt is seized by a predator, it pushes its sharp-tipped ribs through its skin. The ribs pass through its skin glands on the way and release an extremely unpleasant poison.

Breeding time
In most salamander species, male and female do not have to link in a mating position. Instead the male leaves a "packet" of sperm on the ground, which the female then takes into her body. The sperm may join with

The fire salamander has distinctive black and yellow markings. These warning colors are shared by other animals, such as wasps, bees, and poisonous beetles.

The red salamander of North America is also called the eastern newt. It has an extra stage in its life known as the eft. This is a subadult, a halfway form between the tadpole and the full adult. After the tadpole stage, the eft develops and lives on land for up to three years before growing into a mature adult.

laid in water, they hatch out into tadpoles (larvae) with feathery gills. These gradually change to the adult form, developing legs and lungs. However, eggs laid on land usually miss out the tadpole stage and hatch into fully formed miniature salamanders. Some species, such as the fire salamander, do not lay eggs at all. The eggs develop inside the female's body and she gives birth to tiny offspring.

Warning colors
The gaudy markings of many amphibians warn enemies that they are very nasty-tasting indeed. The skin glands of the fire salamander ooze poisonous fluid that causes severe redness, swelling and irritation if another animal bites it. The effects are so severe that they can even kill small mammals. Pet dogs who pick up the salamander may suffer great distress. Potential predators lean to recognize these types of warning colors and avoid the salamanders.

The salamanders that never grow up
The axolotl (page 133) is a kind of mole salamander from Mexico. Some axolotls develop into full adults and live on land, like other salamanders. But others stay in water throughout their lives and keep their larval features, such as feathery gills. They become mature and breed, even though most of the body is still in the immature larval stage. This condition occurs in a few other amphibians. It is called neotony.

Lungless salamanders
As their name suggests, lungless salamanders have no lungs. They must absorb oxygen through the skin and the lining of the mouth. This means the skin must always stay moist. If it dries, oxygen cannot pass through. So lungless salamanders, such as the red, dusky and slimy salamanders, must live in damp places. Most are found in North and South America.

Mudpuppies never lose the feather gills that they have as tadpoles. These salamanders grow to about 16 inches (40 cm) long and inhabit creeks and rivers in North America. They hunt small fish, water worms, and young crayfish.

The olm is a pale, thin, almost blind, cave-dwelling salamander from lands bordering the Adriatic part of the Mediterranean Sea.

The hellbender is 28 inches (70 cm) long. Its head pushes it down onto the rocky bed when facing upstream.

Some groups of salamanders (continued from page 133):

Lungless salamanders (Plethodontidae)
- about 200 species
- long, slender body and tail
- live in water or caves
- includes red salamander, dusky salamander

Mole salamanders (Ambystomatidae)
- 32 species
- broad head, thick body
- adults usually live on land
- includes axolotl, tiger salamander

Newts (Salamandridae)
- about 60 species
- slender body and long tail
- strong legs
- includes fire salamander, warty newt, striped newt

Sirens (Sirenidae)
- 3 species
- eellike body and feathery gills
- live in water
- includes dwarf siren, greater siren

Olm and mudpuppies (Proteidae)
- 5 species
- feathery gills
- long body and short tail
- live in water

Giant salamanders (Cryptobranchidae)
- 3 species
- large, heavy body
- short tail
- live in water
- includes hellbender

Frogs and toads

FROGS AND TOADS ARE BY FAR THE BIGGEST GROUP OF AMPHIBIANS, with more than 3,400 species. They live on all continents except Antarctica, and in habitats ranging from deserts to cold mountain streams. But they are most common in tropical and subtropical swamps and rain forests. The name "frog" was once used for the slender, smooth-skinned types that could leap well, and "toad" for the plump, rough-skinned species that prefer to waddle. Now both names are used for similar species and there is no clear difference between a frog and a toad.

All frogs and toads are tailless and have strong back legs for jumping. The front legs are smaller and cushion the landing. A frog's body is short, with a strong backbone to cope with the physical stresses of jumping, and there is no narrow neck between the head and body. The large eyes are usually on the top of the very wide-mouthed head, so the frog can still see when it is almost submerged in water.

A frog's life cycle

A typical frog or toad lays its eggs in water. These hatch into tiny tadpoles with tails for swimming and fluffy gills for breathing in water. The young tadpole feeds on plants. As it grows, it loses its external gills and develops lungs in its chest for breathing air. It gradually loses its tail too, and develops legs. The head broadens, the body become short and thick, and the tadpole has metamorphosed into a froglet, ready to venture onto land.

Frog calls

Male frogs and toads make loud calls to attract females. Each species has its own particular call, and the green frog can be heard hundreds of yards away. The calls

In Central American rain forests, it is so damp that the strawberry poison-arrow frog (above) can carry her tadpole on her back, without it drying out. The water-holding frog (left) of Australia has a very different habitat – the desert. During the drought, this frog stays in a burrow underground. Its outer layer of slime detaches to form a cocoon that fills with the frog's urine and other body fluids, like a water-filled sleeping bag.

of frogs are made louder in a vocal sac below the chin, as air from the lungs is forced over the vocal cords in the neck. Females do not usually make any sounds.

Caring for young

Some frogs do not leave their eggs in water to hatch, but carry them around to make sure they do

Useful!

The poison fluid or secretion from poison-arrow frog skin may have medical uses. The secretions of the phantasmal poison-arrow frog are far more effective at stopping pain than the usual painkilling drugs. Those of the golden poison-arrow frog may help patients who have had heart attacks.

Tree frogs (above and below) have sucker-like disks at the ends of their toes. They can cling to twigs, wet glossy leaves—and even window glass. Green tree frogs are camouflaged among the leaves as they wait for their small insect prey.

Smallest

One of the smallest frogs in the world was discovered in Cuba in 1997. Its scientific name is *Eleutherodactylus iberia*. It measures only 0.4 inch (1 cm) long.

(!)

not get eaten. As the female marsupial fog lays her eggs, the male fertilizes them and helps her pack them into a backsack-like skin pouch on her back. They hatch into tadpoles and start their development in this pouch. After a few weeks she opens the pouch and her young hop into the water to complete their growth. The female Surinam toad carries her young in separate skin pouches on her back, until they have developed into fully formed mini-toads.

animals to stay away. Glands in the body release extremely strong venom into the frog's skin. Even a few drops of this can be lethal to a predator. Traditionally, local people in Central and South America tip their hunting arrows with this substance by rubbing the arrow head over the frog's skin.

The flying frog lives in Southeast Asian rain forests. It does not really fly, but spreads its huge webbed feet to glide as far as 40 feet (12 m) from tree to tree.

Surinam toad

Many frogs and toads make their calls louder by blowing up the chin skin like a balloon. The stretched skin vibrates or resonates to increase the volume of the sound.

Amazing!

Amphibian species worldwide are declining in numbers because of pollution, pesticides, and habitat destruction. Yet new species are being discovered in remote forests. A four-year survey during the 1990s in Madagascar recorded more than 100 new kinds of frogs.

Poisonous frogs

The bright colors of the poison-arrow (or arrow-poison) frogs warn other

A frog pushes off with its toes, launching its small, streamlined body into a leap at least 10 times its own length.

The cane toad is also called the marine or giant toad. It was taken from South America to Australia, to eat beetle pests in sugarcane fields. But it prefers small creatures that are natural inhabitants in the area, making some of them very rare animals.

Some groups of frogs and toads (continued from page 133):

Ranid or "true" frogs (Ranidae)
- about 650 species
- slim, smooth-skinned body
- pointed head
- mostly live in water but some dwell in trees
- includes common frog, bullfrog

Bufid or "true" toads (Bufonidae)
- about 400 species
- stout body
- often rough, warty skin
- most live mainly on land
- includes cane toad, natterjack

Tree frogs (Hylidae)
- more than 770 species
- slender body
- long legs
- most live in trees
- webbed feet with sticky pads on disklike toetips

Leptodactylid frogs (Leptodactylidae)
- more than 900 species
- varied body form
- land-living and water-living species
- includes horned frog, chirping frog

Narrow-mouthed frogs (Microhylidae)
- more than 320 species
- stout body
- small mouth
- live in burrows or trees
- includes rain frog

Poison-arrow (arrow-poison) frogs (Dendrobatidae)
- over 170 species
- mainly tropical rain forests
- slim, small body
- sticky disks on toes
- brightly colored
- live on ground or in trees

What are reptiles?

REPTILES ARE ANIMALS WITH BACKBONES (VERTEBRATES) THAT ARE COLD-BLOODED, HAVE SCALES ON THEIR SKIN, AND LAY EGGS (page 131). Most reptiles have four legs with five toes on each foot, but snakes have no limbs at all. Most reptiles live on land, but marine turtles and sea snakes stay in the sea, except to come ashore briefly and lay their eggs. Most reptile eggs have shells that are tough yet leathery and flexible, unlike the hard, brittle shells of birds' eggs. However, some snakes do not lay eggs, but give birth to babies.

The main groups of reptiles are the turtles and tortoises, the crocodiles and alligators, the lizards, and the snakes. Most live on land, but many turtles and terrapins, also most crocodiles and alligators, and even some snakes, spend time in ponds, swamps, and rivers. A few, including the saltwater crocodile, venture into the sea.

Reptiles may not seem to be social animals, in the way that birds form flocks or monkeys live in troops. Yet they have many ways of communicating, especially with others of their own species at mating time. Lizards bob their heads and show off their skin crests and brightly colored patterns. Snakes leave chemical messages for their partners, which consist of scentlike substances called pheromones, produced in their bodies. Some reptiles, including crocodiles and geckoes, make hisses, grunts, and calls to attract mates.

When breeding, most female reptiles lay eggs and then leave these to develop and hatch on their own. But a few species,

Marine iguanas are some of the few reptiles that spend time in the sea. These large lizards dive to munch on seaweeds.

such as some skinks, pythons, and crocodiles, guard their eggs and even the babies too, protecting them from enemies. Some snakes and lizards keep their developing eggs inside their bodies, where they hatch and the mother gives birth to the young.

Worm lizards (below) are not worms, or lizards, but reptiles that resemble large earthworms. They burrow in the soil of tropical forests and eat small creatures.

Hingeback tortoises can tilt down the rear of the shell to give extra protection to the back legs and tail.

Scaly!
The skin of a reptile is covered with hard scales. These are made of keratin, the same substance that forms our nails and hair. In some reptiles, such as crocodiles, the scales are strengthened by plates of bones, making a tough armor.

The shell of a softshell turtle does not have hard, horny, strengthening plates, as in other turtles and tortoises. So it feels slightly soft and rubbery.

Cold bodies

Reptiles are cold-blooded creatures. This means they cannot control their body temperatures themselves. They depend on the heat of the sun to become warm, so that they can be active and move about. In cold conditions, reptiles move slowly or not at all. This cold, immobile condition is known as torpor. However, one advantage of being cold-blooded is that reptiles do not need to use so much energy as warm-blooded animals, who must "burn" energy from their food to produce body heat. So reptiles need to eat far less food than warm-blooded birds and mammals of the same body size—perhaps only one-tenth of the amount.

The pond slider is a common turtle in North, Central and South America. It rarely leaves the water.

The reptile's egg

The leathery shell of a reptile egg gives protection and prevents it from drying out, even in the desert heat. Inside are layers of fluid to protect the developing embryo (unhatched baby), and yolk to provide it with nourishment.

REPTILES

- about 6,560 species
- cold-blooded vertebrates
- scaly skin
- lay eggs
- most have four legs
- worldwide except polar regions

Lizards (Sauria)
- about 3,750 species
- long, slim body, long tail
- includes skinks, geckos, chameleons, iguanas, monitors

Crocodiles (Crocodilia)
- 22 species
- long body armored with thick scales, long tail
- includes crocodiles, caimans, alligators, gharial

Tuatara (Rhynchocephalia)
- 1 species
- lizardlike, with head and back crest
- only in New Zealand

Worm lizards (Amphisbaenia)
- about 140 species
- long slender body, no limbs
- includes worm lizards, shield snouts

Snakes (Serpentes)
- about 2,400 species
- long wormlike body, no limbs
- includes pythons, boas, vipers

Turtles and tortoises (Chelonia)
- about 250 species
- body protected by a hard, domed shell
- includes tortoises, terrapins, turtles

Water dragons (below) are mostly large tropical lizards that swim well by lashing their tails from side to side. Caimans (below right) are smaller members of the crocodile group from Central and South America. They grow to about 6 feet (1.8 m) long.

The spotted water snake lives in swamps and creeks in northern parts of Australia. Its nostrils are set high on its head, so it can take a breath without poking its whole head out of the water.

Most terrapins have wide feet with partly webbed toes, for efficient swimming.

Tortoises, turtles, and terrapins

THERE ARE ABOUT 250 SPECIES OF TURTLES, TORTOISES, AND TERRAPINS, FOUND IN MOST WARM PARTS OF THE WORLD. They are easily recognized by the hard, rounded shell that protects the main part of the body. The mostly land-dwelling tortoises thrive in all kinds of habitats, including desert, woodland, and mountains. Turtles and terrapins live chiefly in rivers and ponds. They are slow and ungainly on land, but swift in the water. (Marine turtles are a separate group, page 142.)

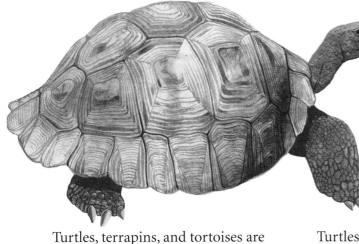

Several kinds of giant tortoises live on Pacific and Indian Ocean islands, such as the Galapagos.

A snapping turtle prepares to eat a young duck that it has grabbed by the legs, while lying camouflaged on the pond bed.

Turtles, terrapins, and tortoises are known as chelonians. They do not have teeth. Instead, a turtle or tortoise has a strong, beaklike mouth with hard ridges along the jaw edges, for biting food. Many chelonians are predators, catching other animals to eat. Others, including many tortoises, are plant-eaters. They swallow each piece they bite since they cannot chew.

Turtles reproduce by laying eggs, usually in a hole in the ground. The female lays her eggs in a warm place and leaves them to incubate and hatch alone. The young receive no parental care.

Galapagos giant tortoise

The largest tortoises are found on the Galapagos Islands, off the coast of Ecuador in the Pacific Ocean. These

Biggest

The largest land tortoise is the Galapagos giant tortoise. It weighs 500 pounds (230 kg) or more and its shell can be 4 feet (1.2 m) long.

!

lumbering giants are strong enough to carry a person. Each island in the Galapagos group has a variety or subspecies of giant tortoise that is recognizable by the shape of its shell or the size and length of its legs. These slight variations were noticed by English naturalist Charles Darwin when he visited the islands on a round-the-world trip by boat in the 1830s. The tortoises, finches, and other animals of the Galapagos set Darwin thinking about the idea of evolution by natural selection. He described this idea in his momentous book *On the Origin of Species* (1859), and it is now central to the study of animals and the natural world.

The turtle's shell

The shell of a turtle or tortoise has two parts—the upper carapace and the lower plastron. Each part has two layers of plates like jigsaw puzzle pieces. These are made of bone on the inside, and horn on the outside like normal reptile scales. The outer plates are called scutes. The two parts meet at the sides, with openings for the turtle's head, legs, and tail. The ribs and backbone are fixed to the upper inside of the carapace.

The matamata is an extraordinary-looking turtle about 16 inches (40 cm) long from the Amazon region of South America. It has an arrow-shaped head and a very wide mouth, to gulp in fish and other water animals. Its tiny eyes are about halfway along the sides of the "arrow."

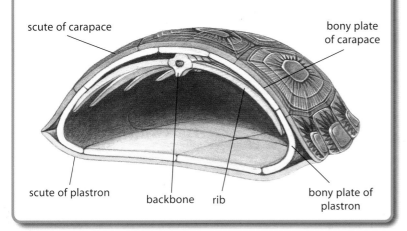

scute of carapace

bony plate of carapace

scute of plastron   backbone   rib   bony plate of plastron

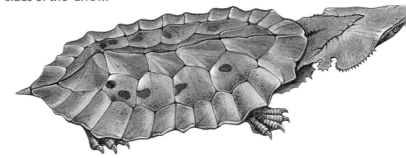

Camouflaged matamata

Many turtles and tortoises are brownish or green, to blend with their surroundings of mud, leaves and waterweeds. This helps them to hide as they wait for prey to come near or stay unnoticed by predators. The matamata is a member of the snake-necked turtle family, and has most unusual camouflage. With its ridged shell and flattened head, fringed with flaps of skin, it looks like a clump of bark and leaves in the water. When a victim passes by, the matamata simply opens its large mouth. Water—and the prey—rush in. The turtle then closes its mouth, squeezes the water out at the sides, and swallows its meal.

The leopard tortoise of Africa has a high-domed shell with bold markings. It lives in woods and grassland.

Leopard tortoise

Named after the color and patterning on its shell, which resemble a leopard's markings, the leopard tortoise is a plant eater. It feeds on thistles, prickly pear leaves, fruits, and grasses. In the breeding season, the female digs a flask-shaped nest for her 30 or so eggs. If the ground is hard and dry she may urinate on the earth first to soften it.

Old!

Turtles are among the longest-lived of all animals. Box turtles of North America and spur-thighed tortoises in Europe survive to over 100 years old. A Marion's tortoise taken from the Seychelles to Mauritius in 1766, lived until 1918. It died due to an accident—at least 152 years old.

Wood turtles catch worms, insects, and grubs, and can climb into bushes. They were once caught and kept as pets, but this has made them rare.

Snapping turtles lurk in ponds and lakes from Canada, south through North to Central America. They grab any small animal as prey.

Circular shell

The spiny softshell turtle has an almost circular shell, covered with leathery skin. Small, spiny projections line the front of the shell. This turtle is a good swimmer and spends most of its life in water where it catches insects, crustaceans, and some fish to eat.

Finger-snapping turtle

The largest freshwater turtle in North America is the alligator snapping turtle. It has a large head and a rough, lumpy shell. Inside its gaping mouth is a small, pink, fleshy flap that resembles a worm. When a fish comes to eat the "worm," it is quickly snapped up in the turtles's jaws. These are easily powerful enough to remove a human finger.

Main groups of turtles (continued from page 139):

Snake-necked turtles (Chelidae)
• about 30 species
• live mainly in water
• most have long necks
• includes giant snake-neck turtle, matamata

Helmeted side-necked turtles (Pelomedusidae)
• about 20 species
• live mainly in water
• includes Arrau river turtle, West African mud turtle

Alligator turtles (Chelydridae)
• 3 species
• large head and long tail
• live in water
• includes snapping turtle, big-headed turtle

Softshell turtles (Trionychidae)
• about 22 species
• shell covered with leathery skin
• live mainly in water
• includes spiny softshell, Indian flapshell

American mud and musk turtles (Kinosternidae)
• about 20 species
• musk glands below carapace give off strong-smelling scent
• live mainly in water
• includes striped mud turtle, common musk turtle

Pond turtles (Emydidae)
• about 85 species
• well-developed shell, strong limbs and webbed feet
• live mainly in water, some stay on land
• includes box turtle, river terrapin, wood turtle

Tortoises (Testudinae)
• about 41 species
• domed shell, strong back legs
• land-living
• includes gopher tortoise, pancake tortoise, spur-thighed tortoise, Galapagos giant tortoise

Sea turtles

SEA OR MARINE TURTLES ARE THE LARGEST MEMBERS OF THE CHELONIAN GROUP. There are only seven species, found mostly in tropical and subtropical seas and oceans. Apart from a few sea snakes, they are the only reptiles that spend virtually their whole lives at sea. Only females come ashore, and then for only a few hours each year, to lay their eggs. Sea turtles have flatter or less domed shells than freshwater turtles, and they swim with their front limbs, which are larger than the back limbs. Awkward on land, they flap their flipperlike front legs to "fly" through the sea with amazing grace. When on the move, they must surface every five minutes or so to breathe air. But when resting or sleeping, they may remain underwater for several hours. They have good senses of sight and smell under the water, to find their food, detect danger, and locate a mate.

Turtle front flippers, like this loggerhead's, are wide and flattened. The turtle does not so much row with them, rather than flap them up and down, like a bird flapping its wings.

The leatherback is the largest of all turtles and tortoises. It can weigh more than 1,100 pounds (500 kg), although most of this great bulk is buoyed up by the water.

Like freshwater turtles and land tortoises, sea turtles do not have teeth. They bite and crush their food with the strong, hard edges to their beaklike jaws. Young turtles feed on the tiny animals and plants of the plankton, and then move on to slightly larger creatures. Adult green sea turtles feed mostly on sea grass. But the other species of sea turtles eat creatures such as jellyfish, squid, shrimps, and fish.

The breeding beach

After mating at sea, female turtles tend to return to the same place year after year, to lay their eggs. At the nesting beach, the female drags herself slowly up the sand to beyond the high tide mark.

A female leatherback digs a hole on a sandy beach, where she will lay 50–150 eggs.

She digs a pit with her flippers, then begins to lay her eggs, 2–3 at a time. She may lay from 50 to more than 150 eggs in the clutch. She then covers the nest with sand and rakes over the site with her flippers, to disguise it as much as possible. Finally she returns to the sea, leaving her eggs to incubate in the sun-baked sand. The leatherback turtle does this several times, laying clutches in different places at intervals of about ten days.

The hawksbill is the most tropical of sea turtles, usually found in shallow coastal waters around reefs and bays. It is one of the few large animals to feed mainly on sponges.

A dangerous journey

Sea turtle eggs take about eight weeks to hatch, depending on the sand temperature. The babies break out of their shells and struggle out of their sandpit nest by themselves. It is a group effort and it may take several days to reach the surface. Once out on the beach, the tiny turtles make a dash for the sea. Many fall victim to predators such as seabirds, crabs, otters, foxes, and lizards, who soon gather for the feast. Those that reach the sea begin to swim at once into deeper water. But here they face new hazards such as predatory fish.

Loggerhead turtle

Leathery back

The huge leatherback sea turtle is named from its unusual shell, which is made of a thick, leathery substance strengthened by tiny bones. Leatherbacks feed mostly on jellyfish, which they catch and cut up with their scissor-like jaws. They are known to dive to depths of more than 3,000 feet (900 m) in their search for food.

The loggerhead sea turtle has a large head, up to 10 inches (25 cm) long, in proportion to the rest of its body. The sides of the head house

powerful jaw muscles that enable this turtle species to crush hard-shelled prey such as clams, scallops, sea snails, crabs, and lobsters.

Migration

Some sea turtles spend their lives within a small area. Others make long journeys between the areas where they usually feed, and the beaches where they breed.

Most green turtles are in the second group. Some feed off the Atlantic coast of South America, then migrate to Ascension Island some 900 miles (1500 km) away.

The green turtle was hunted in great numbers for its meat, shell, eggs, and skin. It has become very rare and, like other sea turtles, it is now on the official list of threatened animals. Trade in its products is strictly controlled.

Turtles continued from page 141:

Sea turtles (Chelonidae)
- 6 species
- flat, bony shell covered with horny plates
- flipperlike limbs
- includes green turtle, ridley sea turtles, hawksbill, loggerhead

Leatherback sea turtle (Dermochelyidae)
- 1 species
- shell covered with leathery skin

Smallest

The Pacific ridley is the smallest sea turtle. It measures about 28 inches (70 cm) long and weighs less than 90 pounds (41 kg).

!

Crocodiles and alligators

CROCODILES HAVE CHANGED LITTLE SINCE THEY SHARED THE PREHISTORIC WORLD WITH THEIR CLOSE REPTILE RELATIVES, THE DINOSAURS, more than 100 million years ago. There are three subgroups in the crocodile group, known as crocodilians. These are the crocodiles themselves, the alligators and caimans, and the single species of gharial (gavial) from northern India. Crocodilians are found in all tropical and subtropical regions of the world. They are are powerful predators, equally at home on land and in water.

The massive saltwater or estuarine crocodile is regularly seen swimming offshore.

The Nile crocodile has become very rare. Its natural river and swamp habitats have been drained and changed to farmland, industrial sites, and tourist areas.

A typical crocodile or alligator has a long body covered with thick scales. Bony plates embedded in the skin along the back give further protection. The snout is long too, with nostrils and eyes set high on the head. The tail is also long and tall, and very muscular, for swimming. The two pairs of legs are short but strong, with five toes on the front feet and four on the back feet. All of these toes are partly webbed.

Lazy days, busy nights

Crocodiles spend much of the day basking in the sun on sandy riverbanks and mudflats. They become active in the evening and usually hunt for prey at night. They are among the most patient, silent, and stealthy of all large predators. Often the croc lurks in water near the shore, almost totally submerged like an old floating log, waiting for an animal to come and drink. When the prey is almost within reach, the crocodile makes a sudden dash from the water, drags the victim below the surface and holds it there, usually with the croc's jaws clamped onto its throat, until it dies.

Croc or alligator?

Crocodiles live in tropical and subtropical areas of Central and South America, Africa, Asia, and Australia. Most alligators and caimans live in North, Central, and South America, with one species, the Chinese alligator, in East Asia. The main difference between a crocodile and an alligator is that, in an alligator, the fourth tooth on each side of the lower jaw fits into a pit in the upper jaw. So it cannot be seen when the mouth is closed. In a crocodile, these fourth lower teeth are visible when the mouth is shut, on the outsides of the upper jaw. The gharial lives in northern India and neighboring countries and is identified by its very long, narrow snout.

Crocodile diet

The food of a crocodile or alligator tends to change as the animal grows. For example, a young Nile crocodile less than 20 inches (50 cm) long feeds mostly on small creatures such as frogs, insects and spiders. As it reaches about 40 inches (100 cm) in length, it starts to catch larger prey such as birds, lizards, small mammals, and fish. The full-grown Nile crocodile preys mainly on larger mammals up to the size of zebras.

Largest

The biggest reptile is the saltwater or estuarine crocodile of the Indian and Pacific Oceans. It grows to 23 feet (7 m) long and about a ton in weight. **!**

A crocodile walks with its legs sprawled out to the sides. But it can also run fast by raising its body high and holding its legs almost vertically.

New teeth

A crocodile has teeth which are strong and pointed, but not especially large. Each tooth is set in its own deep socket in the jawbone. As teeth become worn, they are replaced by new teeth which grow at the bases of the old ones.

On the move

On land, crocodiles walk slowly with the legs splayed out to the sides, swinging the body with a snakelike wriggling motion. But a crocodile in a hurry holds its legs straighter, stiffer, and more upright under its body. This is the "high walk" and allows a speed of about 3 mph (5 km/h). A few species, such as Johnston's crocodile, can even break into a gallop and sprint almost as fast as a person, about 12 mph (20 km/h).

In water, the crocodile is an excellent swimmer. It pushes itself along with side-to-side sweeps of its powerful tail. It can also use its tail to drive itself suddenly and powerfully out of the water, in a sudden upward lunge to snatch prey. The legs are held close against the body to reduce resistance as the reptile swishes along.

A crocodile is almost entirely covered in thick, horny scales, with extra plates of bone along the back.

The half-"smile" of the alligator hides most of its small, sharp, conical teeth. If the animal gets too hot, it gapes—opens its mouth to lose excess body heat from the inner lining.

The gharial's very long, narrow jaws, armed with about 100 teeth, can be swished sideways through the water at speed to grab prey. The lump or "pot" at the upper end of the snout is a feature of old males.

The black caiman (right) is not always black. It may be brown and have creamy patches on its chin and underside. All crocodilians have their nostrils, eyes and ears on the top of the head. They can breathe, see and hear while almost submerged (below).

Main groups of crocodilians (continued from page 139):

Alligators and caimans (Alligatorinae)
- 7 species
- teeth not visible when mouth is closed

Crocodiles (Crocodylinae)
- 14 species
- fourth tooth in lower jaw visible when mouth is closed
- includes mugger, false gharial

Gharial (Gavialinae)
- 1 species
- long, slender jaws

How crocodiles breed

CROCODILES MAY SEEM LIKE ROBOTIC, UNTHINKING KILLERS. We notice few facial expressions or sound signals to show their moods and intentions. But among themselves, crocodiles have surprisingly complicated behavior, social lives, and breeding methods. They communicate using a wide variety of sounds, smells and movements. And, unlike nearly all other reptiles, the female guards her nest and takes care of her young.

Young crocodilians have longer legs, larger eyes, and shorter snouts relative to their body size, compared to the adults. But they are still fearsome hunters.

Crocodiles are polygamous animals. This means a member of one sex, in this case the male, mates with several partners. But the male crocodile must first establish himself in a territory, by threatening and pushing rival males. Then he must attract the attention of possible mates. He swims high in the water with his body exposed to view, occasionally slapping the surface with his head or chin to make loud sounds.

His antics may also attract rival males, who try to take over by having head-butt contests. Females watch the males and, before mating, they also take part by rubbing the male's head or blowing bubbles underwater.

The crocodile's nest

Soon after mating, the female prepares to dig her nest. The details vary slightly among the species, but the Nile crocodile is fairly typical. She finds a suitable site, in sunny soft ground up to 150 feet (50 m) from water. She may have to threaten rival females, since the best sites are in short supply and used year after year.

She digs her nest with her strong back feet and then positions herself over the hole, to start laying eggs. Young females may lay only about 20 eggs, but older ones can spend up to an hour laying about 80 eggs.

She then covers the eggs and settles down to watch over the nest and defend it from enemies. She does not feed during this time, and only moves away from the nest to drink. Even so, rapid predators such as mongooses, foxes, or monitor lizards may dart in and steal an egg or two.

Calls for help

Crocodile eggs usually incubate for 60–100 days, depending on temperature. When the babies are ready and they hear footsteps above, they call from inside their eggs with loud squeals and squeaks. The mother digs down to the eggs, and the hatchlings start to break out of their shells. As they emerge, the mother crocodile reaches down and gently picks them up, one at a time, in her sharp-toothed jaws. When she has collected several, she carries them slowly in her mouth to a safe, quiet "nursery pool," where she carefully releases them into the water. She then quickly returns to the nest to collect the next batch of babies, and so on. Finally all the young and the mother are safe in their nursery pool.

The female crocodile deposits her eggs in the nest hole. Breeding time is usually in the warmest, dampest part of the year. It may be delayed if the rains do not come to soften the soil.

In the backwater swamps of the Everglades National Park, in Florida, a female American alligator provides a safe resting place for her babies.

Inside a reptile

A crocodile has most of the main body parts of other vertebrates, including birds (page 184) and mammals (page 193). However, its digestive wastes (feces), liquid wastes (urine), and reproductive system all open into a common chamber, the cloaca, which leads to the outside. This is similar to birds but different from mammals.

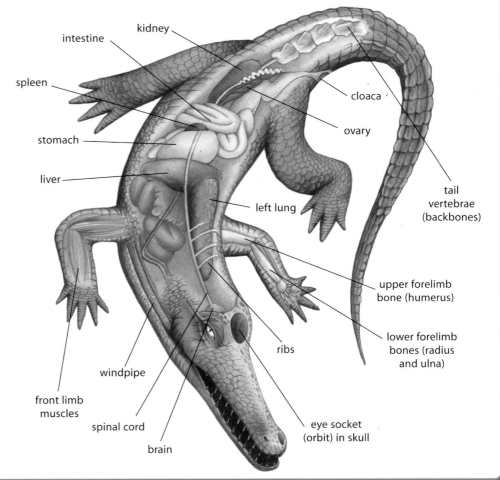

- kidney
- intestine
- spleen
- stomach
- liver
- cloaca
- ovary
- tail vertebrae (backbones)
- left lung
- upper forelimb bone (humerus)
- lower forelimb bones (radius and ulna)
- ribs
- front limb muscles
- windpipe
- spinal cord
- brain
- eye socket (orbit) in skull

Close to mother

For the first few weeks of their lives, the baby crocodiles stay close to their mother, even basking on her back in the sun. At any sign of danger, the mother vibrates her body muscles. The vibrations pass through the ground and water, and are a signal for her young to dive beneath the surface. They stay hidden until the danger is over.

In some species of crocodilians, the male also stays nearby. He may help the female to defend their offspring. However if food becomes very short later, he may turn cannibal and eat one of them!

Grunt!

All crocodiles make some sounds, from simple hisses to husky roars. But alligators are particularly vocal. Baby alligators keep in touch with each other using high-pitched grunting calls, as they search for food in their "nursery" pool. If danger threatens, the youngster who detects it first makes a special distress call. This alerts all the others, and it also attracts the mother's attention so she returns.

Alligator nests

Alligators and caimans do not dig nests in the soil. They lay their eggs in mounds which they scrape together from plants, soil and dead leaves. The mounds are usually up to 6 feet (1.8 m) across and 3 feet (90 cm) high, and the mother guards the eggs and the babies.

Male or female?

The sex of a crocodile is determined by the temperature of the egg during incubation. For example, American alligator eggs at 90–94°F (32–34°C) produce males, while below 86°F (30°C) the babies are females. Both males and females result at 86–90°F (30 and 32°C). In crocodiles, high and low temperatures produce females, while in-between temperatures result in males.

A mother crocodile helps her young out of their eggshells.

WORLD WATCH

Like many large predators, crocodiles and alligators are killed because they occasionally harm people. Their strong, hard-wearing skins have been used for centuries, mainly by native peoples. However, the mass production of crocodile-skin clothing, belts, shoes, and bags led to a surge in the numbers killed for the trade. Some species are now farmed. But others, like the gharial, have recently become very rare.

Iguanas, agamids, and chameleons

LIZARDS ARE THE LARGEST GROUP OF REPTILES. There are more than 3,700 species, and probably still more to discover, especially in rain forests. They are most common in tropical areas, but there are species in nearly all regions except the snowy far north and icy Antarctica. The iguanas are one of the largest lizard subgroups. Most live in North and South America, but there are some in Madagascar and Fiji. The agamids, or chisel-teeth lizards, are similar in appearance and habits to the iguanas but live in the Old World—Africa (except Madagascar), Asia, and Australia, with one species in Europe. Most chameleons come from tropical parts of Africa and India. They are particularly well adapted for life in the trees.

The Madagascan iguana has spiny scales arranged in rings around its tail, almost like a pine cone.

Chameleons change color to blend in with the surroundings.

Some iguanas and agamids are quite large for lizards, growing to more than 20 inches (50 cm) in length (including the tail). Many are adorned with crests and frills, and the males especially are brightly colored. They live on land and in trees, and are active during the day. Most prey on insects and other small creatures but a few species, such as the chuckwalla and desert iguana of North America, feed on plant material.

Running at speed

The basilisk lizard is a type of iguana from South American forests. It has very muscular back legs and long, thin toes. It is one of the fastest runners of all lizards. It can rear up on its back legs and reach more than 6 mph (10 km/h), its long tail held out behind for balance. Male basilisks have a large, bony "helmet" on the head and crests of skin along the back and tail. In females the helmet is smaller.

Diving below

Unlike other iguanas, the marine iguana (page 138) spends much of its life in the seas around the Galapagos Islands. An expert swimmer and diver, it uses its strong tail to propel itself through water, diving to eat seaweeds.

Most anole lizards, which are types of iguanas, have colorful patches and stripes, especially around the head. At mating time the males posture, bob their heads and flick their legs to attract females.

The chameleon's tongue darts out so fast that it can reach its prey in less than one-hundredth of a second.

Some of the larger agamas are known as dragons, like this blue-legged dragon from southern Asia. The large dark patch behind the eye is the ear. Most lizards have very keen hearing.

The basilisk lizard runs so fast that it can even move for short distances over water, its long toes supported by the skinlike film on the surface.

Collared lizard

Although the iguana must come to the surface to breathe, it can eat while submerged. Its heart rate slows as it dives, to reduce its need for oxygen, so it can stay under longer.

Frilled lizard

The frilled lizard is an agamid from Australia and New Guinea. It has a very long tail and an unusual, brightly colored collar of skin, like a ruff, around its neck. Normally this neck frill lies folded flat against the shoulders. If the lizard is alarmed, it opens its mouth wide and spreads out the frill around its head. This makes it appear much larger, to deter possible enemies.

Life in the trees

The chameleon is adapted for hunting insects in trees. Its feet are specially arranged to provide a strong grip on branches, with three toes wrapped around one side and two on the other. The chameleon also has a strong prehensile tail, which can be curled around the branch and used like an extra leg. With these gripping aids, the chameleon can remain still for long periods. It also changes its colour to match the background. When prey comes near, the chameleon takes aim with the help of its excellent eyesight, and shoots out its long, sticky-tipped tongue at the victim.

Striped agama

Frilled lizard in defensive posture

Flying lizards

The flying dragon is another type of agamid lizard, found in Southeast Asia. It lives in thick rain forest and has also taken to rubber tree plantations. It does not really fly, but it can glide tens of metres, to move from tree to tree without having to come down to the ground. It has winglike flaps of skin at each side of its body, which viewed from above, make a circular shape. Normally the flaps are neatly folded against the body. The lizard extends them as it launches itself into the air.

Galapagos marine iguanas grow to 5 feet (1.5 m) in length (including the tail). They vary in colour from green-brown to pink.

Some groups of lizards:

Iguanas (Iguanidae)
- more than 850 species
- limbs usually well developed
- includes marine iguana, basilisk lizard, anole

Agamid lizards (Agamidae)
- about 350 species
- large head and long tail
- includes frilled lizard, flying dragon

Chameleons (Chamaeleontidae)
- 135 species
- flattened body, prehensile tail
- large eyes can move separately
- changes color to match scenery

Geckos, lacertid, and teiid lizards

GECKOS ARE AMONG THE MOST SUCCESSFUL LIZARDS. They live in all warmer areas of the world, and are particularly common and varied in the tropics. Typically, a gecko is active at night. It has large eyes to help it see in dim light. Most geckos do not have eyelids—a special transparent version of the normal reptile scale permanently covers each eye. Most wall and sand lizards, or lacertids, live in warm parts of Europe, Africa, and Asia. But one species, the viviparous lizard, survives in Scandinavia, inside the Arctic Circle—farther north than any other lizard. Most teiid lizards live in South America. In many ways they are the New World versions of the Old World lacertids.

Tail of Collared lizard (page 149)

Geckos are known for their ability to climb smooth surfaces, even glass, with ease. The underside of each toe is covered with many tiny bristles, like a miniature brush. Each bristle ends in a disklike sucker. These disks help the gecko cling to smooth surfaces. The night lizards of the southern USA and Central America look similar to geckos, and are also active at night.

Leafy tail

The leaf-tailed gecko has a spotted body and flattened tail, which gives amazing camouflage as the lizard lies flattened against bark or lichen on a tree trunk. Like other geckos, it often licks its eyes with its long tongue, to keep them clear of dust and dirt.

The tokay gecko, like several other geckos, is a welcome visitor in homes across Asia. It feeds on troublesome insects, from mosquitoes to cockroaches. Like most geckos, the female tokay gecko lays only a couple of eggs at a time. They are slightly sticky and the female attaches them to a rock or tree. Several females may lay eggs in the same place.

The tokay gecko (above) is named from its barking "to-keh!" call.

Lacertids

Lacertid lizards include the green and wall lizards, sandracer, and racerunner. A typical lacertid has a long, slim body and tail. Males usually have larger heads

Leaf-tailed gecko

The caiman lizard, a type of teiid, spends much of its life in water, being an excellent swimmer and diver. It feeds mainly by crushing water-living snails with its strong jaws and flattened teeth. Caiman lizards grow to 3 feet (90 cm) long and have large, rough scales along the back, similar to those of a crocodile.

Day geckos are only about 6 inches (15 cm) long, active by day, and live mainly in forests. Their green color is good daytime camouflage.

The tuatara

The tuatara (or sphenodon) may look like a lizard. In fact, it is a rhynchocephalian—a type of reptile common many millions of years ago, at the time of the dinosaurs. There is only one species alive today, and it is found only in New Zealand. Tuataras shelter in burrows during the day and come out at night to hunt insects, worms, snails, spiders, and other small creatures. They are extinct on the New Zealand mainland, largely due to human-introduced predators such as cats and rats, which eat their eggs. Tuataras survive only on a few offshore island sanctuaries. These "living fossil" reptiles are 18–24 inches (45–60 cm) long including the tail. Their eggs take 15 months to hatch— longer than any other reptile.

than females and are often brightly colored, particularly in the breeding season. Like most lizards, lacertids lay eggs hidden under stones or in holes. Except for the viviparous lizard. It is named because it gives birth to babies rather than laying eggs, as described below. This species lives over much of Europe, including the far north, and Central Asia. In the summer months it is lively and active, feeding on insects, worms, and other small creatures. When the weather gets cold in the north of its range, it becomes inactive or torpid. It stays in its burrow for up to six months.

Lizard eater

Like lacertids, teiid lizards have long bodies and tails, are active during the day, and hunt insects and other small creatures. The jungle runner is a teiid from Central and South America.

Whiptail lizards are among the few reptiles in which females lay eggs without first mating with a male. This is called parthenogenesis.

Soft!
The web-footed gecko lives in the Namib Desert in south-west Africa. It does indeed have webbed feet. These work like sandshoes, to help the lizard run over soft sand without sinking in.

It is an extremely busy predator, catching small birds and mammals, and even smaller lizards. It only grows to about 8 inches (20 cm) in total length, but it has a large head and strong jaws.

Eggs or babies?

Most lizards, like most reptiles, reproduce by laying leathery-shelled eggs. But geckos produce hard-shelled eggs, like those of birds. In most cases the female lizard takes no further interest in her eggs after laying them. The eggs are left to incubate and hatch by themselves. In a few species, the female may curl around her eggs to protect them, but this is rare among lizards.

However, some lizards, including types of geckos, night lizards, anguids, lacertids, and skinks, do not lay eggs. The female keeps the developing babies inside her body, in their thin-walled shells. The young are nourished by their egg yolks in the normal reptile way, and also by substances from the female's body, in a similar way to a mammal mother.

The babies hatch from their eggs inside the mother, and then she gives birth. The viviparous lizard produces about 6–8 young in this way. But after a mother lizard has given birth to her babies, she takes no further interest in them. They must manage for themselves straight away.

The viviparous lizard grows to about 7 inches (18 cm) in total length. It is usually gray, brown, or yellow, but like many lizards, the color varies in different parts of its range. It may also have spots and stripes.

More groups of lizards:

Geckos (Gekkonidae)
· more than 900 species
· large eyes with transparent covering
· climb on smooth surfaces
· includes banded and Tokay geckos

Wall and sand lizards (Lacertidae)
· about 215 species
· long body and tail, well-developed limbs
· includes wall lizard, green lizard, racerunner

Teiid lizards (Teiidae)
· about 105 species
· varied body shape, long tail
· includes caiman lizard, jungle runner, whiptail

Skinks, monitors, and slow worms

SKINKS ARE THE LARGEST GROUP OF LIZARDS, with more than 1,300 species. They live in tropical and temperate areas all over the world, particularly in Southeast Asia and Australia. Skinks are very varied in body shape and are found in almost every type of habitat, from rainforest and stream bank to desert and mountaintop. Some live in burrows and have tiny legs or even none at all. Slow worms also lack legs and look like snakes, but they too are limbless lizards. Monitors are large, muscular, powerful lizards. A monitor has strong legs, a long neck and tail, and a snakelike forked tongue.

The gila monster is one of only two kinds of lizard with a poisonous bite, the other being the Mexican beaded lizard.

Gone!

Many lizards, including most skinks, can break off part of the tail if this is seized by a predator. The break happens at a particular place, the "weak point," causing little harm. The detached piece may wriggle, perhaps confusing the predator. The stump usually grows into a new tail after a few months.

The monitor lizard family includes the largest of all lizards, the Komodo dragon of Southeast Asia. It lives on Komodo and neighboring Indonesian islands, where it is the largest predator. It hunts wild pigs, deer, and monkeys. It also scavenges on carrion. Young komodo dragons catch insects and small mammals. These mighty creatures, once very rare, now benefit from being a tourist attraction. People pay to throw them dead animals to eat, while taking photographs and videos.

Racy monitors

Several other types of monitors grow to more than 3 feet (90 cm) long, and the Nile monitor reaches 6 feet (1.8 m). Monitor lizards live in Africa and Southeast Asia, and also in Australia, where most species are found. Some are known as goannas. The sand monitor is also called the racehorse goanna because it runs so fast. The shy Australian perentie of desert and rocky scrub is the world's second-biggest lizard, at 8 feet (2.5 m) long.

Legless skink

Many skinks are slim and fast-moving. They wriggle on their bellies, rather than walking on their legs. Indeed, some have no limbs. The legless skink has a long, snakelike body and lives in underground burrows in South Africa and Madagascar. It moves surprisingly quickly with curving body movements.

Florida sand skink

The Florida sand skink has four tiny and almost useless limbs, with only one toe on each front leg and two on each back leg. It is an expert digger and uses its chisel-like snout to burrow into sand.

The Komodo dragon grows up to 10 feet (3 m) long and weighs more than 330 pounds (150 kg).

Gila monsters feed mainly on other lizards and snakes, small mammals, and birds, and the eggs of reptiles and birds.

Slow lizards

The anguid lizards include some legless types, such as the slow worms, and also species with large and strong legs, such as the alligator lizard. The galliwasp is an anguid lizard from Central and

The slow worm eats worms, slugs, grubs, and spiders. It is about 20 inches (50 cm) long and lives across most parts of Europe and Asia, and also in North Africa.

South America with an orange head, a red underside, and a dark blue back with black crossways stripes. It has smooth, shiny skin and looks more like a brightly colored salamander than a lizard.

Leg flaps

Scaly-foot lizards, also known as snake lizards, have long snakelike bodies. They have no front legs. The tiny back legs are little more than flaps held close against the body.

Poisonous lizards

The gila monster and the beaded lizard are in a group of their own, related to monitors. They live in southwestern North America and parts of Central America and are the only venomous lizards. They feed mainly on small animals and eggs, so their poison is probably more for defense than for killing prey. The venom flows through ducts into the lower jaw and enters the victim as the lizard bites and chews. Both of these lizards have heavy bodies and thick, plump tails, which can be used to store body fat for times of food shortage.

Snake lizards

Snake lizards are just as they sound—lizards that look like snakes. Burton's snake lizard lives in Australia and New Guinea, surviving in

The blue-tongued skink of Australia grows to about 18 inches (45 cm) long. It lives in dry scrub, eats small animals, and also forages for fruits and berries.

many habitats from rain forest to dry scrub. It hides on the ground among grass and rocks, watching for prey such as insects and small lizards.

Wedged in a crack

Plated lizards live in Africa, usually in rocky, dry areas. The imperial flat lizard, as its name suggests, has a flattened head and body so it can slide into narrow crevices among the rocks. Once in the crack, the lizard puffs itself up with air, wedging its body and making it almost impossible to remove.

Plated lizards include the armadillo lizard from Southern Africa. It is named from its defense of rolling into a ball like an armadillo, its spiny scales sticking out. It is fairly small, only 8 inches (20 cm) long including its tail, and hunts by day for a wide range of small creatures, including spiders.

Worm lizards

The snakelike worm lizards are neither worms, nor lizards, nor snakes. They make up a separate group of reptiles, amphisbaenids. A typical worm lizard has a long, scaly, loose-skinned body, and no legs (although a few have tiny front limbs). It lives underground in burrows, which it digs by forcing its heavy, blunt head through the soil. The worm lizard has powerful jaws and strong teeth, and it preys on any creatures it can find, such as grubs, worms, and slugs. Worm lizards range in size from 4–28 inches (10–70 cm). Most live in Africa, South America and the West Indies, with a few species in southern Europe and the Middle East.

More groups of lizards:

Skinks (Scincidae)
- more than 1,300 species
- body typically long with a small head and short legs
- some limbless species
- includes Great Plains skink, sandfish, blue-tongued skink

Monitor lizards (Varanidae)
- 48 species
- large body, long neck, strong legs and tail
- includes Komodo dragon, Gould's monitor, Nile monitor

Slow worms (Anguidae)
- about 100 species
- long smooth body and tail
- some limbless species
- includes slow worm, alligator lizard, legless lizard, glass snake, galliwasp

Scaly-foot lizards (Pygopodidae)
- about 35 species
- very long slim body, tiny back legs, no front legs
- includes western scaly-foot, Burton's snake-lizard

Girdle-tailed lizards (Cordylidae)
- 50 species
- heavily armored body covered with bony plates
- includes imperial flat lizard, plated lizard, armadillo lizard

Blind lizards (Dibamidae)
- 11 species
- small, long-bodied with tiny limbs
- includes Asian blind lizard

Beaded lizards (Helodermatidae)
- 2 species
- bulky body, large head, short thick tail
- venomous
- includes gila monster, beaded lizard

Pythons, boas, and thread snakes

SNAKES HAVE NO LEGS. Yet they can wriggle at speed along the ground, climb trees easily, swim well—and a few can even "fly"! Snakes are a hugely successful group of reptiles with almost 2,400 species. They live on all continents except Antarctica. They are also absent from Ireland, Iceland, and New Zealand. They are all predators. Most can open their mouths wide to swallow prey whole. Some have suffocating coils and others strike with deadly poison fangs.

The anaconda is a massive-bodied swamp snake from South America. It grows to 30 feet (9 m) in length and can eat animals the size of goats, tapirs, and peccaries. The female anaconda gives birth to about 30 babies, each 2 feet (60 cm) long.

The western blind snake is a type of thread snake. It has very small, simple eyes hidden beneath its scaly skin. It can slide into ants' nests to eat the larvae (grubs).

Snakes evolved millions of years ago, from reptiles similar to lizards which had four limbs. Gradually the limbs became smaller, and in most snakes today, they have completely disappeared. But some snakes have tiny, useless remnants of limbs, such as hip and rear leg bones. These include thread snakes, blind snakes and pipe snakes. They are called primitive snakes because they most resemble their distant ancestors. And, like the first prehistoric snakes, most of them burrow into the soil and spend much of their lives underground.

Blind and thread snakes have tiny eyes hidden beneath scales. Most thread snakes are blunt-headed while blind snakes have narrow heads. Both designs help them to tunnel through earth. They eat small worms, grubs, ants, termites, and similar soil creatures.

Pipe snakes

Pipe snakes also spend much time burrowing underground. Unlike most other snakes, a pipe snake cannot open its mouth very wide. So it feeds mainly on slender-bodied animals such as worm lizards and other snakes, which it sucks in like spaghetti.

The green python coils around itself to rest, almost as it would squeeze or constrict its prey.

Pythons are mainly large snakes of the tropics in Africa, Asia, and Australia. They like to stay near water and climb trees well. Boas are similar snakes of the Americas, although they stay more on the ground. Both pythons and boas are primitive snakes, with tiny hip and back leg bones embedded in their bodies. They all have two lungs as well. Most other snakes have lost one lung during evolution, to help achieve their narrow, streamlined shape.

Both pythons and boas are fierce predators. They kill their prey by coiling their bodies around it and crushing it until the victim suffocates. They prey mainly on mammals and birds. The reticulated python is the longest snake, reaching 33 feet (10 m). Boas have slightly different bones in the head and

The sunbeam snake of Southeast Asia burrows and swims well, and eats fish, frogs, mice, and small birds. Its body has a mixture of primitive (ancient) and advanced (modern) features.

Heaviest

The bulkiest snake is an anaconda. It weighs up to 550 pounds (250 kg), more than three adult humans.

!

This emerald tree boa is just beginning to swallow a wooly opossum. The snake's bright green body gives excell ent camouflage among the leaves and branches of its forest home in northern South America.

Boas often rest in trees. Like pythons, they can tilt forward the large scales on the underside of the body. This raises the rear edges of the scales for extra grip as the snake moves forward.

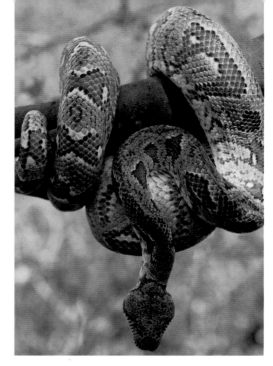

Deadly embrace

Once a python or boa has killed its prey in its crushing embrace, it starts the task of swallowing. This may take an hour or more. The snake gapes its mouth enormously wide so that it can take in a victim larger than its own head. The prey is squeezed along into the snake's stomach. Digestion is very slow. After a large meal, a python or boa may not eat again for three or four weeks.

Caring mother

Most snakes lay their eggs in holes and leave them to hatch. The Indian python is one of the few snake species that incubate their eggs with their own bodies. The female lays up to 100 eggs and curls around them to keep them warm and protected. She also adjusts her body to cover them more or less, according to the weather.

The false coral snake is a type of pipe snake and grows to about 32 inches (80 cm) long.

the teeth compared to pythons. They include the second-longest but heaviest snake, the anaconda. It spends much of its life in swamps and slow-moving streams, in its rain forest habitat. Half-hidden in the shallows, it lies in wait for animals to come and drink. When a victim is near enough, the anaconda bites and envelops it in crushing coils.

Reticulated python

WORLD WATCH

Large snakes such as pythons and boas were once hunted for their leathery, beautifully patterned skin. This was used to make shoes, bags, belts, trousers, and similar hard-wearing items. However, the hunting made some species extremely rare. It is more difficult to farm snakes for the skin trade compared to, for example, crocodiles. Most snakes will only eat a victim if it has only just died and is still warm.

Some groups of snakes (continued from page 139):

Thread snakes (Leptotyphlopidae)
- about 64 species
- small, slender body, blunt head and tail

Blind snakes (Typhlopidae)
- about 150 species
- smooth, cylindrical body
- teeth only in upper jaw

Pipe snakes (Aniliidae)
- 11 species
- blunt head
- body often boldly marked
- includes coral pipe snake, false coral snake

Pythons and boas (Boidae)
- about 60 species
- flexible jaws
- tiny remnants of rear limbs
- squeeze or constrict prey

Colubrid snakes

THE COLUBRIDS ARE THE LARGEST GROUP OF SNAKES. Found on all continents except Antarctica, they are the most common snakes everywhere except Australia, where they are outnumbered by the various types of cobras. Most colubrids are medium-sized snakes, about 20–60 inches (50–150 cm) long. Unlike pythons, they have no remnants of any limbs, and the left lung is either very small or absent, in order to streamline the body. Colubrids live on land, in burrows under the ground, in trees and even in water. They eat a wide range of foods, from eggs to mice and small birds. Most species are harmless to humans. But a few, such as the boomslang, have poisonous bites. They are called back-fanged venomous snakes because their poison fangs are near the rear of the jaws, not at the front.

The poisonous types of colubrid snakes are few in number, and they do not have hollow fangs at the front of the mouth like other venomous species. Instead they have grooved teeth at the back of the upper jaw, which are linked to a poison gland. As the snake bites, the poison flows down the groove into the prey. This means the snake must get its mouth well over the victim, to deliver its venom.

Thumb-thin snake

The venom of the African boomslang is strong enough to kill a human. But this dark or olive green snake usually prefers to slide away if threatened, rather than strike. It needs to conserve its poison to kill its prey, which is mostly birds and lizards such as chameleons. The boomslang is up to 6 feet (1.8 m) long but its body is very slender, hardly thicker than a thumb. This means it is also very light and a good climber, spending much of its life among the branches.

The grass snake is extremely varied in color and pattern. Its bite is poisonous, but only to small animals such as frogs, fish, and voles. It grows to about 4 feet (1.2 m) in length.

Eggs and snails

Some colubrids have very specialized diets. Many snakes eat eggs as part of a varied diet. But the egg-eating snake of Africa eats only eggs—and these are the hard-shelled eggs of birds. It can open its jaws very wide to take the whole egg into its mouth. As the egg passes into its throat, spiky projections on the snake's neck bones just above jab and saw the shell open, allowing the contents to ooze out and be swallowed. The snake then brings up or regurgitates the bits of shell and settles to digest its meal.

The snail-eating snake is another specialist. Its lower jaw is long and slender, and equipped with strong, curved teeth. The snake thrusts its lower jaw into a snail's shell, hooks its teeth into the fleshy body, and drags the snail out to swallow.

Mangrove snakes hunt crabs, fish and frogs among the mangrove swamps of Southeast Asia and Australia.

An egg-eating snake is ready to crack the egg with its spiny neck bones.

Babies!

Garter snakes are among the most numerous and widespread snakes in North America. In autumn, in the north of their range, they gather in holes and caves to spend the winter. However, they may mate first, each large female hidden by a writhing mass of smaller males. She does not lay eggs. Up to 80 babies develop inside her body. They are born as the warmth returns in late spring.

Water snake

Although water snakes bask on land, they spend most of their time in swamps, streams, and rivers. They are excellent swimmers and pursue fish and other water-living creatures, such as frogs and crayfish.

The brown water snake lurks in muddy creeks and ponds, ready to strike. There are about 30 kinds of water snakes, and they all have their nostrils on the top of the snout for breathing while almost submerged.

Flying snake?

The tree-living paradise snake from Southeast Asia is sometimes known as the flying snake, because it can glide through the air. As it hurls itself off a high branch, it spreads its ribs out sideways and draws its belly up and in, to make a long, ribbonlike shape with a curved underside. This shape works almost like a bird's wing to provide an upward force. The snake wriggles its body as it would on the ground, and glides perhaps 60 feet (18 m) to the ground or to a lower branch. It is not a very well controlled glide, however, and a gust of wind can blow the snake into the trunk of a tree. The "flying" snake is about 50 inches (1.3 m) long and feeds on small birds and lizards.

The vine snake may be more than 6 feet (1.8 m) long. Yet its body is as thin as a little finger. This amazing camouflage hides it among the creepers and vines in trees. If the wind increases, the snake sways with the stems around it. Vine snakes eat small tree-dwelling lizards and baby birds.

Another—and the largest—group of snakes (continued from page 155):

Colubrid snakes (Colubridae)
- about 1,600 species
- no remnants of limbs
- flexible lower jaw to allow mouth to open very wide, for biting and swallowing
- most lack venom, or the venom is not strong enough to harm humans
- includes grass snake, garter snake, rat snake, cat-eyed snake, milk snake, mud snake, slug snake, spotted water snake, gopher snake

Cobras, vipers, and rattlers

THERE ARE TWO MAIN GROUPS OF VENOMOUS SNAKES. These are the cobras and the vipers. The cobras have short fangs, fixed in position at the front of the upper jaw. When the snake bites, venom passes from the poison glands through the fangs and into the victim. The fangs must be relatively short or the snake would not be able to close its mouth. Vipers have longer fangs that fold up and back when not in use, to keep them safe and sharp.

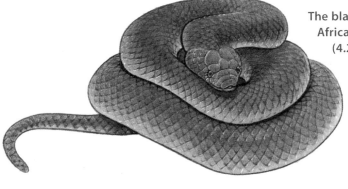

The black mamba, from Africa, is 14 feet (4.2 m) long. It is one of the deadliest snakes. It can slither along at more than 7 mph (11 km/h).

Snakes have necks and tails, but they usually merge into the main body. The Gaboon viper has a very noticeable neck for its size. It is one of the largest vipers, at up to 6 feet (1.8 m) long. Its brown pattern makes it blend in among old leaves on the rain-forest floor.

The cobra group includes many kinds of poisonous snakes besides the hooded species named cobras, which live in Africa, the Middle East, and Asia. Other group members are the brightly colored coral snakes of North and South America, the highly venomous mambas of Africa, and the fish-eating sea snakes which live all their lives in the oceans. The cobra group is particularly common in Australia, with far more members there than any other type of snake. They include the eastern brown snake of forests and swamps.

The cobra's hood

To warn off enemies, hooded cobras raise the front of the body off the ground, spread the ribs and loose skin at the sides of the head to make the cloaklike hood, and sway gently. This makes the snake look bigger than it really is, and warns the enemy that it may strike. In the Indian cobra, the hood has eyelike markings to further alarm the attacker.

Snakes at sea

About 50 species of sea snakes, such as the banded sea snake, spend all their lives at sea. The female carries the developing babies inside her body and gives birth to the young, so does not need to go onto land to lay eggs.

Sea snakes have other adaptations to a watery life, including a flattened tail that works as a paddle, and nostrils on top of the head so the snake can breathe even when most of its body is underwater. Flaps close the nostrils when the snake dives. Sea snakes feed mostly on fish and have extremely powerful venom. On land, without the water to buoy them up, they are floppy and can hardly move.

After making its warning noise, a rattlesnake is in mid-strike, mouth wide open and fangs about to stab poison. The largest rattlers grow more than 7 feet (2.1 m) long and are the most dangerous snakes in North America.

The bandy-bandy is a distinctive black and white snake from Australia. It eats mainly smaller snakes, especially blind snakes, and lives in a wide variety of habitats.

Viper fangs

Vipers have the most complicated killing equipment of any snake. A viper's large, thin teeth, or fangs, are much longer than the fangs of a cobra. Also they are hinged so that they can be folded back against the upper jaw when not needed. When the viper attacks, it opens its mouth wide and the fangs swing forward. Venom is pumped into them from the poison glands behind the eyes. Members of the viper family include pit vipers and rattlesnakes. While cobras tend to chase after their prey, vipers usually lie in wait and ambush their victims.

venom duct
venom gland
jaw joint
hinge of fang
fang
back-curved teeth
upper jaw
tongue
lower jaw

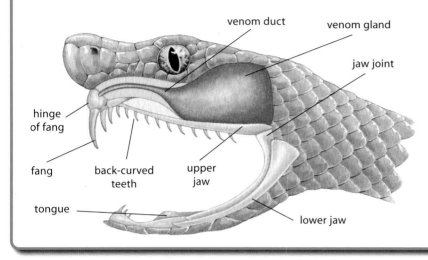

Wagler's viper

Mambas
The African mambas are feared for their surprising speed, their readiness to strike, and their venom. Mamba bites are fatal more often than the bites of almost any other snake. Mambas chase birds and small mammals to eat. They can crawl with a large part of the front body held upright, so the head is almost one metre high.

Pit vipers
The types of vipers called pit vipers can hunt even on the darkest night. They are named from the small, sensory holes or pits on each side of the head. These detect heat (infrared rays) coming from warm-blooded prey.

Like infrared "night binoculars," the two pit organs provide a "heat picture" of the surroundings. The pits are so sensitive that they can recognize variations in temperature of as little as one-hundredth of a degree celsius. By moving its head from side to side, the snake can pinpoint the exact position of a mouse or small bird.

The warning buzz
North America rattlesnakes belong to the pit viper group. At the end of the tail is a rattle made of hard rings of skin. When the snake shakes this, the rings make a buzzing, rattling sound to warn enemies. New rings are added to the rattle as the snake grows.

WORLD WATCH

Most snakes that become rare have been killed for their skins or because humans fear their poisonous bites. Others suffer from loss of habitat. The Australian broad-headed snake, for example, usually shelters under sandstone boulders. But these are rapidly being cleared from the wild for use as garden decorations and to build walls. The snakes are left with nowhere to hide. This species is now endangered.

An Indian cobra spreads its "eyed" hood when ready for action, to look more menacing.

Main groups of poisonous snakes:

Cobras (Elapidae)
- about 250 species
- fixed fangs at front of upper jaw
- usually slender-bodied
- includes black mamba, king cobra, banded sea snake

Vipers (Viperidae)
- about 200 species
- tilting hollow fangs in upper jaw
- heavy-bodied
- includes common viper, puff adder, rattlesnakes

Largest

The largest venomous snake in the world is the king cobra, which grows to more than 16 feet (5 m) in length.

!

The sidewinder, a type of viper, pushes up and forward mainly with its head and tail, leaving J-shaped indents in the desert sand.

BIRDS

Birds are probably the most easily recognized of all animals. Any creature with wings, feathers and a beak must be a bird. But not all birds use their wings for flying. The ostrich uses its wings as a sunshade to keep its eggs cool in the desert heat. Puffins, razorbills, and guillemots flap their wings to swim underwater, with the help of their webbed feet.

Feathers and beaks vary enormously, too. The kiwi is flightless, like the ostrich, and its feathers look like hairs. The peacock's colorful tail feathers are longer than your arm. The shape of a bird's beak usually shows the type of food it eats. An eagle's beak is sharp and hooked, for tearing flesh. A parrot's beak is thick and massive, for cracking nuts. A pelican's beak has a stretchy throat pouch which it uses as a fishing bag. A curlew's beak is like long, slim tweezers for probing into mud.

Birds are one of only two groups of animals that are warm-blooded. (The other group is mammals.) Being warm-blooded means being able to stay active even in cold conditions. Penguins survive some of the lowest temperatures on Earth, in the bitter cold and driving snow of Antarctica. Other birds experience intense cold at great heights, on mountains and during long-distance journeys. Some migrating geese fly as high as jet planes.

Flightless birds

ALL BIRDS HAVE WINGS, BUT NOT ALL OF THEM CAN FLY. Penguins are so well adapted to life in the sea that they use their short, stubby wings for swimming, not flying. The rare kakapo parrot of New Zealand has lost the power of flight because it has no natural predators in the areas where it lives and so it does not need to escape by flying. The most distinctive flightless birds are the ratites. These are mostly big—ostriches, emus, cassowaries, rheas, and kiwis. They are part of a group of birds that never evolved the ability to fly. Ratites have always walked or run everywhere. Their small wings are used mainly for balance and for displaying to mates at breeding time.

The dodo was a huge-beaked, turkey-sized flightless bird from the Indian Ocean island of Mauritius. In this remote place it had no natural predators and so no need to fly. But when European people came to the island in the 1500s, they brought rats, pigs, and monkeys, which ate the dodos' eggs. By 1680, they were extinct—"dead as a dodo."

The cassowary uses its helmet-like head crest for pushing through thick scrub.

Birds like the kakapo of New Zealand, and various kinds of rails, have lost the power of flight during evolution. But there are two main kinds of birds which could never fly. These are the ratites and the penguins.

Biggest birds
Millions of years ago there were many species of ratites all over the world. Now there are just ten species left, scattered as far apart as Africa and New Zealand. They are different to other birds in various ways, besides being flightless. For example, their feathers lack the smooth, flat, airproof surfaces which other birds have for flying. Instead, ratites have downy, "hairy" feathers.

The leg bones of ratites are sturdy, more like a mammal's legs than a bird's. This is why some ratites can grow so large. The ostrich is the biggest living bird, towering up to 9 feet (2.75 m) tall. Even bigger was the giant moa of New Zealand. Some moas were 10 feet (3 m) tall and weighed as much as a pony. They became extinct after people arrived.

Ostriches and rheas
With their soft, downy plumage and bare necks, ostriches look rather comical and vulnerable as they strut around the savanna grasslands of Africa. But they can sprint at up to 35 mph (60 km/h)—faster than a race horse. Even when they are tired and cannot run any more, their leg muscles are so big and strong that they can turn around and kick like a mule—

The emu of Australia grows up to 68 inches (170 cm) tall and weighs almost 100 pounds (45 kg). In some areas they have become pests because they eat crops and break sheep fences.

which is why they very rarely fall prey to lions. The idea that ostriches bury their heads in the sand when they are afraid is a myth. It comes from the way that this bird moves its eggs around in the nest so that they stay evenly warm.

The rhea lives on the plains of southern Brazil and Argentina. It looks like a small ostrich. But it has more feathers on its neck, and also larger wings. On rare occasions it can struggle a few feet through the air. It also has three toes on each foot, not two like an ostrich.

The world's biggest bird, the ostrich, is also the only bird with just two toes on each foot. The toes have sharp claws and a kick from an ostrich can be deadly.

Penguins dive into the water in a large group to hunt for their food. The mass dive helps to confuse any predators such as leopard seals and killer whales that may be lurking nearby.

Male Emperor penguins keep their egg warm by balancing them on their feet.

Largest

The biggest bird of historic times was the elephant bird of Madagascar. This gigantic ratite almost lived up to its name. It grew up to 15 feet (4.5 m) tall and weighed as much as an ox. Its eggs had a volume of 2 gallons (7 l), the size of a soccer ball. These giant birds may have given rise to many myths. **!**

The males of both rheas and ostriches do most of the work at breeding time. This is very unusual among birds. The male scoops out a hole in the ground for a nest. Then he leads several females to it, to lay their eggs. The male keeps the eggs safe and at the correct temperature until they hatch, and he cares for the young chicks too.

Australian ratites
In the thick forests of tropical Australia and nearby islands, such as New Guinea, live three species of shy ratites called cassowaries. They are the same size as rheas, about 5 feet (1.5 m) tall. But they look more like long-legged turkeys, with a brightly colored neck and a bony crest. They eat fruits, seeds, and other plant parts.

Ouch!
The kiwi's huge white eggs are the biggest eggs of any bird, compared to the size of the adult. Each weighs about a pound (454 g), which is almost one quarter of the mother's normal body weight—and she may lay two!

Another Australian ratite is the emu. It is second only to the ostrich in size, and can run almost as fast. It lives in grassland, dry scrub, and woodland, and eats an extremely varied diet of seeds, grass, leaves and fruit, and also insects and other small animals.

New Zealand's ratites are kiwis. They are about the size of chickens. Their wings are tiny, hidden beneath their furlike feathers. Kiwis are extremely secretive birds, active only at night in bushy country or forests. They are rarely seen as they search for grubs, worms, insects, berries, and fruit.

Flying in water
Penguins are so well adapted to life in the water that their wings are more like flippers. Their coats are so thick and well waterproofed with oil that they can survive even in the icy waters of the Antarctic. They are superb swimmers, and dash through the water by flapping their wings with the same motion that other birds use to fly through the air. On snow and ice penguins often slide head-first down slopes, as if tobogganing.

Kiwis are tubby birds, covered in shaggy feathers like a furball. They have the best sense of smell of almost any bird, using the nostrils on the end of the beak to sniff out food in the leaves and soil. The male and female keep in touch using soft calls.

In the water they are swift and agile, pursuing their prey with ease. They eat mainly krill, squid, and fish. Emperor penguins are the largest species and they can dive as deep as 800 feet (250 m) in search of food.

The flightless kakapo of New Zealand is the world's largest parrot. It was once thought to have been wiped out by cats, rats, and dogs. But recently, a few survivors were found and taken to a protected area on Little Barrier Island near Auckland, where there are no such predators. There the kakapos can breed and the species might be saved.

BIRDS (AVES)
- about 8,800 species
- warm-blooded
- feathers
- beak or bill

Some flightless birds:

Ostrich
- 1 species
- Africa
- savanna
- male black and white; female brown

Rheas
- 2 species
- South America

- scrub, grassland
- brown or gray

Emu
- 1 species
- Australia
- woodland, scrub, and grassland
- dark brown

Cassowaries
- 3 species
- Australia, New Guinea
- rain forest
- mainly black

Penguins
- 16 species
- Antarctic region and southern parts

of main oceans
- rocky islands and icebergs
- mainly black and white
- expert swimmers

Kiwis
- 3 species
- New Zealand
- forest and scrub
- brown or gray

Tinamous
- 49 species
- Central and South America
- resemble guinea fowl or pheasants
- some can fly but do so rarely

Seabirds

HUGE NUMBERS OF
BIRDS LIVE BY, OR
ON, THE SEA. Some
feed mainly along the
shore or dive for fish in
coastal waters, such as
various gulls, cormorants and
gannets. Others, such as auks,
terns, skuas, and frigate birds, live for weeks far out in the ocean. They come to
the surface occasionally in calm weather, to float and rest. Still others,
such as albatrosses, shearwaters, and petrels, spend weeks at a time in the air.
They land only rarely, usually to breed. They are superb fliers, soaring
across the oceans for
thousands of
miles.

Common gulls use the wind
to stay aloft without flapping.

Albatrosses may be at sea for 2–3 weeks at a
time. The wandering albatross has the longest
wingspan of any bird, up to 12 feet (3.5 m). The
waved albatross shown here is slightly smaller.

Great black-
backed gull

There are about 90 species of
gulls, skuas, and terns. They
usually wheel and call along
the coast, but gulls especially
have adapted to new
sources of food far
inland. They hunt for
worms and grubs in
freshly plowed fields, and squabble
over leftovers on dumps, especially
in winter. The herring gull, in
particular, is aggressive and threatens
other birds. Gulls eat almost anything,
including fish, crabs, insects, rotten
meat, and even the eggs of
other birds.

Shearwater

Most gulls have white and gray plumage,
matching the reflections of sunlight
on the sea. Some species have
black markings on the
back, wings and
head. The larger gulls,
like the great
black-backed, have heavy,
hooked beaks. They can easily
kill smaller birds, baby rabbits,
and similar prey.

Pirates among birds
Skuas resemble the larger
gulls and have fearsome
hooked beaks. In North
America they are known by
the German name of jaeger,
meaning "hunter," due to their habit
of chasing other
birds who are
carrying food.
They harass the
other bird, force it
to drop its meal,
then swoop to
steal it. Big skuas
like the great skua
may catch and kill
birds even larger
than themselves.

Terns are like
slim, graceful
gulls. Many have
forked tails, earning
them the nickname of
"sea swallows." Many
terns catch their fish prey
by plunge-diving straight
down into the water. They
are mainly summer visitors
to temperate regions,
migrating to warmer areas to avoid
the cold winter months.

Skimming along
Skimmers are ternlike
birds, but with an
unusual feature. The
lower mandible
(part of the beak) is longer
than the upper part. The
skimmer flies low and
dips this mandible in
the water, to snatch
any fish.

Royal terns

Fulmar

Gannets and boobies are powerful oceangoing seabirds with torpedo-shaped bodies and long, pointed beaks. They glide and soar over the sea, watching for schools of fish just below the surface. When they find their food, the birds drop like arrows into the sea, folding their wings at the last split second, to emerge with their fish.

Masters of the ocean winds

Albatrosses and petrels are master fliers, feeding far out at sea. Albatrosses are so big and heavy that they usually need a cliff to leap from, or a headwind to launch themselves into the air. Once aloft, they glide for hours in winds and air currents, without flapping. Shearwaters are smaller but have similar bodies, with long, narrow wings. Storm petrels are smaller and darker.

Cormorants are related to pelicans and have a similar but smaller throat pouch. Their feet are webbed across all four toes. They are black or dark birds, expert at diving and swimming after fish. They prefer rocky coasts and, unusually for seabirds, the oily waterproofing on their feathers is not very effective. So they spend long periods sitting with their wings spread out to dry in the sun, between bouts of diving after food.

Frigatebirds

Frigatebirds live along tropical coasts and are among the most graceful seabirds. The magnificent frigatebird has long wings and a long tail, which it uses as an aerial rudder and air brake. It can swoop to catch fish leaping above the surface or snatch baby turtles hatching from their eggs on the beach.

The puffin is a strange-looking seabird that nests in clifftop burrows. Its brightly patterned beak is large enough to hold a dozen small fish such as sand eels.

Light!

Arctic terns fly 25,000 miles (40,000 km) each year! In the northern summer they breed in the Arctic. At the end of the summer, they migrate all the way to Antarctica, in time for the southern summer. So they live in almost endless daylight.

The male frigatebird has a bright red, balloonlike skin pouch on his throat. He blows this up to attract a female.

Plump divers

Auks are plump seabirds resembling penguins. Their tight feathering keeps body warmth in and water out, they spend much time diving for food. Guillemots and razorbills breed in colonies on rocky ledges and cliffs, where most predators cannot reach.

Guillemot

Boobies were named from the Spanish word *bobo*, meaning "stupid," because these birds were easily caught by sailors for food.

Some groups of seabirds:	
Gulls and terns • 95 species • mostly white or gray • narrow wings	• dive well • black and white plumage
Skuas (jaegers) • 6 species • brown and white • hooked beak	**Cormorants** • 29 species • black or dark plumage • swim low in water
Skimmers • 3 species • black or dark brown and white • long lower bill	**Gannets and boobies** • 9 species • white, with black or dark markings
Albatrosses, shearwaters and petrels • 93 species • oceanic • long, narrow wings	**Frigatebirds** • 5 species • large and long-winged • black or dark and white
Auks • 22 species • compact and dumpy	**Tropicbirds** • 3 species • white with black markings • graceful fliers • tail streamers

Shorebirds and waterbirds

THE WATER'S EDGE IS ONE OF THE RICHEST OF ALL BIRD HABITATS. The shallows of marshes, and the shores of lakes, estuaries, and seas, are home to hundreds of small wading birds, such as oystercatchers, plovers, avocets, stilts, sandpipers, and curlews. They stride through the water on spindly legs, dipping their long beaks into the water to grab worms and other food in the mud. There are bigger wading birds, too, such as flamingoes (page 168), herons and storks which feed mainly on fish. Many other birds live in these water-edge and shallow-water habitats, but they dive or swim after food, rather than wading. The largest diving birds are pelicans. Expert underwater swimmers include grebes, darters, and (despite their name) divers.

The avocet is a graceful wader that sifts tiny worms, shrimps, and similar animals from the water with its slender, distinctive, upcurved beak. It skims its beak from side to side across the surface to gather food.

Many wading birds have clear, sad-sounding cries, like lonely wails. The curlew's "koor-lee" call can be heard far across the marshes, moors, and mudflats. The curlew is northern Europe's largest wader, 22 inches (55 cm) from bill to tail tip.

The stilt sandpiper has long, thin legs, as its name implies, to wade in deeper water. The sandpiper family includes about 80 species of waders, found across the world.

Almost any kind of bird is found occasionally on the shore. But the water's edge is home to many of the 300 bird species in the huge group called the Charadriiformes. They include most types of waders, as well as seabirds which fly rather than wade, such as skuas, gulls, and auks.

Waders have long, spindly legs for walking through water, and widely spread toes for standing on soft mud.

The black-winged stilt has the longest legs of any bird compared to its body size—they are over half the stilt's total height of 16 inches (40 cm). Waders' beaks are mostly also long and thin, for probing in water and mud. The precise shape of the beak varies according to how the bird feeds, and on what. Most waders poke about in mud and sand for small insects, worms and shellfish. Sandpipers have long, sensitive beaks for gently digging softer sand and mud. Curlews are larger and have longer bills. They gouge further down for deeper-dwelling worms. The oystercatcher uses its strong, chisel-like bill to hammer and prise apart shellfish such as mussels and oysters.

The white pelican is one of the biggest waterbirds, with a wingspan of 8 feet (2.7 m). It is known for its big beak with a stretchy pouch.

The pelican's fishing bag

Pelicans are among the largest and heaviest waterbirds. They live on shallow coastal lagoons and inland lakes throughout the warmer parts of the world. They waddle awkwardly on land, but they swim and dive well, and soar gracefully through the air. The Australian pelican has the longest bill of any bird, measuring up to 18 inches (47 cm).

Pelicans are fish eaters. They feed by dipping their heads under the surface and scooping up a huge mouthful of water and fish, in their big beaks. The chin and throat have loose skin that stretches like a balloon. The pelican tips out the water and swallows the fish.

Jacanas or lily-trotters are waders that spend much time walking across lilies and other floating plants. They have the longest toes, for their body size, of any bird—as long as your fingers.

to feed along estuaries, mudflats, and saltmarshes. Grebes are known for their elaborate courtship "dances." At breeding time, the female and male often swim and dive together. They surface holding waterweeds in their beaks, which they exchange with each other as though swapping presents. Then they circle round, approach front-to-front, touch breasts, and stretch up with their beaks pointing skyward, like synchronized swimmers.

walking on land. When a diver swims, it almost lies on the water, so that it can slip easily beneath the surface. It may stay submerged for minutes at a time, dashing about with the ease and grace of a penguin—although divers propel themselves with their webbed feet, not their wings.

African darter

Darters

The darter is one of the most streamlined swimming birds. It has a slender body, snakelike neck, and dagger-shaped beak. It is very agile on and under the water but it swims quite slowly, creeping up on its prey to deliver a stabbing peck. Darters are found mainly in the tropics and prefer large, quiet lakes with plenty of insect and fish life.

Trapped!

White pelicans sometimes work together as a team. Up to 40 of them surround a spread-out shoal of fish, then they beat their wings on the water and kick their feet. This drives the fish into a smaller, denser shoal, in shallow water where they cannot escape by swimming deeper. Every 20 seconds or so, all the pelicans plunge their beaks into the middle of the shoal and scoop up their prey.

A saying about the pelican is: "Its beak can hold more than its belly." And it is true because the chin-and-throat bag, or gular pouch, expands to hold more than twice as much as the stomach. But not all pelicans scoop for fish. The American brown pelican dives from heights of 30 feet (9 m) into the sea, to dive-bomb and catch fish.

Supreme swimmers

Divers or loons are streamlined waterbirds of northern regions. In the breeding season they make ghostly, wailing cries to attract a mate. They spend most of their time on lakes or out at sea, swimming with ease because their legs are set far back on their bodies. But this makes them unbalanced and clumsy when

Zoom!

Courting western grebes rear up and run at amazing speed across the surface. They zoom along like powerboats, driven by their splashing feet. This shows that they are fit and healthy, and so suitable as breeding partners.

Grebes

Grebes, unlike pelicans and divers, have lobed rather than webbed feet. They are found in most parts of the world, mainly in freshwater lakes, rivers, and marshes. In the winter, many grebes move toward the coasts,

A red-necked grebe sits on its floating nest. Most grebes build nests of water-plant stems and leaves, piled up so that they float.

Some groups of waterbirds:

Waders
- 200 species
- most are wetland birds
- long legs, many have long bill
- medium-sized or small

Pelicans
- 7 species
- gliding and soaring flight
- feet completely webbed (all four toes)
- balloonlike throat pouch

Divers or loons
- 4 species
- waterbirds, excellent swimmers and divers

Grebes
- 20 species
- waterbirds, very good swimmers and divers
- 3 species are flightless

Darters
- 4 species
- thin, snakelike, darting neck

Herons, ducks, and geese

THE FRESH WATERS OF LAKES, RIVERS, AND MARSHES are home to a wealth of birds. There are long-legged waders like herons, storks and flamingoes, smaller cranes and rails, and hundreds of species of waterfowl—ducks, geese, and swans. Many are excellent swimmers and can cope with fast-flowing rivers, but they prefer the calmer waters of lakes and swamps, where there is no energy-sapping current. Some species nest on the water, among reeds and other vegetation, but most nest on the shore and feed in the water. The taller waders are mostly predators, using their long, sharp beaks to spear fish, frogs, shellfish, and other water creatures. Waterfowl are mainly vegetarians, feeding on grass, waterweeds, and other plants, although some ducks take insects and shellfish.

The roseate spoonbill is one of the most colorful of waders. It dwells in the warmer areas of the Americas.

Most wading birds have long, featherless legs for striding through the water, a long neck to reach down and feed, and a long beak to grab or stab prey. The biggest group of large freshwater waders is the herons, egrets and bitterns, with 60 species throughout temperate and tropical regions. Most are gray or brown. They look stately and walk in an elegant fashion, yet for fish and frogs, they are deadly hunters. A heron stands motionless on one leg in the shallow for ages, but just when it seems to have gone to sleep—WHAM, it spears the water with a sudden lightning dart of its beak. The victim may wriggle but the heron soon flips it around to swallow. If prey is lacking, the heron may kick around in the mud to disturb small creatures.

Herons fly slowly with extravagant, steady wingbeats. They keep their long necks tucked into their shoulders— unlike cranes, storks and ibises, which fly, with the head and neck extended. Herons usually nest in colonies called heronries, building their untidy pile-of-sticks nests high in trees.

Soaring storks
Storks are even bigger than herons, some standing 4 feet (1.2 m) tall. They fly through the air with slow, strong wingbeats, neck stretched out in front and legs trailing behind. On their long annual journeys, or migrations, they find an upcurrent of warm air to gain height, then flap on their way.

In Europe and Asia, white storks often build their great twig nests on the roofs of houses. Many people see the return of the same pair, year after year from Africa, to build their nest in the same place, as a sign of continuing good luck. Storks are renowned parents. They raise their young with such great care that, in legend,

Scarlet ibis

they have become the birds which deliver new babies to human parents.

Spoon-fed
Spoonbills are medium-sized waders named after their flattened, spoon-shaped beaks. The spoonbill swings and swishes its beak from side to side through the water, to catch prey such as fish and small crabs.

The heron is a patient hunter, standing still and silent on one leg for hours. Then it makes a lightning dart with its long beak, to spear a fish which mistook the heron's single leg for a reed stem.

The mute swan weighs 40 pounds (18 kg). It needs a long stretch of water for takeoff and landing.

Spoonbills are close relatives of ibises. An ibis has a long, thin, down-curved beak. Like spoonbills, ibises have toes webbed at the bases to help them swim and walk on soft mud. Both ibises and spoonbills feed in water that is so muddy that they cannot see their prey. But the beak is so sensitive that the bird can touch an animal, feel it move, and snap it up—all in a second. The brilliant pink plumage of the scarlet ibis grows more glowing with age, making it one of the most striking of all tropical birds.

Boom boom!

The male bittern has one of the loudest bird calls. It is an extraordinary boom, made to warn others off its territory. The bittern makes this deep booming in its throat, and it can sound almost like a bull roaring as it echoes across the marsh at night. The bittern's scientific name is *Botaurus*, which comes from an ancient Latin term meaning "bellow of the bull."

Waterfowl

The body of a duck or goose is so buoyant, it can float for hours, paddling with its big webbed feet. But on land, waterfowl—especially ducks—waddle awkwardly since their legs are set far back on the body for better swimming. The pochard and tufted duck are diving ducks, descending to the bottom to find roots, shoots, shellfish and insects. Dabbling ducks such as the mallard, widgeon, and teal lap at the water's surface, or up-end in the shallows to sift waterweeds and pond snails from the muddy bed.

White and black swans

Swans are the largest waterfowl. A swan uses it long, elegant neck to reach down and grab plant bits and small creatures. Most swans have pure white plumage, apart from the black swan of Australia and the black-neck swan of South America. Geese are slightly smaller than swans and spend less time on the water. They come onto land to graze on grass.

Geese and ducks are powerful long-distance fliers and reach speeds of 55 mph (90 km/h). Bar-headed geese have been seen from planes at altitudes of 36,000 feet (9,000 m), crossing the Himalayas. Many geese breed in the Arctic, where there is plenty of food during the brief summer. They migrate south in autumn as the days shorten, to appear in flocks on lakes and estuaries in North America, Europe, and northern Asia.

Flamingoes live and nest in enormous colonies in the tropics. To feed, a flamingo bends its neck down and tips its head over, to hold its strange, kinked beak upside down and sweep it from side to side. Inside the beak, the tongue works like a piston to suck water in and squirt it out. Hairlike fringes on the beak filter out small shrimps and similar food.

At more than 10 feet (3 m), the marabou stork of Africa has the largest wingspan of any land bird.

Herons, egrets, and bitterns
- 60 species
- long legs, long neck, long bill
- most species are quite large
- neck curved or hunched back in flight

Storks
- 17 species
- long legs, long neck, long bill
- most species are quite large
- neck outstretched in flight

Spoonbills and ibises
- 31 species
- long legs, long neck, bill curved or flattened
- neck outstretched in flight

Flamingoes
- 4 species
- long legs, long neck, stubby bill
- large, with pink plumage
- neck outstretched in flight

Cranes
- 15 species
- tall, with long legs and neck
- white or gray
- neck outstretched in flight

Ducks, geese, swans
- 150 species
- webbed feet, good swimmers
- most species are long-necked
- bill usually flattened, quite short and wide (spatulate)

Some groups of ducks, geese, and swans:
Swans and geese
- 21 species
Dabbling ducks
- 40 species
Sea ducks
- 20 species
Diving ducks
- 16 species
Shelducks
- 16 species
Perching ducks
- 13 species
Whistling ducks
- 9 species
Stifftails
- 8 species

Birds of prey

A SHARP, HOOKED BEAK AND CURVED CLAWS CALLED TALONS mark out the raptors—birds of prey— as the deadly hunters of the bird world. Most are masterful fliers, able to stay aloft for hours while searching for prey with their incredibly keen eyes. Then they dive like a bullet onto the chosen victim. Smaller raptors like the sharp-shinned hawk are no bigger than a robin. They eat mainly insects, frogs, and similar small creatures. Hawks and eagles take larger prey, including rats and rabbits, snakes and lizards, and other birds. The huge harpy eagle of the Amazon jungle snatches monkeys and sloths from the treetops. The osprey and fish eagles grab fish. All of these predators will feed on carrion if it is available, but vultures and condors feed on carrion most of the time.

There are some 295 species of raptors. They hunt across a huge range of habitats, from icy mountaintops to lush rain forests. The condors are among the largest flying birds, with wingspans of 10 feet (3 m). Falcons such as the peregrine are the greatest winged acrobats, able to catch other birds in midflight with astonishing power and agility.

All kinds of large predators, such as sharks and tigers, are scarce because of the balance of nature. This also applies to large birds of prey, especially eagles. Sadly, people also try to kill them in case they attack farm animals or gamebirds. And they are shot as trophies, or their eggs are stolen for collectors. So, many large raptors survive today only in remote, often mountainous terrain. However others, like certain kestrels and kites, have adapted to living near people. They wheel over high-rise city buildings and by highways, just as they would soar along cliffs or shores.

Despite wildlife protection laws, golden eagles are still shot and poisoned by farmers and gamekeepers.

The bald eagle (above) is not bald, but its white head looks featherless from a distance. Like the osprey (left), it is a fish-eater. These birds have rough-skinned toes which help the sharp, curved claws to grip slippery prey.

Symbol of power

Eagles and vultures are the biggest hunting birds. Eagles, with their graceful soaring that can turn into a deadly swoop, have long been symbols of power. The golden eagle was the figurehead of the armies of Ancient Rome. The bald eagle is the national bird of the USA. The golden eagle is often called the "king of birds." It hunts rabbits, marmots, ground squirrels and birds. Its nest, or "eyrie," is a bed of twigs perched high on a cliff to which pairs return year after year.

A buzzard glides on a warm air current, waiting to spot its prey.

The American bald eagle has been the victim of hunting, water pollution and loss of natural habitat where it fed and bred. By the mid-1970s there were just 2,000 left in the USA. Just in time, conservation laws were introduced and now there are more than 20,000.

Smaller raptors

Hawks, sparrowhawks, goshawks, falcons, kestrels, and hobbies are smaller than eagles. They often take other birds as well as ground-living animals, using their mastery of the air to strike in midflight.

There are two main kinds of hawks, accipiters and buteos. Accipiters, such as the goshawk, tend to wait on a branch and then dash out to ambush smaller birds under the cover of the foliage. They have short, rounded wings and a long, narrow tail, for great maneuverability. Buteos, such as the kestrel, have longer wings and fan-shaped tails. They soar high and scan the scene below, ready to swoop. The kestrel is often known as the windhover because it hovers in midair, wings and tail moving but head held still, focusing on the ground below. When it sees a victim the kestrel drops suddenly like a stone and pounces on its prey.

Even as an animal gasps its last breath, vultures swoop in to scavenge on its carcass. Different species feed on different parts. Here white-backed vultures and a white-headed vulture peck into the body. The naked face and neck mean no feathers to clog with blood.

Falcons like the red-footed falcon (right) and gyrfalcon (left) are powerful fliers. They plunge, or stoop, from above at tremendous speed, to grip the victim in their sharp-taloned feet. Hawks do this too, but they kill their prey with their claws, whereas a falcon's fatal blow is a sharp bite to the neck.

Winged scavengers

The biggest birds of prey are not really predators, but carrion feeders. Vultures and condors have weak bills and the flesh they eat must be soft and rotten before they can rip off mouthfuls. The bearded vulture or lammergeier takes bones from the carcass and flies high to drop them onto rocks. The bones smash to reveal the soft, juicy marrow inside. All of the vultures have vast wings and spend hours soaring high, peering across the landscape for corpses.

Condors have such keen smell that they can even locate dead meat under a canopy of trees by scent alone.

Condors are among the biggest flying birds. The wingspan of the Andean condor of South America can exceed 10 feet (3 m). Sadly, as a result of human persecution, the Californian condor is now one of the world's rarest birds. It also tends to crash into power cables. In the 1980s, conservationists captured the few remaining wild birds in a desperate bid to breed them in captivity. Some of the young have been released into the wild, but this species remains on the very edge of extinction.

The rare Everglade kite feeds only on one type of water snail, the apple snail.

The hobby is one of the most brightly colored of hawks. It is so speedy and agile that it can catch dragonflies, swallows, and swifts.

Dive!
The peregrine falcon is the fastest-moving of all animals. It can streak down onto prey, or charge at an intruder in its territory, in a powered dive called a stoop. Some stoops have been timed at more than 210 mph (350 km/h).

Main birds of prey:	
Eagles, hawks, buzzards, and vultures	• hunts fish • brown and white
• 224 species • worldwide • medium to large • sharp hooked beak • sharp curved talons	**Falcons, falconets, and caracaras** • 62 species • worldwide • small to medium • long tail
American vultures • 7 species • large • naked head and neck • soaring flight	**Secretary bird** • 1 species • African grassland • long legs • feathered head crest • eats reptiles
Osprey (fish eagle) • 1 species • worldwide	

Gamebirds and rails

MANY LARGE BIRDS THAT LIVE MAINLY ON THE GROUND have such tasty flesh that they have long been hunted for meat, and so are called gamebirds. They include pheasants, grouse, partridges, capercaillies, quails, wild turkeys, guinea fowl, curassows, and the guans of South America. Most of the females have dull, mottled brown plumage that blends in well with their woodland, scrub or moor home. Their chicks also have this camouflage plumage. Yet some of the males, especially pheasants and their relatives the tragopans, have extremely striking coloration. Their huge and brilliantly patterned feathers shimmer in all the hues of the rainbow.

Cock common pheasant

A male monal pheasant displays his breeding plumage.

The gamebird group, Galliformes, includes more than 240 species. The world's most numerous bird, the domestic chicken, is among them. Gamebirds are mostly quite large, stout-bodied, heavily built birds that spend their time on the ground, pecking for seeds, buds, shoots and fruits. They can fly but prefer to run, and only take to the air in emergencies.

Pheasants

Many of the 165 species of pheasants lived originally in China and central Asia. But they have been taken to many other parts of the world, mainly to be hunted. They range in size from the sparrow-sized painted quail to the turkey-sized argus pheasant. The smaller species, including quails and some partridges, are usually drab browns and grays. So too are the females or hens of the larger species, to escape the notice of

predators while sitting on their eggs. But in the breeding season the larger male or cock pheasants are extremely noticeable with flowing tails and beautiful blue, red, and gold feathers. The peacock's amazing "eyed" tail is well known. The Himalayan monal pheasant also has brilliant iridescent plumage in shiny shades of blue, green, purple, and orange. The male argus pheasant has long wing feathers, adorned with eye spots.

Why are these birds so colorful?

To attract a mate. The cocks strut and fluff out their plumage to show how fit and fine they are, using cackles, whistles and screams to increase the effect. The Reeves cock pheasant shakes its feathers and jumps up high in the air,

Several types of flightless rails are at risk from dogs, rats, and other animals brought to their region by people (page 162). The takahe of New Zealand is a flightless rail that looks more like a parrot. It was thought to be extinct until its rediscovery in 1948. Only a few hundred takahes survive in the Murchison Mountains of New Zealand's South Island. Introduced deer compete for their food.

again and again, to make sure the females notice. Rival cocks may threaten or even battle with each other to gain a mate.

A peacock is a male peafowl. He is the most spectacular pheasant, with a metallic turquoise neck, shimmering indigo breast feathers and a long train of brilliant green tail feathers. A courting peacock throws up his tail feathers into a gigantic fan, revealing dozens of beautiful eyelike spots.

Battle at the lek

Grouse, partridges, and ptarmigan are hunted by many birds of prey and by mammals such as foxes and cats. So they are usually well camouflaged, to blend in with the undergrowth. They may be dull in color, but grouse mating displays are just as dramatic as those of pheasants. Male capercaillies, the largest of the grouse, gather at a traditional breeding place called a lek. They strut aggressively to and fro and make extraordinary hissing, popping, and gurgling sounds, while the females watch from nearby. Each male tries to gain a site near the centre of the lek area, which will guarantee a mate.

The habitat of the ptarmigan (pronounced "tar-mig -un") is the cold mountains and treeless tundra of the north. This bird changes with the seasons. In summer (left) it has dull brown feathers, like most other grouse. In winter (right) its plumage turns mostly white, to blend in with the snow and ice. Its diet changes too, from buds and insects in summer to seeds and shoots in winter.

The word "grouse" covers a wide range of birds, including quails and partridges. Also, grouse are often called partridges! The spruce grouse (right) of conifer forests is also known as the swamp partridge and spruce partridge.

Bustards are strong, turkey-sized birds of open habitats. Most species live in Africa, with a few in Asia and one in Australia. They are heavily built and stride along on their powerful legs, reluctant to fly. When they do take to the air, it is a struggle since they are heaviest of all flying birds.

A bustard's varied diet includes seeds, fruits, insects, and other small animals. Like most gamebirds, the female nests on the ground or on a low branch, usually in dense undergrowth.

Skulking rails

Rails are related to cranes (page 168). Like cranes, they are found mainly in wetland habitats. All rails swim extremely well, and when they are not in the water, they walk in a slow, deliberate, creeping fashion. They are shy birds and skulk in the undergrowth, camouflaged by their drab plumage. The rail group includes moorhens, coots, and the endangered flightless takahe of New Zealand.

Sandgrouse are pigeon-like birds of dry, desert habitats. The males fly tens of miles to a water hole, soak their breast feathers, and then fly back to the nest so the chicks can sip the water.

Rotten!

The megapodes ("big feet") are strong-legged gamebirds from Southeast Asia and Australia. They do not sit on eggs in a nest, but bury them under a huge mound of rotting plants 30 feet (9 m) across! The decaying vegetation is like a compost heap, giving out warmth so the eggs develop. The bird adds or scrapes away plants to keep the eggs at the best temperature.

The great bustard (left) and the kori bustard are the world's heaviest flying birds, weighing some 44 pounds (20 kg).

Gamebirds
- about 250 species
- mainly ground-living
- includes pheasants and grouse
- males often have elaborate plumage at breeding time

Rails
- 124 species
- mostly small, drab gray or brown
- a few are brightly colored
- make calls that sound like engines or machines
- some are flightless
- rivers, lakes, and marshes

Bustards
- 21 species
- large, heavy
- open plains and grassland

Sandgrouse
- 16 species
- resemble pigeons
- deserts and other dry habitats

Pigeons, doves, and parrots

CITY PIGEONS MAY NOT BE THE MOST APPEALING BIRDS, drab and gray, leaving a mess as they flock around litter. Parrots, on the other hand, are among the most attractive of birds, with their vivid colors of scarlet, emerald, and turquoise, their beady eyes, and their ability to mimic our voices and "talk." But pigeons and parrots have several features in common. Both eat mainly seeds and fruits. Both are bold and curious, but also placid and easy-going. And both have long associations with people. Parrots and doves live near or even in our villages, towns, and cities. Many kinds, including the small members of the parrot group called parakeets, are kept as cage birds and pets. Pigeons and doves are entered for shows and competitions such as racing, and they are even used for carrying messages because of their amazing homing instincts.

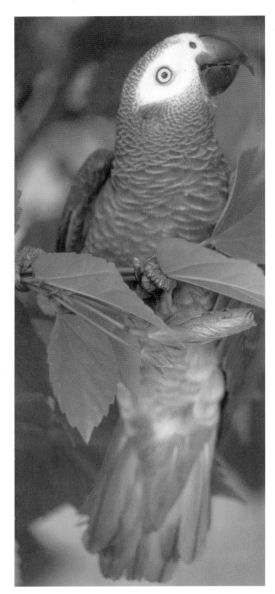
African gray parrots roost by night in tall trees, often on islands in lakes.

Parrots have strong hooked beaks to crack open nuts and scoop out soft fruits.

Besides familiar town pigeons, there are nearly 300 other pigeon species around the world, ranging from the large and spectacular crowned pigeons of New Guinea to tiny ground doves. In general, the larger and plumper types are called pigeons and the smaller, slimmer species are known as doves. All are mainly seed-eaters, and most build untidy stick nests in trees. Pigeons are also among the strongest-flying birds, and many migrate long distances.

The pigeons in our cities are not truly wild, but part-wild or feral. This means they are descended from domestic pigeons, which were kept widely in the past, both to carry messages and to eat! Those domestic pigeons, in turn, were descended from wild rock doves, whose natural habitats are sea cliffs and rocky crags.

Most pigeons and doves have soothing, rather sad-sounding, cooing songs. These can often be heard in woods, parks, and gardens, especially in early morning and evening. Pigeons and doves are the only birds that feed their young on "milk," like mammals. The parent produces a milky substance from the lining of its throat, to feed to the chicks.

Crowned pigeon

Parrots

Parrots are tropical birds with strong hooked beaks and bright plumage. They also have clinging feet, with two toes pointing forward and two backward. This design allows a parrot to clamber in trees, using its beak as a "third foot." The real foot can also hold fruits and nuts, to eat.

There are more than 500 species in the parrot group, including macaws, lories, lorikeets, cockatoos, lovebirds, and parakeets. Many are inquisitive and investigate objects with great care, holding and pecking them to see if they are good to eat. Many of the larger species are also long-lived, surviving for 30, 40, or more years in captivity. These are further reasons why they are so popular as cage birds and even as pet "companions." Sadly, this popularity means thousands of parrots are illegally captured from the

The budgerigar is a small species of parrot from Australia. It is mainly green to blend in with trees and grass. Flocks of budgies swoop and chatter around waterholes at dusk.

The crested cockatoo only erects its crest when aroused in some way.

The real macaw

Macaws are big, long-tailed parrots that live in the forests of Central and South America. They rest and nest in tree trunk holes. They are colorful even by parrot standards, in shades of brilliant blue, red, yellow, and green.

Most parrots have few natural enemies, apart from hawks and eagles, and monkeys who may steal eggs and chicks. But continuing threats from the pet trade mean many are still endangered.

wild each year. And perhaps half suffer and die before they even reach the pet shops. Several kinds of parrot are now endangered in the wild as a result of this cruel and unlawful trade.

Brush-tipped tongues

Lories and lorikeets are colorful parrots from Southeast Asia and Australia. Unlike most other parrots they feed, not on seeds and fruits, but on pollen and nectar from flowers. They have brushlike tips on their tongues to lick up these foods.

Crested cockatoos

The cockatoos have feathered crests on their heads, which they fan out when excited, such as when a predator or rival approaches. Some species are white or pinkish. Largest is the palm cockatoo of New Guinea and northeast Australia.

Lorikeets like the Australian varied lorikeet, have long beaks to reach nectar in flowers.

The gold-and-blue macaw has a beak so strong that it can easily crack Brazil nuts.

Pigeons and doves
- 300 species
- dumpy bodies
- tree-dwelling
- mournful calls

Parrots, cockatoos, and lories
- 330 species
- strong hooked beak
- two toes facing forward, two backward
- bright colors, especially greens or reds
- mainly tropical or southern hemisphere

Cuckoos and turacos

IN EUROPE, A SOFT "CUCK-OO" CALL HERALDS SPRING, as these birds arrive from southern Africa or Asia to breed. The cuckoo is also known from its habit of laying eggs in the nests of smaller birds. The large cuckoo egg develops rapidly for its size, so that it hatches at the same time as the smaller eggs of the unknowing foster parents. The baby cuckoo is looked after by its foster parents—even though it grows far bigger than them. There are about 130 other kinds of cuckoos, roadrunners, and coucals all over the world. Many of the tropical species are large and colorful. The heavy-bodied turacos or plantain-eaters are also colorful birds. They dwell in the tropical forests of Africa. They include the go-away bird, named after its persistent, piercing "g-way! g'way!" call.

Some Eurasian or Old World cuckoos, like the common cuckoo, get other birds to rear their young. Most American or New World cuckoos, such as the black-billed and yellow-billed cuckoos, do not.

About one third of all cuckoo species, including the common or European cuckoo, are brood parasites. Instead of hatching their own eggs, the male and female mate, and then the female lays her eggs in the nest of another bird species, such as a reed warbler, meadow pipit, dunnock, or redstart. She chooses the foster parents carefully. Usually, they are the same species as her own foster parents when she was a chick. She must also choose her moment with care, otherwise the foster parents may abandon the nest and eggs. So the female cuckoo spends hours perched nearby, watching and waiting. She must put her own egg into the nest as soon as the foster mother has laid her own eggs, and while she has left for a short while to feed, but before she has started to incubate (sit on) her eggs.

A female cuckoo may lay more than 20 eggs, each in a different nest. When the cuckoo chick hatches it tips out the other eggs or chicks. The foster parents feed it as if it were their own, desperately trying to keep up with the appetite of

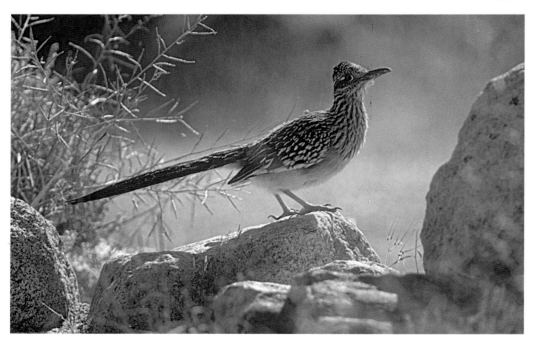

The roadrunner of southwestern North America can fly, but prefers to run. It can do so at more than 20 mph (30 km/h), outpacing most predators. It eats a wide variety of foods, from insects and snakes to fruit.

Many birds have feathers in shades of green. But turacos are the only birds that actually make a green pigment, or coloring substance, in their feathers. In other birds, the green color is due to tiny ridges on the feathers. These split up the white light of sunlight into the rainbow colors of the spectrum, and reflect only the green rays.

Turacos such as the red-crested turaco (right) are weak fliers. They prefer to climb and run along tree branches, almost like squirrels, hunting for fruit and insects.

Tropical cuckoos

Coucals are mostly large, ground-dwelling members of the cuckoo group that live in the tropics. The pheasant coucal of New Guinea and Australia stalks through dense undergrowth for small insects and other prey. The buff-headed coucal of the Solomon Islands is one of the largest cuckoos, with a beak-to-tail length of 28 inches (70 cm). It eats a wide variety of prey, including lizards, snakes, and frogs.

Coucals are among the many colourful cuckoos living in the forests of the tropics. Unlike European and American cuckoos, they stay mostly on the ground.

Running the roads

The roadrunner of desert scrub in Mexico and the southwestern USA is another type of ground cuckoo. It is about 24 inches (60 cm) long, but most of this is tail. It gets its name from its habit of racing along roads in front of cars, then quickly darting off into the

bushes on the roadside. Roadrunners do not deliberately dice with death by dodging vehicles. They simply choose the road as an easy place to walk, and also as a source of injured animals which might be good to eat.

Feeding on fruits

The turacos of Africa are forest birds with colorful, silky plumage. Many have bright flashes of yellow, red, green, and blue on their wings and bodies. Some have bare areas of brilliantly colored skin around the eyes or on the face. A few turacos eat a mixed diet of plants and small animals, but most are specialist fruit-eaters, feeding their chicks mainly on fruit pulp. The drabbest member of the group is the go-away-bird, which is gray all over apart from dark wingtip feathers.

their giant baby. After six weeks the young cuckoo can fly and leaves its tiny, exhausted foster parents.

Bash!

The roadrunner kills its prey in a very simple way. When it catches a snake or lizard, it simply bashes the reptile to death by pecking, pounding and banging it with its beak. Then the roadrunner swallows its meal head-first.

The hoatzin of the Amazon region is one of the world's oddest birds. The chick clambers about in trees using its legs, beak and two claws, one halfway along the front of each wing. The adult hoatzin loses the claws but it is the most vegetarian of all birds, browsing only on certain types of leaves, such as arum and mangrove. This unique bird may be related to the cuckoo group.

Cuckoos and coucals
- 130 species
- most continents
- slim body, long tail
- most are gray or brown
- about one third of species are brood parasites
- mixed diet

Turacos
- 22 species
- Central and southern Africa
- mostly brightly colored
- fruit-eaters

Hoatzin
- 1 species
- Amazon region of South America
- chickenlike with head crest
- leaf-eater

Owls and nightjars

MOST HUNTING BIRDS FLY BY DAY. BUT OWLS, NIGHTJARS, AND FROGMOUTHS HUNT AT NIGHT. They rely on their amazing twilight vision and even more astonishing hearing to locate their prey in the dark. Owls have enormous eyes that take up over half of the skull. They can see in almost pitch darkness. Also their ears are four times more sensitive than a cat's ears. On a quiet night an owl can hear a mouse move 150 feet (45 m) away. It can also pinpoint the direction of sounds with incredible accuracy. Nightjars, too, have large eyes that see especially well at twilight. They feed mainly on moths and other night-flying insects. Frogmouths are also dusk-flying birds but they tend to swoop from a perch onto prey on the ground.

Most owls are mottled gray or brown. But the male snowy owl is almost pure white, the perfect disguise in its snowy Arctic habitat.

The potoo (right) is a relative of the nightjar. Its name comes from its ooo-ing call. The frogmouth (below) hunts on the forest floor for beetles, snails, and other small animals. It has even been known to take whole mice and small birds into its gaping mouth, which is surrounded by sensitive bristles for feeling food in the dark.

Owls live in most parts of the world, from the tropics almost to the arctic regions. There are some 135 species. They vary in size but all are similar in appearance with a big, broad head, no obvious neck, and a saucer-shaped ruff of feathers, called the facial disk, around the huge eyes. Both eyes face directly forward, unlike those of most birds, which look partly to the side.

The wise old owl

The owl's intense forward stare has made it a symbol of wisdom since ancient times (although owls are no more intelligent than other birds). In fact the eyes fit so tightly in the skull bone that they cannot swivel in their sockets.

To look to the side, an owl twists its neck and turns its whole head. It can do this to look directly behind!

The tiny elf owl from the southern USA and Mexico is one of the smallest owls. It measures only about 5 inches (12 cm) from beak tip to tail tip. Largest is the European eagle owl, which can be 28 inches (70 cm) long, with a wingspan of 5 feet (1.5 m).

Owls are wonderfully adapted for night hunting. They have sharp sight and keen hearing, and their wing feathers have soft, almost furry, edges.

The great horned owl does not have horns. Its earlike tufts are simply extra-long feathers. It is one of North America's largest owls, standing almost 2 feet (60 cm) tall.

This muffles the sound of the wings' beating and swooping, so the owl's prey is not disturbed. Smaller owls eat mostly insects. Medium-sized owls, like the barn owl and boobook (morepork), eat mice, rats, lizards, and similar creatures. The biggest owls catch rabbits and squirrels. Eagle owls prey on other birds, including owls and hawks, and even carry away young deer. The fishing owls of Africa and Asia swoop on fish, frogs, and crayfish, dipping just under the surface to grab prey with their sharp claws.

Big-mouthed birds

Nightjars glide gracefully after flying insects, which they snap up in their wide, gaping mouth. Like bats and the oilbird (left), they may use a type of sonar or echolocation to find their way and avoid obstacles in the dark. After the hunt, nightjars roost by day—but not hidden away in holes, caves, or buildings, like owls. The nightjar rests in the open. It nestles against a tree branch or among leaves on the forest floor. This may sound risky but its mottled plumage is such perfect camouflage that the bird is almost impossible to spot.

Frogmouths are named for their wide, gaping mouths. They are not very agile in flight. Instead, they catch their prey by dropping onto the ground from a twig or rock. Like nightjars, frogmouths rest by day in the open, relying on their camouflaged plumage for protection.

The nightjar's (above) song is a mechanical "churring" that resembles the sound of a distant motorcycle.

The short-eared owl (right) is one of several owls that hunt by day as well as by night.

The oilbird of South America is a relative of the nightjars. It is unusual among the owl-like birds, in many ways. It spends all day deep in its breeding cave, then comes out at night to feed—not on insects, but on oily fruits. Oilbirds find their way in the total darkness of their cave in the way that bats do, by making loud clicking sounds and analyzing the echoes.

The little owl has the dished face typical of all owls. The dish shape acts as a sound trap to funnel the faintest noises toward the owl's super-sensitive ears, under the feathers on the sides of its head.

Owls	Nightjars and frogmouths
• 135 species	• 100 species
• most are nocturnal	• nocturnal
• soft feathers	• sleek and graceful
• large, flat face	• large eyes
• huge eyes	• gaping mouth
• hooked beak	• camouflaged plumage
• sharp claws	
• camouflaged plumage	

Swifts and woodpeckers

A WALK THROUGH A TROPICAL RAIN FOREST reveals a host of small birds, chattering in the treetops and darting between the branches. They include hummingbirds, jacamars, toucans, barbets, bee-eaters, and many more. Most have such startlingly brilliant colors that they seem to have little in common with the drabber birds of temperate woodlands. Yet many of them are closely related. Hummingbirds belong to the same group of birds as swifts. Toucans and jacamars are cousins to the woodpecker. Kookaburras and hornbills are related to the kingfishers, bee-eaters, rollers, and hoopoes. Most of these birds have large beaks compared to their body size.

Few birds have a beak which is as distinctive as the toco toucan's. The beak is as big as the bird itself, and strong and stiff. But it is made of a very light spongy, horny substance, so the toucan has no problem flying, balancing and moving its beak to peck at fruits.

Common swifts only land when they are breeding. Apart from incubating eggs or raising chicks, they are airborne. They even rest on the wing. Swifts have extremely short beaks, but they can open their mouths very wide.

Most birds spend some time in the air. But swifts are so well adapted for flight that they rarely settle on a perch. They are on the wing nearly all the time, swooping and hovering, soaring and diving, courting and resting, and, of course, feeding. As a result, their legs and feet have become quite weak. Swifts and hummingbirds belong to the same bird group, the Apodiformes, which means "footless ones." They are not actually footless, but the legs and feet are certainly tiny.

Swift by name and nature

Swifts really live up to their name. They are among the fastest flying birds. The spine-tailed swifts of eastern Asia have been timed at over 120 mph (200 km/h) in level flight. Swifts catch insects on the wing, swooping through swarms of gnats with their gaping mouths wide open. They often fly through the night without landing. When they do touch down, they cling clumsily to upright surfaces such as cave walls, tree trunks, brickwork, and chimneys.

The alpine swift wheels over mountains, uplands, and cliffs across southern Europe, Africa, the Middle East, and Asia. It flies even faster than the common swift.

Smallest

The world's smallest bird is the bee hummingbird of Cuba. Its body is hardly larger than a bumblebee's, with a total length of 2 inches (5 cm)—including its beak and tail! (!)

The male crested tree swift has a red-brown eye patch; the female's eye patch is green.

The hornbill is mainly black and white. It uses its enormous beak for picking fruits.

Hummingbirds like this Violet crowned hummingbird, beat their wings up to 80 times every second. This produces the beelike humming sound of their name.

The kingfisher sits on its perch above a stream, watching for food. When it sees a fish or frog it dives like a flash into the water, swims below with its wings, and bobs up with its catch. Back on its perch it swallows the meal whole.

Sipping nectar

Hummingbirds are the helicopters of the bird world. They are brightly colored and sip nectar as they hover close to flowers. They are incredibly agile, flap their wings faster than we can see, and hover in midair, fly sideways, go straight up or down, or even fly backward. The long, thin, curved beak probes deep into flowers for the sugary nectar that fuels their high-energy life. There are more than 300 species of hummingbirds, mostly in tropical America. In the 19th century, millions were killed and made into feathered jewelry such as brooches. Luckily the fashion died out before the birds did.

pointing forward and two backward (rather than three forward and one backward as in most other birds). A woodpecker uses its feet to cling to the tree while hammering at the wood with its large, powerful beak, to search for insects below the bark. The toucans of tropical South and Central America have massive, brightly colored bills, which they use to feed on berries, fruit, and soft-bodied insects.

The kookaburra of Australia is a type of kingfisher, yet it is quite at home in dry scrub far from water. It eats mainly insects and reptiles. Its cackling call has earned it the nickname of the laughing jackass.

The white-fronted bee-eater (above left) is a tropical bird related to hornbills and kingfishers. It catches bees and wasps in mid-air and bashes them on a branch to kill them and so reduce the risk of being stung.

Unusual feet

Woodpeckers, toucans, barbets, jacamars, and honeyguides all have the same type of feet. Each foot has two toes

The honeyguide of Africa eats mainly beeswax—but it cannot obtain the wax for itself. Instead, it perches near a wild bees' nest, and calls out. The sound draws honey-eating mammals, such as the honey badger, which break open the nest to get at the honey. The honeyguide then feasts on the wax.

Woodpeckers like the Downy woodpecker hammer at trees to find wood-boring grubs and also to make nest holes.

Woodpeckers
• 200 species

Hornbills
• 45 species

Toucans
• 38 species

Kingfishers
• 86 species

Bee-eaters
• 24 species

Rollers
• 16 species

Barbets
• 78 species

Honeyguides
• 15 species

Swifts
• 74 species

Hummingbirds
• 315 species

Crows, shrikes, and bowerbirds

MORE THAN TWO THIRDS OF BIRDS—more than 5,000 different species—belong to the group known as perching birds or passerines. Of course, many kinds of bird perch. But passerines have a special design, a four-toed foot, with three toes pointing forward and one facing backward. This allows them to cling securely to a twig, branch or other perch, but not to swim easily or run fast on the ground. So passerines tend to live in or near trees and bushes, where they can hop among the branches and find places to build nests. Most passerines are small. Crows, shrikes, bowerbirds, and the lyrebird are among the the biggest species.

A black cuckoo shrike feeds its chicks.

A male blue bird of paradise shows off his plumage.

There are more than 100 species in the crow group, including rooks, jackdaws, jays, magpies, and the largest types, ravens. Most are noisy, bold, aggressive birds, which bully other bird species and are not especially afraid of other animals or even people. Jays screech and squawk all year except during the breeding season, when they go quiet so as not to give away their nests. Most crows collect and hoard bits of food and other items. European jays even "steal"

The male spotted bowerbird builds an elaborate courting area, or bower, of twigs and grass decorated with fruits, seeds, and pebbles. The bower helps to attract a female.

The hill mynah, from India, is sometimes kept as a cage bird for its skill in imitating noises, especially the human voice.

shiny objects such as bottletops and rings. Most crows have black or drab plumage, except (again) for jays such as the blue jay, and also some magpies, which are quite colorful.

The butcher birds

Shrikes are like birds of prey, but smaller. They lack sharp talons, but they do have a fierce-looking hooked beak, used to catch large insects, mice, lizards, and frogs. A shrike usually sits in a bush or similar lookout, watching for prey. It may store surplus food by impaling the carcasses on long thorns, to eat later. This gruesome "larder" has earned the shrike the name of butcher bird.

Starlings

Starlings are active, noisy birds that often gather together in huge flocks, to feed or roost. In winter a starling roost may number thousands of birds. As dusk falls they gather somewhere such as a clump of evergreen trees or the ledges of a building. Mynahs, bulbuls, and mockingbirds, which live in the Americas, are related to starlings. Mockingbirds mimic human laughter, hence their name. Their songs are loud, clear and musical.

White-cheeked bulbul

The male Baltimore oriole sings his courtship song for a female.

Come into my bower

Bowerbirds take courtship to an amazing extreme. These medium-sized birds from the forests of New Guinea and Australia build elaborate bowers. These are places where the male bird displays to his mate. Each male decorates his bower with flowers, shells, pebbles, berries, leaves, and moss. He may even use natural colored plant juices to "paint"some of the decorations.

Paradise

Perhaps the most spectacular of the larger passerines are the birds of paradise. They inhabit tropical forests,

Mimics!

Many perching birds mimic sounds, including the songs of birds, human voices, and even engines and machines. Members of the starling family, which includes mynahs, are some of the most skilled. They learn animal noises, whistles and even words, but of course they do not understand what they say. The superb lyrebird of south east Australia copies the calls of local birds, and even imitates car sirens, telephones, and chainsaws.

The male satin bowerbird waits in his decorated bower.

mainly in Southeast Asia. The males are adorned with amazing colored plumes and perform elaborate dances to attract the females during the breeding season. The male lyrebird of southeast Australia also sings and displays to attract a female. He fans out and tips forwards his lyre-shaped tail streamers, while producing a rich, melodious song that includes various sounds, even the sound of car engines and burglar sirens!

A male lyrebird courts the female from the top of an earthen mound about 3 feet (90 cm) across, which he builds himself.

Blue jays frequent parks and gardens in eastern North America.

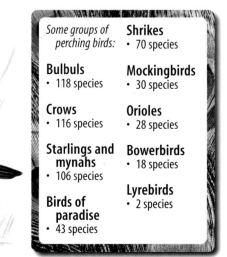

Some groups of perching birds:

Bulbuls
- 118 species

Crows
- 116 species

Starlings and mynahs
- 106 species

Birds of paradise
- 43 species

Shrikes
- 70 species

Mockingbirds
- 30 species

Orioles
- 28 species

Bowerbirds
- 18 species

Lyrebirds
- 2 species

Sparrows, finches, and weavers

SPARROWS, FINCHES, AND WEAVER BIRDS are familiar in gardens and countryside around the world. Many species migrate to warmer places for the winter, such as from Europe to Africa. Most of these birds have short, strong, stubby, pointed beaks designed for feeding on seeds. They are sometimes called seed-eating passerines (page 182). There are some 315 species in the New World (the Americas), including cardinals and buntings, and 375 in the Old World, including goldfinches, waxbills, and weavers. They tend to be sociable, feeding and roosting in flocks so as to gain safety in numbers. Some kinds, especially weavers, even breed in groups or colonies. Weaver birds get their name from their nests, woven like baskets from plant stems, twigs, grass, and strips of leaves.

A species of bunting is found almost everywhere in the world, from the Equator nearly to the Poles. The snow bunting ranges into the Arctic Circle, and also up near the summits of the world's highest mountains.

Inside a bird

No birds have teeth, so they cannot chew their food. This means the inner parts must grind and mash the food into a pulp. This happens in a muscular, strong-walled section of the digestive system called the gizzard. First, the swallowed food enters a stretchy

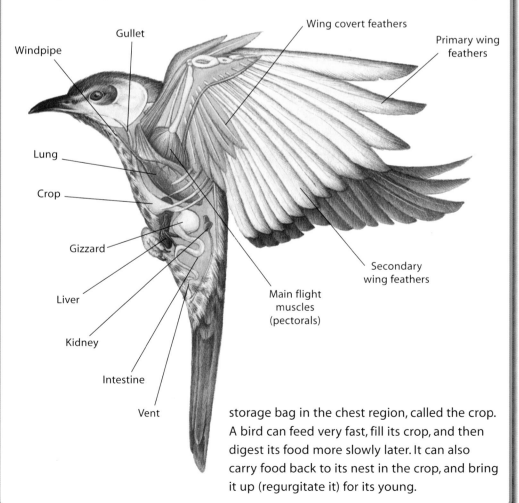

Windpipe

Gullet

Wing covert feathers

Primary wing feathers

Lung

Crop

Gizzard

Liver

Kidney

Intestine

Vent

Main flight muscles (pectorals)

Secondary wing feathers

storage bag in the chest region, called the crop. A bird can feed very fast, fill its crop, and then digest its food more slowly later. It can also carry food back to its nest in the crop, and bring it up (regurgitate it) for its young.

Most sparrows are stocky, active birds with drab brownish plumage. Few birds are more familiar in towns and cities, and their chirruping song is a common garden sound. House sparrows nest under the eaves of buildings even in the centre of a busy city. Other sparrows occupy a huge range of habitats—the swamp sparrows in swamps, the fox sparrows in forests, sage sparrows in deserts, and song sparrows in scrubland. Some sparrows are called buntings and these tend to be more

The song of the corn bunting sounds like a bunch of jangling keys. This bird is found in farmland and similar open areas.

The male paradise whydah's tail feathers are four times as long as his body. He flies with them angled almost straight up when courting the female.

Hawfinches are big, orange-brown finches that live in broadleaved trees, such as beech or hornbeam, across most of Europe and Asia. The thick, strong beak can crack open nuts and even the seed stones of fruits such as cherries. The hawfinch is very shy. It is often only glimpsed in the treetops when it is feeding or when it makes its loud "tik" call.

brightly colored, especially the male indigo bunting, painted bunting and lazuli bunting.

Nutcracker beaks

Finches of various kinds, with their powerful seed-cracking beaks, are found throughout the world. They often visit bird tables for extra food, especially in the winter. The chaffinch is one of Europe's most common birds, nesting in a wide range of wooded or bushy habitats. Goldfinches, with their attractive red, gold, and black plumage, often feed in small flocks on the seed heads of flowers such as thistles or teasels. The powerful bill of the hawfinch can even crush cherry stones with ease. The tips of the crossbill's beak actually cross over at the tip, like a pair of twisted pliers. This allows the bird to extract seeds from pine cones.

Expert weavers

Weaver birds are related to sparrows and are similar in body shape. But most are larger and more colorful than sparrows, with yellow, black and red plumage—especially in the males. Weavers make the most complex nests of any bird. Even the simplest designs have long funnels or tubes at the nest entrance to keep out predators (and cuckoos).

The sociable weavers of Africa work together to build the most elaborate constructions in the bird world. Their huge colonial nest

Lots!
The red-billed quelea of Africa is one of the world's most abundant birds. It is a kind of weaver and gathers in gigantic flocks numbering a million or more birds. They wheel and turn together, darkening the sky. They also ruin crops.

looks like the thatched roof of a cottage, transported to the branches of a tree. Each pair of weavers has their own entrance on the underside. The whole multinest may measure more than 23 feet (7 m) across. Village weavers also build a colonial nest from intertwined grass stems, with up to 100 compartments inside.

Male village weaver

The snow bunting nests farther north than any other land bird. It also breeds on high mountains, where its black and white plumage gives good camouflage among the rocks and ice.

More perching birds:

Buntings
- 552 species

Finches
- 155 species

Weavers
- 95 species

Sparrows
- 35 species

Warblers, thrushes, and flycatchers

MOST BIRDS MAKE THEIR OWN DISTINCTIVE NOISES OR CALLS. But perching birds or passerines (page 182) do not simply call. They sing. A bird's song is not just a single sound, but a sequence of musical-sounding notes. Perching birds admired for their beautiful songs include thrushes, warblers and nightingales. Indeed, these species are sometimes known as songbirds. Songs have a different purpose to the simpler, shorter calls. A call is designed to communicate a brief message. Chicks call to tell their parents they are hungry. A bird makes an alarm call to warn of possible danger. But the songs of songbirds are usually made only by the males, and only in the mating season. The male flits from twig to twig around his own patch of land, or territory, and sings loudly at each stop. He is warning off rival males of the same or competing species. He may also be trying to attract a breeding partner of his own species.

Many warblers have drab plumage in shades of yellow, green, and brown. This makes them hard to see as they dart among the leaves and twigs. But they make up for this with their loud, melodic songs, which are such a feature of temperate regions in late spring and summer. Most warbler species are

European robin

visitors to these temperate regions. They time their breeding to fit in with the huge increase in grubs, caterpillars, flies, and other insects each summer. They snap up the food in their narrow beaks as they flit about, rarely coming into the open. Most then fly south to warmer climates in autumn, to avoid the cold of winter.

Most perching birds build small, neat, cup-shaped nests in the branches of trees and bushes. The inside is carefully lined with moss and grass, or perhaps with soft mud, to protect the eggs from drafts. The cup shape reduces the risk of the eggs falling out even if the nest rocks in a high wind. This is an Australian pied monarch flycatcher at its nest.

The song thrush lives up to its name, producing a loud and beautiful song that lasts for five minutes or more. This thrush is often seen hopping across the garden, head cocked on one side, listening for worms. It also eats snails, which it smashes on a stone "anvil" to break the shell and expose the juicy flesh.

The male Asian paradise flycatcher shares the task of sitting on the eggs to keep them warm. This species has two distinct types, or phases, of males. Both have blue heads. But a white phase male has a white body and tail, while the rufous male (shown here) is reddish.

In spring the male redwing blackbird sings a rich, short, warbling song that sounds like a flute, with short pauses between phrases.

The varied thrushes

The thrush group includes redstarts, wheatears, chats, and the European blackbird. Most thrushes have loud songs that carry well through trees and bushes, and even better across gardens and parks. The nightingale often sings at night. Its loud, rich voice echoes through the darkened woods in spring. This shy bird usually stays on or near the ground, where there is plenty of undergrowth.

The cock-of-the-rock, from Colombia is one of 90 species of tropical perching birds called cotingas.

Thrushes feed on a mixed diet of worms, insects and other small animals, and fruits and berries. Some adults have bright plumage, but most are dull and mottled or spotted for camouflage. Exceptions are the red-breasted European robin and the similar but slightly larger American robin. Robins are also unusual because they sing in autumn and winter, as well as spring. But not all robins are so common and familiar. The Seychelles magpie-robin is one of the world's rarest birds. Only about 50–100 survive on a couple of Seychelles islands.

Catching flies

Flycatchers like to sing from tree stumps and dead branches. Most catch insects in midair. But the pied flycatcher of Europe and Asia uses its singing perch to watch for food. It waits patiently, then darts out to snap up a fly and return to a different perch.

Monarch flycatchers are found in Africa, Asia, and Australia. They have bold, bright plumage, especially the paradise flycatcher. The male's long tail streamers measure 6 inches (15 cm), about twice as long as the bird's head and body. The African paradise flycatcher is rich chestnut brown with a black head. The Seychelles paradise flycatcher is similar in shape, but the male is glossy black with a deep blue sheen. Fantail flycatchers include the willy wagtail of Australia. This bold little bird is not afraid of larger animals, and often hitches a ride on the back of a sheep!

The American redstart is a small perching bird with a loud, reedy song. Its warning alarm call sounds like a rattly ticking clock.

Sing!
Most songbirds have their own distinctive songs (which often help us to recognize them!). But the marsh warbler produces "song samples" from perhaps 100 other bird species. It even copies species that it hears only while migrating.

Antbirds are forest-dwellers from South America. Not all feed on ants. Some eat beetles and other animals escaping from marching army ants.

More perching birds:	**Old world warblers**
Flycatchers	• 340 species
• 156 species	• mainly Europe, Africa and Asia
• Europe, Africa, Australasia	
	New world warblers
	• 120 species
Monarch flycatchers	• Americas only
• 133 species	
• Africa, southern Asia, Australasia	**Australian warblers**
	• 60 species
	• Southeast Asia, Australasia
Fantail flycatchers	
• 38 species	**Thrushes**
• India, Southeast Asia, Australasia, New Zealand	• 304 species
	• worldwide

SECTION
7

MAMMALS

For many people, the most familiar group of animals is the mammals. This is partly because we keep many kinds of mammals as pets and on farms, including dogs, cats, rabbits, horses, cows, sheep, and pigs. Also, the best-known animal in the world, and one of the most numerous, is a mammal—the human being.

A mammal is warm-blooded and has a body covering of fur or hair. Most mammal babies grow in their mother's womb, and are born quite well developed. But in marsupial mammals, such as kangaroos, the babies are born tiny and hardly developed at all. They continue their growth in the safety of the mother's pouch. Monotreme mammals do not give birth to babies at all. They lay eggs, like birds, and the eggs hatch into babies. But all female mammals make milk to feed their babies. This is produced by special glands called mammary glands—which is how the group got its name.

There are some 4,000 kinds, or species, of mammal. They include the largest creature ever to live on Earth, the blue whale. Most mammals walk and run on land. However, the whales, dolphins, porpoises, and sea cows spend all their lives in water. Another group of mammals, the bats, have taken to the air. Others, such as moles and mole rats, tunnel underground and rarely see the sun.

Egg-laying mammals

PERHAPS THE ODDEST OF ALL MAMMALS ARE THE MONOTREMES, OR EGG-LAYING MAMMALS. There are only three kinds—the platypus and two species of echidnas or spiny anteaters, the short-beaked and long-beaked echidnas. They all live in Australia or nearby New Guinea. The platypus is also called the duck-billed platypus because its mouth is shaped like a duck's beak. These highly unusual mammals do not give birth to babies, like the other 4,000-plus mammal species. The females lay eggs, like a bird or reptile.

The female platypus digs a very long breeding burrow, 60 feet (18 m) or more into the riverbank, with a nest of dry leaves and grass at the end.

The male platypus has a poison spur hidden in the fur on each hind leg. If threatened, he kicks out and causes the attacker great pain.

The platypus lives in eastern Australia, including Tasmania. It is one of the strangest of all mammals. When a preserved platypus body was first studied by scientists in 1798, they thought it was a fake made of several animals sewn together. The platypus has a wide beak like a duck, a flattened tail like a beaver and webbed feet like an otter. These body features make it ideally suited to swimming, and a platypus spends up to half its time nosing and grubbing in the water for food. It uses the tail as a rudder and to store a reserve of fat to help the platypus to survive during winter when food is often scarce.

Electric bill

Platypuses are not often seen since they live along creeks, rivers, and lakes, and are usually active at night. They have an extraordinary method of feeding. They hunt at night along the stream or lake bed, detecting prey hidden in the mud by the tiny electrical impulses given out by the muscles in the prey's body. The platypus does this using its wide, leathery bill. This is very sensitive to touch and movements, and also has tiny pits which can detect electricity, like some fish (page 107). As it hunts, the platypus keeps its eyes and nostrils tightly closed.

The platypus catches mainly insect grubs, worms, little shrimps, and similar small freshwater creatures. It stores them in its cheek pouches and eats them later, when it returns to its burrow in the bank. Then the platypus grinds up its food using horny ridges in its jaws, since like the echidnas, it has no teeth.

Wow! The mouth of a long-beaked echidna is just a small slit at the end of the snout. The tongue can poke out 7 inches (18 cm) beyond the snout tip. The echidna has no teeth. It squashes its tiny prey between its tongue and the roof of its mouth.

Sticky tongue

The echidnas look similar to porcupines, being covered with long, sharp, protective spines. They use their powerful front claws to dig into soil, or ant or termite nests. Then they lick up the prey using their long, sticky tongue.

Unlike the platypus, who lays her eggs in a breeding burrow, the echidna keeps her single egg in a temporary brood pouch which develops on her belly. The egg hatches after about ten days. Then, like the mother platypus, she feeds the tiny, helpless baby on her milk, as other mammals do.

The long-beaked echidna (left) grows to about 28 inches (70 cm) in length, and the short-beaked echidna (right) to 14 inches (35 cm). Both types have strong claws for digging up their prey and excavating nest burrows.

The platypus catches small creatures including frogs and fish, and even water plants. Each dive lasts about one minute. The head and body are about 18 inches (45 cm) long, and the tail 6-8 inches (15–20 cm). Once very rare, platypuses are now protected by law and have become more common in some regions.

MAMMALS
- 4,150 species
- young fed on mother's milk
- body with fur or hair
- warm-blooded
- most have four limbs

One major subgroup of mammals:

Monotremes
- 3 species, platypus and 2 echidnas
- only mammals that lay eggs
- adults have no teeth
- found only in Australia and New Guinea

The short-beaked echidna is quite common in Australia and New Guinea. It is found in a wide range of habitats, from dry deserts to cold uplands, scrubland and forest. The long-beaked echidna is only found in the highlands of New Guinea. It is larger than its short-beaked cousin, with fur longer than the spines, and a longer, down-curved snout. Despite its name of spiny anteater, this echidna feeds mostly on earthworms, which it catches using the tough spines on its tongue.

Inside a mammal

All mammals have the same basic parts inside. The body has an internal skeleton made of bones, which give strength and support. In the chest are the heart and lungs. The abdomen contains the digestive, waste-disposal, and reproductive parts.

brain

jaws and teeth

kidney

stomach

vertebrae (backbones)

intestines

neck muscles

shoulder blade

lungs

penis

heart

humerus bone

testes (male organs)

ulna and radius bones

leg muscles

toe bones

Marsupial mammals

MARSUPIALS ARE POUCHED MAMMALS, NAMED AFTER THE POUCH OR POCKET OF THE FEMALE. She gives birth to babies that are at a very early stage of development, tiny and helpless. The babies crawl to the pouch, or marsupium, and continue to develop there in safety, feeding on her milk. There are about 120 species of marsupial in Australia, 50 species in New Guinea, and 90 species in South and Central America. One species, the Virginia opossum, has spread through southern North America. The largest marsupials are kangaroos and wallabies. They have big, muscular hind legs and can bound along at great speed, head and neck stretched forward, and thick tail to balance behind.

The brushtail possum once lived in forests, but has now spread to towns.

One of the smallest marsupials is the honey possum. It is about the same size as a house mouse and lives on nectar and pollen from flowers. The possum licks up its food using its long, bristly, brush-tipped tongue.

Largest

The largest marsupial is the red kangaroo or marloo, at 2.7 m from nose to tail-tip and 80 kg in weight. It can jump 10 m in a single leap, clear a height of 3 m, and bound along at speeds of over 55 km/h.

!

Compared to placental mammals (page 197), the babies of marsupial mammals are born tiny and undeveloped. At birth, a baby kangaroo is hardly larger than a grape, and its legs have only just begun to grow. Even so, it can crawl from the birth opening to its mother's pouch, where its mouth latches onto her nipple, to suck her milk. The baby lives like this for six months. As it grows larger it begins to leave the pouch for short periods. Meanwhile another tiny, newborn baby arrives.

Even when a youngster is more than a year old, it may dash back to the safety of its mother's pouch if danger appears, and still pokes its head in to feed on her milk. Most kangaroos and wallabies eat leaves, stems, shoots, and other plant parts. And the smaller, shorter-legged tree kangaroos really do live in trees!

The appealing koala

The koala is one of the most appealing marsupials, looking like a teddy bear soft toy. In fact it has very sharp claws to cling onto the branches of the gum (eucalyptus) trees where it lives. So it can give a deep scratch if threatened.

The female red kangaroo is smaller than the male, weighing less than 30 kg. The young in the pouch is called a joey.

Koalas spend much of their lives either sleeping or munching on gum leaves. They get all their nourishment and moisture from these, so they rarely come down to the ground. Another bear like marsupial is the wombat. It lives in a complex system of burrows and chambers, which it digs using its powerful, large-clawed feet.

The marsupial mole has shiny golden fur.

Wombats (above) feed on roots, shoots, and other plant material. They sometimes raid farm crops.

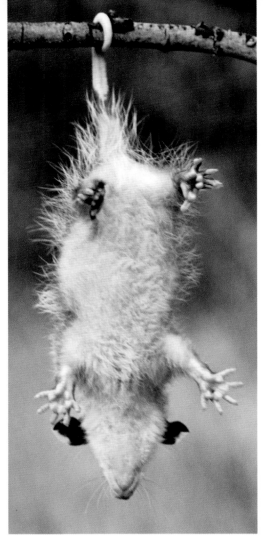

The Virginia opossum (left) is an agile climber and usually lives in trees. But it has adapted to life in towns. It clambers over fences and buildings, and scavenges for food in trash cans and dumps.

The Tasmanian devil (right) has a body length of about 24 inches (60 cm). It lives on the Australian island of Tasmania. Its massive teeth and jaws can easily crunch bones.

Marsupial versions

There are many other kinds of marsupial. Some resemble mammals living on other continents. For example, there are marsupial mice, marsupial cats or quolls, marsupial shrews or planigales, rat- and rabbit-like marsupials called bandicoots, and even marsupial moles. The pouches of tunneling marsupials, such as the wombat and marsupial mole, open backward, so they do not fill with soil as the female digs her way through the ground.

Koalas look peaceful and quiet. But they can defend themselves with their sharp claws, and the bellowing call of the male koala can be heard over a distance of several miles. Koalas are a threatened species and are fully protected.

Marsupial gliders

Several species of marsupials can swoop from tree to tree, using winglike flaps of skin stretched between the front and rear limbs. These include various types of gliders, and the pygmy possum or feathertail glider. The greater glider, which weighs 3 pounds (1.4 kg), can travel 300 feet (91 m) in a single 'flight'.

Creatures very similar to marsupial gliders are the colugos or flying lemurs. There are only two species, living in the forests of Malaysia and the Philippines. They swoop through the air in a similar way to marsupial gliders but with better flight control, covering more than 500 feet (150 m). However these animals are not marsupial mammals, they are placental mammals (page 197).

Rare and common

About 20 species of Australian marsupials have become extinct during the last 200 years. Dozens more are threatened today, mainly because of habitat loss or competition from introduced animals. However, there are

a few successes too. The mahogany glider was believed to be extinct, but it has been rediscovered recently in the forests of North Queensland. The brushtail possum, which resembles a large squirrel, has become common in Australian suburbs. It climbs across buildings, nests in roof spaces and eats leftover food scraps.

Rabbit-eared bandicoot

The second major subgroup of mammals:

Marsupials
- about 270 species
- tiny young raised in mother's pouch
- live mainly in Australia, New Guinea, South and Central America

Marsupial groups include:

American opossums	**Pygmy possums**
• 75 species	• 7 species
Marsupial mice	**Shrew (rat) opossums**
• 53 species	• 7 species
Kangaroos and wallabies	**Wombats**
• 50 species	• 3 species
Bandicoots	**Bilbies**
• 17 species	• 2 species
Ringtail possums	**Honey possum**
• 16 species	• 1 species
Brushtail possums and cuscuses	**Koala**
• 14 species	• 1 species
Rat kangaroos	**Marsupial mole**
• 10 species	• 1 species
Gliders	**Monito del monte**
• 7 species	• 1 species
	Numbat
	• 1 species

Colugos (flying lemurs)
- 2 species of placental mammals (page 197)
- cat-sized gliders on skin stretched between legs
- live in Southeast Asian forests

Insect eaters

THE INSECT-EATING MAMMALS, OR INSECTIVORES, ARE MAINLY SMALL AND VERY ACTIVE. They include shrews, hedgehogs and moles, and also tenrecs, solenodons, moonrats, and desmans. Most types eat mainly insects, from soft caterpillars, maggots, and grubs, to hard-cased beetles and biting ants. But they consume other small prey too, from juicy worms and slugs, to spiders, snails, and woodlice. Insect-eating mammals are generally nocturnal (active at night). They sniff and feel for food with their sensitive noses and whiskers. But some types, especially shrews, are so small and busy that their bodies soon run out of energy. They must eat every hour or two to survive.

Desert hedgehog

The common shrew's small eyes and little rounded ears are almost hidden in its fur. Its main senses are smell and touch.

The moonrat (opposite), with its striped badgerlike face, is one of the largest insect eaters. It has a head and body 16 inches (40 cm) long. It is active at night and has a hairless, scaly tail like a rat, hence its name. It is also one of the worst-smelling animals, making a foul odor from glands at the base of its tail to repel enemies.

Many insect-eating mammals resemble rodents such as mice or rats. But rodents have long, chisel-like front teeth (page 206). Insectivores have sharp, pointed teeth, almost like a miniature cat. They are fierce hunters and despite their size, if they are threatened, they leap at the enemy in a frenzy of bites and squeals.

Going cold

The biggest problem faced by tiny and active mammals such as shrews is that they are warm-blooded. Being so tiny, the surface area of the body is very large compared to the volume of the body. So enormous amounts of body heat are lost through the body surface, compared to larger mammals. To keep up its body temperature, a shrew must "burn" lots of energy, which it gets from its food. So it must eat—or go cold and die. The pygmy shrew is one of the smallest mammals, with a head-and-body as small as your thumb. It hunts for 2–3 hours, has a short rest, and hunts again, so on. It may starve to death after 12 hours without food.

The desman (upper right) has a long, flattened tail for swimming. The tailless tenrec (lower right) is from Madagascar.

A shrew tackles a lizard almost its own size. Shrews have poisonous saliva (spit) which helps to paralyze victims when the shrew bites them.

Tree shrews live in the forests of Southeast Asia. They are not insectivores, but they are very similar in their habits and food, except that they are perfectly at home in trees, and also they eat some fruits and berries.

Prickly ball

The prickles of a hedgehog are long, thick, extra-sharp hairs. A fully grown European hedgehog has about 5,000 of them. They normally lie flat along the body, but the hedgehog can raise them by tensing muscles just under its skin. With its back arched, head and legs tucked in and spines pointing out, the hedgehog then becomes a spiny ball. This deters most predators, but is no defense against road traffic.

Living underground

Moles are well suited to life in the soil. The cylindrical body, short limbs, and soft, thick fur allow a mole to slide through the soil, as it digs tunnels using its flattened, strongly clawed front paws. Here and there the mole heaves loose soil to the surface through an upright tunnel, to make a molehill. A mole's tunnel network may stretch more than 500 feet (150 m). It feeds on animals like worms that fall in through the sides.

Golden moles are only found in southern and central Africa. They have shiny fur with a golden sheen, and their eyes are covered by hairy skin. Like other moles, they spend most of their lives in tunnel systems below the ground.

More insectivores

Tenrecs are another group of African insectivores. Some resemble large shrews, others have hedgehog-like spines. The most unusual tenrecs are called otter shrews. They live in West Africa, swim well and hunt for water insects, small fish, and frogs.

Solenodons are like giant shrews. There are only two species, both from the West Indies region and both rare. One is found just on the island of Cuba. The other lives only on nearby Hispaniola (Haiti and the Dominican Republic).

The golden mole (upper left) often comes to the surface to feed. The Cuban solenodon (middle left) is 12 inches (30 cm) long. It tackles animal prey as large as rats. The pygmy white-toothed shrew (lower left) is the smallest insectivore.

Insect-eating mammals
(insectivores)
- 345 species
- eat insects, worms, slugs, and similar small animals
- small and active
- long snout, small eyes and ears

Groups of insect eaters include:

Shrews
- 246 species

Tenrecs and otter shrews
- 33 species

Moles and desmans
- 29 species

Golden moles
- 18 species

Hedgehogs and moonrats
- 17 species

Solenodons
- 2 species

Tree shrews
- 18 species
- resemble squirrels with long legs and long, bushy tail

Elephant shrews
- 15 species
- small with pointed shrewlike face
- long nose, almost like an elephant's trunk in some species

ABOUT ONE QUARTER OF ALL MAMMAL SPECIES ARE BATS. They are the biggest mammal group, after rodents. About 960 different species are found throughout the world, except in the coldest regions. Although some mammals can glide, bats are the only mammals that can truly fly. There are two main kinds of bats. One is the fruit bats and flying foxes. These are mostly large, with a body the size of a small dog and wings about 6 feet (1.8 m) across. They eat fruits, flowers, leaves, and other plant parts. The other main kind is the insect-eating bats. These are much smaller, with a body the size of a mouse or rat. Surprisingly insect-eating bats do not only eat insects, some also prey on mice, voles, frogs and fish.

The pipistrelle is one of the smallest bats, with a head and body 1.6 inches (4 cm) long and a wingspan of 8 inches (20 cm).

Most bats are nocturnal, or active at night. Apart from flying foxes, they find their way by a sound-radar system called echolocation (opposite). Most smaller bats feed on night-flying insects such as moths. But some bats specialize on other foods. The fisherman bat of Central and South America swoops over rivers and lakes, and hooks fish from just under the surface using its long, curved claws. Mastiff bats catch bees and wasps. Greater horseshoe bats, named after their horseshoe-shaped noses, dive onto beetles and other ground-dwelling insects. Others catch night-flying birds such as nightjars and even small owls.

Legend of a vampire

Vampire bats feed on blood. But they are not dangerous to people, as the legends say. Vampire bats live in Central and South America and are quite small, with a head and body length of only 3 inches (8 cm). They usually feed on the blood of sleeping cattle, pigs, or horses. The vampire lands near its victim, crawls over the ground, and makes a small slit-like wound with its sharp teeth. Then it dribbles spit to stop the blood clotting and licks up the oozing blood.

Flying foxes like the common long-tongued fruit bat have dog- or foxlike faces. They roost by day in trees, often making chattering noises.

WORLD WATCH

In some parts of the world, especially the tropics, bats are among th most common mammals. In other are such as Europe, they have beco extremely rare. Modern farming met using pesticides mean that their insect p scarcer now. The old hollow trees that roost in have been felled, or their ca have been blocked up. In som countries, such as Britain, all bat species are protected by law

The vampire bat has four razorlike canine t and makes only a tiny slit in its victim's skin usually chooses a fur-less or featherless pa the body, such as the ankle. It feeds for abo half an hour each night. In some areas vam bats spread diseases such as rabies.

A bat's wing

The wing (arm) of a bat is different from the wing of a bird. It is a thin skinlike membrane, the patagium, stretched between enormously long arm, hand and finger bones. The patagium is a thin layer of blood vessels and elastic threads sandwiched between two layers of skin.

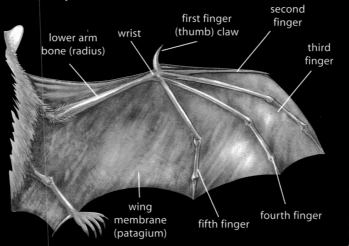

lower arm bone (radius)

wrist

first finger (thumb) claw

second finger

third finger

wing membrane (patagium)

fifth finger

fourth finger

Resting or roosting bats hang upside down by their foot claws. They wrap their wings around the body, to keep in warmth.

The huge ears of long-eared bats can turn and swivel with great accuracy, like radar dishes. They catch the returning echoes of sound, which a bat uses to find its way in the dark.

The mouse-eared bat's high-pitched squeaks of sound emerge from its mouth. Some bats emit sounds through the nose.

Some bats catch prey in their tail membranes, others in their foot claws.

The biggest group of bats is the common or vesper bats. It includes common European species such as the pipistrelle, long-eared bat, and noctule. The smallest mammal is a bat – Kitti's hog-nosed bat from Thailand. Its head and body are just 1.2 inches (3 cm) long and it weighs 0.07 ounces (1.5 g). And one of the biggest gatherings of mammals is of bats. Some colonies of the Mexican free-tailed bat contain up to 10 million bats, all clustered together in a single cave.

Many bats roost together in colonies, in caves or hollow trees, and also inside modern "caves" such as church towers and mine shafts. In tropical areas bats are active all year. In temperate lands, most bats hibernate through the winter, emerging from their deep sleep when the weather warms up again in spring.

How bats fly in the dark

Most bats use echolocation to find their way even in total darkness. They emit very high-pitched pulses of sound, called ultrasound, which are too high for most humans to hear. The sound pulses bounce back as echoes off nearby objects. The bat hears the pattern of echoes and analyzes it to give a "sound-picture" of the surroundings. Flying foxes and fruit bats have good eyesight and smell, and fly mainly at dusk and dawn. Most do use echolocation.

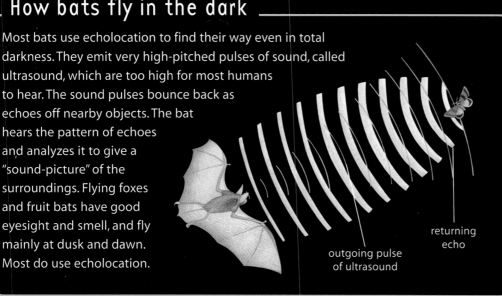

returning echo

outgoing pulse of ultrasound

The third major subgroup of mammals:

PLACENTALS
- about 3,880 species
- unborn develop in the womb, nourished by the placenta (afterbirth)
- worldwide, in all habitats, mountain to deep sea

Bats
- 960 species
- the only mammals with true, powered flight
- front limbs are wings
- most are nocturnal

Some groups of bats:

Flying foxes, fruit bats	**Sheath-tailed bats**
• 175 species	• 50 species
Common or vesper bats	**Slit-faced bats**
• 320 species	• 12 species
Spear-nosed bats	**Ghost-faced bats**
• 140 species	• 8 species
Free-tailed bats	**Vampire bats**
• 90 species	• 3 species
Horseshoe bats	**Bulldog bats**
• 70 species	• 2 species
Leaf-nosed bats	**Hog-nosed bat**
• 60 species	• 1 species

Anteaters, sloths, and armadillos

SOME MAMMALS LIVE AT A SLOW PACE. They include anteaters, armadillos and pangolins, and especially sloths. These creatures share other features too, such as long, sharp claws, and very small teeth or none at all. They feed on soft or tiny food items that do not need much biting or chewing. For defense, armadillos and pangolins have a covering of bands or scales made from very tough bone and horn, like a suit of armour. Sloths rely on staying still and unnoticed. Anteaters use their large claws to slash out at the enemy.

A sloth is so well suited to hanging around, it can hardly walk on the ground. It has to drag its body along with its curved claws.

The tree pangolin has a gripping or prehensile tail. A rough, scaleless patch of skin on the underside near the tip helps to give extra grip.

An anteater eats not only ants. It also licks up termites and small grubs with its very long, sticky tongue, which emerges from the small mouth at the end of the long snout. The anteater digs out or rips open the ant nest or termite mound with its large front claws, and licks up the milling insects in their hundreds. But it does not eat them all. It soon moves on, leaving the nest to be repaired as a larder

Largest

The largest armadillo is the giant armadillo of Brazil and Peru, at 5 feet (1.5 m) long. It is endangered by the loss of its dense forest habitat.

!

for the future. The giant anteater is the largest of the four anteater species. It is 80 inches (200 cm) in length, but much of this is its long, down-curved nose and brush-like tail. It also has a

The nine-banded armadillo is the most common and widespread type. Like the others, it feeds mainly at night.

shaggy coat and an awkward, rolling way of walking. Giant anteaters roam forests and scrub in Central and South America. The other three anteater species are smaller and stay mainly in trees, using the strong, curly tail as an extra limb to clasp tightly to branches.

Slow as the sloth

The sloths of South American rain forests are named from their very slow movements. They spend most of their

The tongue of the giant anteater is 2 feet (60 cm) long. It can collect hundreds of termites or ants with a single lick. One anteater may eat 20,000 ants in a single day.

A sloth feeds mainly on fruit and leaves, hanging by its long, hooked claws. Even its digestion works slowly. It can take as long as a month for a meal to pass through its body. Most sloths come down from their trees about once each week, to leave their droppings on the ground. And they spend about two thirds of their time asleep!

lives hanging upside down from tree branches, either munching leaves, crawling slowly along, or staying perfectly still, asleep. A sloth relies on its stillness and camouflage to escape detection. The hairs of its fur have furrows where microscopic plants (algae) grow, giving the animal a greenish tinge among the leaves.

Armored armadillos

The most obvious feature of an armadillo is the hard, protective covering over its back, like armor plating. Each plate or band has a hard, bony core covered by a tough, horny substance (like our fingernails). Flexible skin between the bands allows the armadillo to hunch up its body and tuck its legs underneath when a predator comes near. Some armadillos can roll up into a tight ball, for greater protection. Most armadillos eat ants, termites and similar small animals. Some are also fond of fruit. They live in South and Central America, and the nine-banded armadillo ranges into southern North America.

Mammal "pine cones"

Pangolins, like armadillos, are protected by hard, bony plates. But the plates consist of flat, point-edged scales which overlap like the scales on a pine cone. Most pangolins lick up ants and termites, using their long tongue in the same way as an anteater.

Most of the armadillo's body is protected by bony plates. However, a predator may succeed in flipping the armadillo onto its back, to get at the soft underside.

A pangolin sheds a few of its scales each month, and new ones soon grow. As it licks up ants with its strap-shaped tongue, the pangolin closes its eyes and nostrils to stop the ants biting them.

Edentates (small-toothed or toothless mammals)
- 36 species
- slow-moving
- most have long claws
- small simple teeth, or toothless

Groups include:
Armadillos
- 20 species
- South and Central America
Pangolins
- 7 species
- Africa, India, and Southeast Asia
Sloths
- 5 species
- South and Central America
Anteaters
- 4 species
- South and Central America

Rabbits, hares, and pikas

EVER ALERT TO DANGER, RABBITS AND HARES ARE ALWAYS READY TO DASH FOR SAFETY. They live in open, grassy country, and have large eyes and huge ears to look and listen for predators. Their back legs are long and muscular, ideal for running at high speed from danger. Although they resemble rodents such as squirrels and rats, rabbits and hares belong to a different mammal group, the lagomorphs. This name means "leaping shape", which is what these creatures do to survive. The lagomorph group also includes pikas. These are like small, dumpy rabbits with shorter ears and little legs. They also lack the rabbit's bobtail.

"Mad March hares" are usually males battling for a female at breeding time in spring. Or …

The hare's prominent eyes allow it to see above and even behind itself, so it can spot predators such as eagles from almost any direction.

There is no exact difference between rabbits and hares. Generally, the larger types with longer legs and longer ears are known as hares, or jackrabbits in North America. The smaller species with shorter ears are usually called rabbits. Hares that live in the far north, such as the Arctic and snowshoe (or varying) hares, molt into a white coat during the snowy winter season. The numbers of snowshoe hares in the northern forests of North America vary on a regular cycle.

They reach a peak roughly every ten years, then fall again. Why this is so, is not clear. But it affects the populations of lynx, snowy owls, and other predators in the same way, since they depend on the hares for food.

The volcano rabbit lives only on grassy mountain slopes in Mexico. It has short ears and a small tail. It is a very rare species, and protected by law.

The winter fur of Arctic and snowshoe hares is white, for camouflage in snow and ice. It moults in spring. The summer fur is brown.

The large ears of a rabbit or hare not only pick up the faintest noises, like an elephant's ears; they also help to lose body heat into the air during very hot weather. If a rabbit or hare detects danger, it races away, propelled by great leaps of its large back legs. It may thump the ground first with its rear feet to warn others nearby, and it can zigzag at great speed. Some hares sprint at more than 50 mph (80 km/h). However, they do not have great stamina, and predators such as wolves soon tire them out.

… the pawing and boxing may be a jill (female) chasing away an unwanted jack (male).

Gnawing teeth

Rabbits and hares have strong teeth for gnawing grasses, stems, seeds, roots, bark, and other plant foods. Some rabbits live in groups or colonies in networks of underground tunnels, called warrens, which they dig in the soil

of hedges and banks. Most hares live alone and rest in the open, in shallow bowl-like areas in the grass or scrub, called forms. They also have their babies in these forms. For this reason, young hares (known as leverets) can run and hide almost as soon as they are born.

Breeding like rabbits

Baby rabbits born in the safety of the breeding chamber or "stop," are blind and helpless at first. Their eyes open at a week old and they venture out of the nest at three weeks. But at only four months of age they can breed. Since one female may have up to 20 babies each year, rabbits have a deserved reputation of increasing numbers very quickly.

Hay for winter

Pikas look like a combination of rabbit and guinea pig or vole. They live in mountainous country in Asia, with one species also in north west North America. Most pikas prefer rocky slopes. The large-eared pika of the Himalayas and nearby mountains is one of the highest-living mammals, found at heights of more than 20,000 feet (6,000 m). Pikas graze on a range of plants, mostly grasses, flowers, and young stems. In autumn they pull hay, soft twigs and other stores of food into their burrows, to eat during the long, cold winter.

The American black-tailed jackrabbit is actually a type of hare. It uses its large ears to listen for danger and also to keep cool in the great heat of summer.

Most pikas, like the northern pika, are about 8–10 inches (20–25 cms) long.

The running hare kicks off with its long back legs, and cushions its landing on the two front legs with paws held together. Then it thrusts its rear legs forward on either side of the front paws, and makes another leap.

Rabbits and hares
- 44 species
- large ears
- long back legs
- eyes face sideways
- very short "bob" tail
- slitlike nostrils
- eat plants

Pikas
- 14 species
- rounded ears
- almost tailless
- eat plants

Hyraxes and the aardvark

HYRAXES (ALSO CALLED HYRACES) ARE SMALL PLANT-EATING MAMMALS ABOUT THE SIZE OF RABBITS. They also resemble rabbits in appearance, but with shorter ears and legs, and a short, stumpy tail rather than a "bobtail." Hyraxes are found over much of Africa, and also in parts of the Middle East. Most types live in rocky country and sit on boulders or outcrops, sunning themselves as they rest. Rock hyraxes are commonly known as dassies, and some types are also called conies. The aardvark is another African mammal, and quite unlike any other— it is the only member of its group, the tubulidents.

The tree hyrax climbs nimbly even on damp, slippery branches. Hyraxes are long-lived for fairly small plant-eating mammals. Some survive for more than 12 years, compared to 2–3 years for most rabbits.

A hyrax has a small face and an upturned mouth that always seems to "smile." But this is only our own interpretation, based on human facial expressions (page 249).

Cousins!

Hyraxes look similar to rabbits and hares (lagomorphs), or to rodents such as rats and guinea pigs. But scientific studies show that their closest mammal relatives are elephants! Hyraxes and elephants, and also aardvarks, share similarities in their teeth, jaw bones, muscles, and other internal body parts.

Rock hyraxes make their homes on rocky outcrops or hills known as kopjes (koppies). They usually live in colonies of about 10–30, including adults and young. Rock hyraxes eat a wide variety of plants, especially grasses, even when dry and tough. Bush and tree hyraxes prefer softer leaves and fruits.

Hyraxes are stocky, well-built mammals suited for clambering over rocks or climbing trees. Their small feet have thick, rubbery, moist soles to give a firm grip even on smooth rocks and branches. The feet are also equipped with nail-like hooves rather than proper claws, and are not designed for digging burrows or scraping up food. So hyraxes make their nests in caves or cracks between rocks, under tree roots, or inside hollow trees.

Rock hyraxes form family groups. The adult male defends the territory against neighboring groups of the species.

The "earth pig"

There is only a single species of aardvark, a name that means "earth-pig" in the Afrikaans language. This strange animal is quite unlike any other mammal, especially its teeth and claws (below). Its teeth are covered, not with hard white enamel as in most mammals (including ourselves), but with a soft, grey substance called cementum. The aardvark is also something of a mystery.

Although it is the size of a large pig, it is hardly ever seen by day, since it hides in one of its many burrows. At night, it roams in search of its food, ants and termites. But it is extremely shy and secretive, and darts away into the darkness if it senses danger.

Aardvarks live in open woodland, scrub and grassland across much of central and southern Africa. They find their

The aardvark has a head-and-body length of about 4 feet (1.2 m), with a tail of 20 inches (50 cm). Its head is narrow, with long ears and a long, flexible snout tipped by a piglike nose.

food by nosing about, sniffing and listening. After digging out the tiny prey, the aardvark gathers them using its long, sticky tongue. It may need to hunt for several hours each night, covering 9 miles (15 km) or more, to find food.

The aardvark's odd claws

The aardvark is a very efficient burrower. If a predator threatens, it can dig itself into even hard ground in just a few minutes. It also digs for food, and it excavates several burrows around its home territory for shelter and safety. The main breeding burrow of the female may be 39 feet (12 m) long. The aardvark does all this digging using its powerful feet with their unusual curved claws. There are four on each front foot and five on each rear foot. They jab into the hard soil even through matted grass roots.

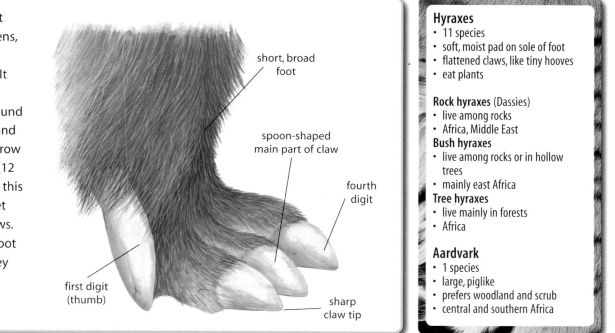

short, broad foot

spoon-shaped main part of claw

fourth digit

first digit (thumb)

sharp claw tip

Hyraxes
- 11 species
- soft, moist pad on sole of foot
- flattened claws, like tiny hooves
- eat plants

Rock hyraxes (Dassies)
- live among rocks
- Africa, Middle East

Bush hyraxes
- live among rocks or in hollow trees
- mainly east Africa

Tree hyraxes
- live mainly in forests
- Africa

Aardvark
- 1 species
- large, piglike
- prefers woodland and scrub
- central and southern Africa

Mice, rats, and cavies

THE RODENTS OR GNAWING MAMMALS ARE BY FAR THE LARGEST MAMMAL GROUP. The 1,700 species mean that almost one of every two mammals is a rodent. Some three quarters of these are types of mice and rats, and their South American relatives called cavies—the best-known being the guinea pig. The rodent's key feature is its four long, sharp, chisel-like incisor teeth at the front of the mouth. These can chew even the hardest foods, such as nuts or tree bark. Some small rodents, including mice, rats, hamsters, gerbils, and guinea pigs, are often kept as pets. (More rodents are described on pages 208 to 211.)

The cavy group of rodents include guinea pigs, porcupines, spiny rats. and mole rats.

The yellow-necked mouse is common in farmland and woods across Europe. It may even come into houses in autumn, to escape the cold and look for food. It eats mainly seeds, berries and other fruits, also small animals like insects.

Black or ship rats have spread around the world, from their original homeland of tropical Asia. They travel on ships, being agile enough to climb aboard along the mooring ropes.

Mice and rats range in size from the pygmy mouse, less than 4 inches (10 cm) long including its tail, to rats that reach a total length of 32 inches (80 cm). The harvest mouse is one of the smallest, with a body hardly larger than a thumb. It is a very agile climber and uses its long tail as an extra limb to grasp grass stems. It spread rapidly when people began to plant wheat and similar crops. But then it suffered as machines took over harvesting from people. It could not escape from its ball-shaped nest as the combine harvester approached.

Jumping mice bound along like miniature kangaroos. They can cover more than 6 feet (1.8m) in a single leap. Fast reactions and speed help small rodents elude their many predators.

Some mice and rats have taken to living near people, especially in our houses, farms and food stores. They cause damage and also spread diseases. The fleas that live on certain rats may bite people and spread plague. House mice get into pantries and larders. Brown and roof rats are a nuisance in grain stores.

Lemmings have blunt noses, small ears, rounded bodies, and thick fur. These features help them stay warm in their cold northern homelands. They live among grasses and bushes on the ground, feeding on roots and shoots. When conditions are good and food is plentiful, lemmings breed so fast that they end up eating all of the available food. Then many of them set off on a mass migration to find new places to live. During these "lemming years" they become bold and aggressive. At first they travel only at night, being nocturnal like most small rodents. But soon they journey by day too. The urge to move on is so strong that they enter towns and cross streets, and even dive into rivers or tumble off cliffs. These migrations have led to legends that the lemmings really want to die!

Big cheeks

The hamster is a familiar pet, yet it is rarely seen in the wild. Its original home was the steppe grasslands of Eastern Europe, but it has now spread into Central Europe too.

Hamsters eat many foods. They carry what they cannot consume in their stretchy cheek pouches, back to the nest. In the wild, many hamsters hibernate during winter. But they wake up every few days to nibble at their store of nuts, berries and other food.

Hamster

Another group of small rodents is the jerboas. They have very long back legs and jump exceptionally well, using the long tail to balance. Their large ears give good hearing. Jerboas live in the deserts of North Africa, the Middle East, and Central Asia. They feed mainly on seeds and insects. Gerbils are similar to jerboas, but they have shorter back legs and smaller ears. Like jerboas, they spend the day in their burrows, to avoid predators and also the intense desert heat.

Sleeping mice

Common dormice are about the same size as house mice. But they have soft, light brown fur and a furry tail. They are well known for their long winter sleep or hibernation. The name "dormouse" comes from the French word *dormir*, "to sleep." In summer they eat flowers, shoots, nuts, berries, and small animals such as insects, and spiders.

The jerbil (right) lives wild in the deserts of Mongolia. The jerboa (below) has huge back feet that work like sandshoes so it does not sink into the desert surface.

Naked mole rats work together for the good of the colony, like bees or ants. Only the chief female, or queen, can have babies. The rest are "workers" and do specific jobs.

When lemmings become too numerous in an area, they have a strong instinct to set off and look for less crowded places.

A dormouse may hibernate for up to eight months, depending on the climate of the region.

The most unusual small rodents are African naked mole rats. They have hardly any fur and live entirely underground, in large colonies. They chisel through the soil with their huge front teeth. Even more amazing, different members of the colony have different jobs— just like bees in a hive. Some are diggers, some gather food and some are guards to fight intruders. Only one female, the queen, can produce young. Apart from certain insects, this type of colony is unique in the animal world.

Rodents
- 1,700 species
- long, sharp gnawing front teeth
- most are small and nocturnal

Some groups of small rodents:

Old World rats and mice
- 480 species

New World rats and mice
- 365 species

Pocket mice
- 65 species

Spiny rats
- 55 species

Jerboas
- 31 species

Jumping mice and birch mice
- 14 species

Dormice
- 10 species

African mole rats
- 9 species

Cane rats
- 2 species

Chinchilla rats
- 2 species

Rock rat
- 1 species

Large rodents

MOST RODENTS ARE LESS THAN SIX INCHES (15 CM) IN BODY LENGTH. BUT THERE ARE SEVERAL MUCH LARGER KINDS, including porcupines, beavers, chinchillas, coypus, and the biggest of all rodents—the capybara of South America. The size of a sheep, the capybara lives in forests near lakes and rivers, and feeds on waterside vegetation. It has partly webbed toes and is at home in the water, spending much of its time wading and swimming. The American beaver is another huge rodent, with a head and body about three feet (90 cm), and webbed feet suited to life in water. The crested porcupine of Africa is large too, with a head and body about 32 inches (80 cm) long. Like other porcupines, it is protected by spines which are thicker, longer, sharper versions of the normal mammal fur.

The biggest spines on the crested porcupine's back are a foot (30 cm) long. This rodent rattles special hollow tail spines as a warning that it may charge backward at an attacker.

Most porcupines come out at night to feed. By day, ground porcupines sleep in their burrows. Tree porcupines rest in hollow trees.

Oldest

Porcupines are among the longest-lived rodents. The oldest known individual was at least 27 years of age when it died in a zoo. Since porcupines are so well protected by their spines, they may live almost as long in the wild. **!**

The beaver's sharp gnawing teeth, the incisors, can cut down a small tree in a few minutes.

Porcupines cannot "shoot" their spines, or quills, at enemies. Instead, they rush at an attacker and turn around to jab in the spines. If the spines pierce the skin, they come away from the porcupine's body and work their way into the flesh.

There are two main groups of porcupines. The American or New World porcupines live mainly in trees and most have prehensile tails. They feed on leaves, fruits and shoots. The Old World porcupines of Europe, Africa, and Asia are ground dwellers. They grub around in the soil for roots and other plant food. They also feed on fruits and berries, and sometimes damage crops.

The beaver has a unique feature among rodents—its flat, scaly, paddle-like tail. This has two main uses.

The tree porcupine has long toe claws and a muscular, curly, prehensile tail, for gripping branches.

Inside the beaver lodge, a mother suckles her young. When they reach two years of age, they will leave and build their own lodges.

The capybara grows to 53 inches (135 cm) in length, stands 24 inches (60 cm) tall at the shoulder, and weighs more than 130 pounds (59 kg). **!**

When the beaver swims with its webbed back feet, the tail is used as a rudder for steering. If the beaver senses danger, it slaps its tail onto the water's surface with a loud splash, to warn others of its family group.

Beavers gnaw through trunks to fell trees. They feed on the soft, sap-rich bark. They also use the logs and branches to build a wall or dam across a stream. Then they construct their home or lodge in the pool that forms behind the dam. The lodge gives protection against winter weather and predators such as wolves. Both dam and lodge are strengthened and cemented with stones and mud. The lodge has several tunnels leading from the living quarters down into the water. It also has a "chimney" leading upward for fresh air. In cold weather, the beaver family stay in the lodge. They feed on twigs, bark, and leaves that they have stored in the lodge or jammed under stones in their pool. If the lake freezes they can swim under the ice to collect food.

Among the South American cavy group (page 206), there are several large species. The mara of Argentina has a head and body up to 30 inches (75 cm) long, and long legs. It grazes in open grassland and can outrun most predators, sprinting at 30 mph (45 km/h). Agoutis are also large cavies. They look like giant, tailless rats. They feed by day on plants and rest at night in burrows. An agouti can leap 6 feet (1.8 m) straight up to avoid danger.

In the wild, chinchillas live in multifamily groups of about 50–100. They eat almost any kind of plant food.

Another group of cavies is the chinchillas and viscachas. The chinchilla itself is now rare in its natural habitat, the rocky uplands of the Andes mountains. But it is commonly kept as a pet, and some are still farmed for their fur, which is the finest and softest of any mammal. In the wild, this fur keeps the chinchilla warm in the bitter Andean winter, and is kept in good condition by regular dust baths.

Young capybaras can run and swim a few hours after birth. Capybaras live in family groups and feed mainly at dusk and dawn. They are preyed on by large cats, especially jaguars, and big snakes such as anacondas.

The coypu is yet another large rodent of the cavy group. Swimming in the water, it looks similar to a beaver but has a rat-like tail. Coypus eat water plants and rest by day in long bankside tunnels.

Coypus (above) can cause damage because they raid farm crops and dig burrows in the banks of drainage channels.

Maras are active by day. They search for any type of plant material to eat, including grass, shoots, leaves, and fruits. They can run almost as fast as a hare, bounding along in a similar manner using their strong back legs.

Main groups of larger rodents (from page 207):

Porcupines	Pacas
• 21 species	• 2 species
Beavers	**Degus**
• 2 species	• 8 species
Mountain beaver	**Tuco-tucos**
• 1 species	• 33 species
Springhare	**Gundis**
• 1 species	• 5 species
Agoutis	**Chinchillas**
• 13 species	• 6 species
Hutias	**Capybara**
• 13 species	• 1 species
Pacarana	**Coypu**
• 1 species	• 1 species

Squirrels and chipmunks

SQUIRRELS ARE BRIGHT-EYED, PERT-EARED, SHORT-NOSED, BUSHY-TAILED RODENTS THAT LEAP AROUND IN TREES AND FEED ON NUTS. Actually, this is true of most squirrels, but not all. Some members of the squirrel family live on the ground and hardly ever venture into trees. In fact, rather than climb above the surface, they tunnel beneath it and live in underground burrows. These ground squirrels include marmots, chipmunks, prairie dogs, and sousliks. But most squirrels stay high above ground in the branches, and flying squirrels can even glide from tree to tree.

There are at least 50 species of flying squirrels, most from Asia. They glide on furry flaps of skin stretched between front and back legs.

Some ground squirrels sleep very deeply, or hibernate, in their nests during the cold season. The Arctic ground squirrel of Alaska and northern Canada is perhaps the record-holder. It hibernates for up to nine months of the year.

Tree-dwelling squirrels are skilled climbers and leapers. They cling onto the bark with their sharp claws, and use the long, bushy tail as a balance when running along a branch, and as a rudder when leaping to another bough. The claws grip so firmly that a squirrel can race head-first down a tree trunk.

The familiar gray squirrel lived originally in eastern North America. It has spread to Europe and southern Africa. Like its cousin the European red squirrel, it builds a main nest, or drey, from twigs and leaves. About the size of a soccer ball, the drey is usually anchored high in the fork of a tree branch.

It has a soft lining of grasses and moss. Smaller dreys are used as temporary shelters. A larger, stronger drey is built to rear the young and as a winter refuge. In cold weather, tree squirrels stay in their dreys and sleep. Unlike some ground squirrels, they do not go into the very deep sleep of true hibernation. They emerge from time to time and search for food, especially in mild weather.

Many squirrels store food, mainly seeds and nuts, when it is plentiful. This happens especially in autumn, as the squirrel prepares for the cold season.

European red squirrel

Golden-mantled ground squirrel

Tassel-eared squirrel

Thirteen-lined ground squirrel

Gray squirrels regularly bury acorns or beech mast (nuts) in the soil, returning to dig them up later. But they lose or forget about many of the nuts. However, in doing this, they act as tree planters. This helps to offset the damage that some squirrels do in woodlands and timber plantations. They nibble bark and injure or even kill trees.

Marmots and prairie dogs are stout-bodied, short-tailed or tailless ground squirrels. Most dwell in underground burrows. In Europe, Alpine marmots scamper over high meadows and rocky slopes. Many family groups live close together, their burrow entrances dotted over the ground. The burrows may go down 10 feet (3 m), ending in a hay-lined sleeping chamber. In autumn the marmots collect grass, seeds, nuts, fruits, and other plant food.

The rat-sized European souslik inhabits warm, dry grasslands, where it digs deep tunnels in the soil.

The groundhog or woodchuck (above) is one of the largest marmots, with a head and body length of 32 inches (80 cm).

Then they retreat underground, sealing the entrances with soil and hay, and hibernate huddled together. North American prairie dogs live in bigger colonies called townships, some with thousands of members.

The scaly-tailed squirrels of West African forests are not true squirrels, but they are rodents and have a similar lifestyle. They glide like flying squirrels and feed mainly on fruits and nuts. The pocket gophers of North America are expert diggers, using their large front claws and chisel-like teeth. Both grow about 0.04 inches (1 mm) each day to replace the wear.

Prairie dogs are named after their doglike, yapping "barks." Shown above is a black-tailed prairie dog.

Hoary marmot

Eastern chipmunk

Main groups of squirrel-like rodents (from page 207):

Squirrels and marmots
- 267 species
- Includes tree squirrels, ground squirrels such as prairie dogs, chipmunks, marmots, sousliks

Pocket gophers
- 34 species

Scaly-tailed squirrels
- 7 species

Pocket mice
- 65 species

Deer, camels, and pigs

MAMMALS WITH HOOVES, RATHER THAN CLAWS, ON THEIR FEET ARE CALLED UNGULATES. There are 203 species, all plant eaters, in two main groups. The larger group is the even-toed ungulates, with two or four hoofed toes on each foot. They include deer, cattle, antelopes, giraffes, hippos, pigs, camels and llamas. The odd-toed ungulates have one, three or five hooves per foot (page 216). All even-toed ungulates, except pigs and peccaries, have a special form of digestion. The stomach is divided into several chambers. Food goes into the first chamber, the rumen, where it is part-digested. Then the animal brings it up and "chews the cud" before swallowing it again for the rest of digestion.

A fallow deer youngster, or fawn, feeds on its mother's milk.

Llamas are South American relatives of camels. They eat mainly grass.

Deer are among the most common and widespread hoofed mammals. They live mainly in woods and forests, browsing on leaves. Some, like red and fallow deer, have spread to other habitats, such as moors and parks. Male deer have antlers, which they shed and regrow each year, and which they use to battle with rival males at breeding time. Only in reindeer, or caribou, do females also have antlers. Deer live in herds for safety, have keen senses and flee danger at great speed.

Camels survive for days without food and weeks without a drink. They obtain some moisture from food, and also make water in their bodies because of their specialized body chemistry. When a camel finally has a drink it can gulp 14 gallons (50 Litres) in a few minutes.

Most camels today are domesticated, used as pack animals in dry scrub and desert, and to provide meat, milk, skins, and hair. But some wild camels can still be found in the remote grasslands of Mongolia. These are bactrian or two-humped camels. Domestic one-humped or dromedary camels live throughout the Middle East and North Africa. Some dromedaries were taken to Australia, as pack animals for the inland deserts, and now live wild in the outback.

Woolly cousins

The llama, alpaca, guanaco, and vicuna of South America are close relatives of camels. They live mainly on the slopes of the Andes mountains and have thick, woolly coats to keep out the cold. Most llamas and alpacas are domesticated, as pack animals and for their fine wool. The rare vicuna is a protected species.

During the breeding season, male deer like this elk bellow and threaten rival males for control of the herd. This is called the rut.

The tusks of a hippo are really large canine teeth. They may be 20 metres (50 cm) long. Male hippos sometimes fight each other for females or territory and can inflict nasty wounds with their tusks. Hippos are the third largest land animals. A big male may reach a length of 13 feet (4 m) and weigh well over 3 tons.

Giraffes are so tall they are easy to spot in their homeland of the African savanna (grassland). They use their great height to reach tasty buds, leaves and fruits in the tree tops. The okapi is a close relative of the giraffe.

The hippopotamus is the largest even-toed ungulate. Hippos live in Africa, in groups of 10–15. They spend the day lazing in rivers, lakes or water holes. They emerge at night to graze waterside plants, moving along regular pathways. The much smaller pygmy hippo is a rare animal of swampy forests in west and central Africa. It is an endangered species, with just a few thousand left.

Wild pigs like the warthog use their tusks and strong snouts to grub in the soil for their varied food of roots, bulbs, and small animals.

Ungulates
- 203 species
- hoofed feet

Even-toed ungulates:
Deer
- 36 species including red, fallow, sika, roe, caribou (reindeer), moose, (elk) muntjac
Camels and llamas
- 6 species
Giraffe and okapi
- 2 species
Wild pigs
- 8 species
Peccaries
- 3 species
Hippos
- 2 species
Chevrotains
- 4 species
Musk deer
- 3 species

Tallest

An adult male giraffe may be 6 m tall at the base of its short horns. And it can poke out its long tongue to reach leaves almost 50 cm higher.

!

babirusa of Sulawesi in Southeast Asia. Most have tusks formed from their up-curved canine teeth. Peccaries are very similar to wild pigs but have tusks in the upper jaw that grow downward. They live in scrub and forests mainly in South and Central America.

Giraffes live in groups, called troops, of about 6–10. A troop consists of females and their young, and a senior male who defends their territory.

This extremely shy forest dweller is seldom seen in the wild. It stands almost 6 feet (1.8 m) tall and has a giraffe-like head, neck and body, although the neck is not quite as long in proportion to the body. It also has striped legs like a zebra.

Wild pigs
The wild ancestor of our domestic pigs is the wild boar. It has thick fur and a large, powerful head. Wild boars are common in woods and forests in many parts of Europe and Asia. There are another seven species of wild pigs, including the African warthog and the very rare, protected

Antelopes, wild cattle, and sheep

CATTLE, SHEEP, AND GOATS WERE PROBABLY TAMED FROM ABOUT 9,000 YEARS AGO, making them some of the first domesticated animals. The many breeds of cows today are descended from the wild auroch, which roamed the forests of Europe and Asia, but which finally died out in the 17th century. Like antelopes, cattle have horns that grow throughout their lives and are not shed, unlike the antlers of deer. Most antelopes and gazelles are fairly large, long-legged, fast-running grazers and browsers of grasslands and open scrub.

Gerenuk are long-necked gazelles of African deserts.

There are two varieties of American bison. The wood bison (above) is larger and darker than the plains bison which lives further south.

The wild cattle group, known as bovids, includes the American and European bison. Both species became rare due to hunting by humans. American bison or "buffalo" are now protected in sanctuaries in the open plains and Canadian woodlands. European bison were almost extinct but now live in several forest sanctuaries, especially in Poland and Russia.

The yak is another species of cattle. It lives on the high plains of Tibet, at altitudes of 20,000 feet (6,000 m). Few wild yaks survive, but there are many domesticated yaks which are kept by local people for their meat, milk, skins, and hair.

Another domesticated species of cattle is the water buffalo, which came originally from India and

Wild water buffalo survive in a few parts of Africa and Asia, mainly in swampy areas.

Southeast Asia. It has the largest horns of any living animal, with a record tip-to-tip spread of more than 13 feet (4 m). Water buffalo have been taken to Africa, South America, and Australia, where some have returned to the wild.

Sheep and goats

As with cattle, there are various species of wild sheep and goats, and some have been domesticated. Wild species include the wild goat of eastern Europe and Asia, the chamois and mouflon of Europe and the Middle East, and the American bighorn sheep. Chamois are very agile and sure-footed, leaping over

Wild goats live from Greece and Turkey across to India. They are the ancestors of farmyard goats.

North American mountain goats live high on snowfields and along edges of glaciers.

high mountain crags. Their hooves have soft pads with hard edges, to help them grip even on smooth, slippery, wet rocks. The ibex of eastern Europe, north Africa, and Asia is another mountain dweller, normally found above the timber line. It climbs to even higher levels to avoid the summer heat, then descends to sheltered lower slopes for the winter.

The longest coat

Musk ox from northern North America look like wild cattle, but they are members of the sheep and goat group. They stand about 56 inches (1.4 m) tall at the shoulder and have the longest hair of any wild mammal, reaching 3 feet (90 cm) on the neck and flanks. This thick coat protects them from fierce Arctic storms. Like most cattle, sheep, goats, antelopes, and gazelles, they dwell in herds. If danger or bad weather threatens, the adults huddle together and face outward to protect the young calves in the middle.

Some antelopes and gazelles, like springbok (above), leap straight up more than 10 feet (3 m). This is called pronking. It shows predators such as lions that they are fit, and difficult to catch.

Male cattle, sheep, goats, antelopes, and gazelles use their horns to battle with rivals at breeding time. In Thomson's gazelles (below), the male has much larger, thicker horns than the female.

Keen senses

Antelopes and gazelles are known for their speed and agility. Keen senses give them early warning of predators. Most antelopes live on the African savanna (grassland). Several species, such as springbok, Thomson's gazelles, and Grant's gazelles, gather in huge herds. Some antelopes, such as hartebeest, have short horns. Others, such as the sable antelope and gemsbok, have longer horns. The largest antelope species is the giant eland of Africa, 10 feet (3 m) long and 6 feet (1.8 m) at the shoulder.

More groups of even-toed ungulates (continued from page 213):

Cattle
- 23 species, including domestic cattle, yak, water buffalo, African buffalo, American and European bison, kudus, elands, bongo, nyala

Sheep and goats
- 26 species, including saiga, musk ox, chamois, ibex, markhor, mountain goat, Barbary sheep, mouflon, bighorn sheep

Gazelles and dwarf antelopes
- 30 species, including Grant's gazelle, Thomson's gazelle, dikdik, blackbuck, springbok, gerenuk

Grazing antelopes
- 24 species, including waterbuck, wildebeest (gnu), impala, sable antelope, oryx, lechwe, addax

Duikers
- 17 species

Pronghorn
- 1 species

Horses, zebras, and rhinos

THE HOOFED MAMMALS CALLED ODD-TOED UNGULATES are a much smaller group than the even-toed ungulates (page 212). They include wild horses, asses, and zebras, which are very similar in general body size and shape, and also rhinos and tapirs. Horses and zebras have long legs for fast running in open country. Like cows and sheep, horses have been domesticated and there are now many breeds of different sizes and colours. Rhinos are huge mammals—the white rhino is the third—largest land animal, after the two kinds of elephants. Tapirs are smaller, piglike animals of South America, with one species in Southeast Asia.

No one knows why zebras have such vivid stripes. Each zebra's stripe pattern is unique, so perhaps herd members use the markings to recognize each other.

Horses, donkeys, asses, and zebras are all known as equids. All domestic horses belong to the species *Equus caballus*. They are probably descended from horses that looked very similar to Przewalski's horse, *Equus przewalskii*, of the Mongolian steppe (grassland) in Central Asia. There are no longer any truly wild members of this species. It was rescued from extinction by being domesticated by local Mongolian people, and being breed in various wildlife parks. It may be possible to re-establish wild herds of Przewalski's horses in their Mongolian homeland.

There are two species of wild ass, one in Africa and one in Asia. Domestic donkeys are descended from a form of the African wild ass. Asses are smaller than horses and have longer ears, a more uneven mane, and a tufted tail.

In many parts of the world, horses have escaped from captivity to run free on plains and hills. They grow up wild but they can usually be caught and tamed.

Striped horses

Zebras are "striped horses." The three species live mainly on the plains of east and southern Africa. Like all equids, zebras live in herds. They use their speed to flee from large predators such as lions, hunting dogs, and hyaenas.

All equids have just one large hoofed toe on each foot. Rhinoceroses—rhinos for short—have three hoofed toes per foot. They are bulky animals with very thick skin, almost like armor plating. Unlike horses, rhinos generally live alone and have small eyes and poor sight. But their large ears can pick up the faintest sounds and they also have an excellent sense of smell.

Like all odd-toed ungulates, rhinos are plant eaters. They graze on tough grasses and scrubby bushes. Both males and females have horns, but these are not true horn or bone, they are made of very tightly packed hairs. The white rhino reaches 14 feet (4.3 m) in head-

All rhinos are very similar in appearance. The white or square-lipped rhino (above) has a small hump on its back, just in front of the hips. The exceptionally thick skin of the Indian rhino (below) is creased into deep folds at the shoulders and hips. Rhinos are usually peaceful but if they are threatened they charge in defense.

body length, stands over 6 feet (1.8 m) tall at the shoulder, and weighs over 3 tons. Smallest of the five species is the Sumatran rhino, 8 feet (2.5 m) in length.

Tapir "trunk"

Tapirs live deep in the tropical forests and swamps of South America and Southeast Asia. They resemble pigs, but without the flat-ended snout. A tapir has a long, flexible upper lip, which it uses almost like an elephant's trunk to gather food. The South American tapirs are reddish-brown;

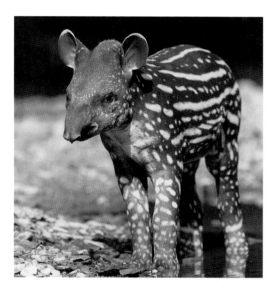

A baby Brazilian tapir (above) is born with spots and stripes, but these fade to an even dark brown coat (left).

the Malayan tapir is black and white. All are about 8 feet (2.5 m) in length. They are active at night, feeding on grasses, water plants, fruits, shoots and buds.

Odd-toed ungulates (from page 213):

Horses, asses, and zebras
- 7 species, including domestic horse, Przewalski's horse, African ass, Asiatic ass, Grevy's zebra, mountain zebra, plains zebra

Rhinos
- 5 species, including black rhino, white rhino, Indian rhino, Javan rhino, Sumatran rhino

Tapirs
- 4 species, including Malayan tapir, Brazilian tapir, Baird's tapir, mountain tapir

Elephants

ELEPHANTS ARE THE LARGEST LAND ANIMALS. African elephants, with their huge ears and longer tusks, are bigger than Asian elephants. These great mammals are famed for their size, strength, and stamina, and also for their long lives and complex herd behavior. People have long trained elephants, especially in Asia, for farming, logging, hunting, warfare, and ceremonies. Sadly, people also threaten their survival, especially in Africa, mainly through killing them for their ivory tusks.

An elephant herd is led by the matriarch (senior female). She remembers the location of seasonal feeding places.

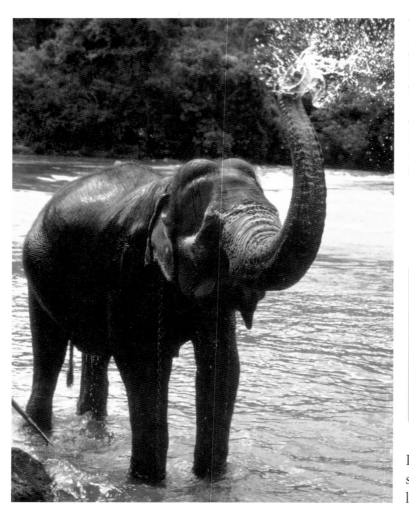

The Asian elephant has a more domed forehead and humped back than the African elephant. It squirts water, mud, or dust over itself to keep cool and to get rid of irritating skin pests.

Elephants sniff and caress each other when they meet, to make sure that they are from the same herd, not intruders.

Largest

The largest African male elephants stand 13 feet (4 m) tall at the shoulder, measure 33 feet (10 m) from trunk tip to tail tip, and weigh over 6 tons. The tusks can be over 10 feet (3 m) long. A few rare "giant" Asian elephants are almost this size, but most weigh 2–3 tons.

!

African elephants live mainly south of the Sahara Desert, in a wide range of habitats including grassland, forests, and dry, thorny scrub. Asian elephants are found mainly in the forests of India, Sri Lanka, and Southeast Asia. Most Asian elephants are kept and trained by people. Fewer than 50,000 live in the wild, in hilly and remote jungle.

In each species, a small family group lives together. They move slowly and steadily, feeding mainly on grasses, bark, leaves, and twigs. They spend up to 18 hours feeding and consume about 330 pounds (180 kg) of food each day. An elephant walks at an average speed of 3 mph (5 km/h). However, if it senses danger, it can sprint away or charge at the attacker at up to 25 mph (40 km/h)—faster than a human.

As drinking holes shrink in the dry season, the herd relies on the long memory of the matriarch, who may be more than 60 years old. She knows places where there may still be water. The elephants gouge a hole with their tusks and sip the water that collects in it.

Elephant anatomy

Elephants are some of the most specialized of all mammals. Their tusks, trunks, ears, and feet are very different from those of most mammals.

The ear of the Asian elephant (below) has tapered lower points.

The foot rests on a broad pad of tough fibers and fat that works as a cushion to spread the animal's weight.

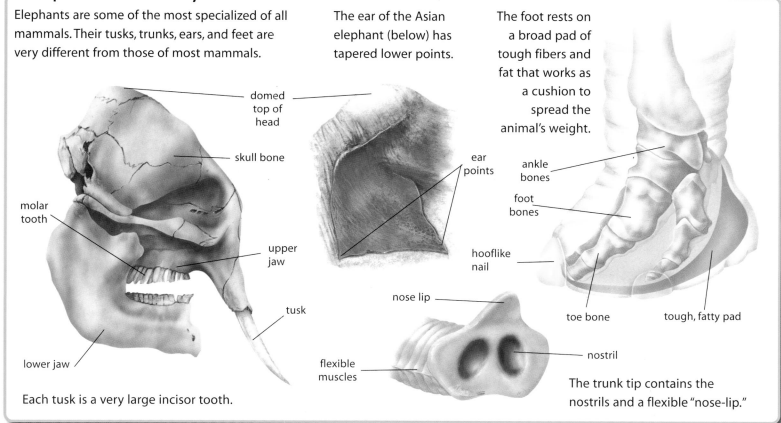

domed top of head

skull bone

molar tooth

upper jaw

tusk

lower jaw

Each tusk is a very large incisor tooth.

ear points

hooflike nail

nose lip

flexible muscles

ankle bones

foot bones

toe bone

tough, fatty pad

nostril

The trunk tip contains the nostrils and a flexible "nose-lip."

Elephants keep in touch with their herd members in several ways. They have a simple language of deep growls and rumbles which carry for hundreds of metres in open country. They also sniff the air with their trunks, and they touch other herd members with their trunks too. In fact the elephant's trunk, which is its greatly lengthened nose and upper lip, has many jobs. It is used almost like our hand and arm for grasping food, greeting other elephants, and guiding babies or calves.

Keeping cool

An elephant cannot drink through its trunk. But it sucks water into the trunk and then squirts the water into its mouth—or over its back for a cooling "shower." Elephants also keep cool by bathing in mud and flapping their ears. The ears work like radiators to lose excess body heat into the air.

Elephant tusks are made mainly of a hard, white substance called ivory. This has been treasured through the ages for making tools, ornaments, weapons, and decorative carvings. Despite wildlife laws and patrolling wardens, many elephants are still killed illegally for their tusks. However in a few areas where elephants are common, limited legal hunting may be allowed in future.

Oversized teeth

An elephant's tusks are its incisor teeth. They start to grow at about two years of age, and continue to grow throughout the animals life. Both males and females have them, but usually in female Asian elephants, they are short and hidden by the trunk and lower lips.

Elephants
- 2 species
- African elephant scattered across central, east and southern Africa, common in a few small areas
- Asian elephant found in India, Sri Lanka, southern China, and Southeast Asia (rare in wild)

Cats

"CARNIVORE" MEANS "MEAT-EATER."
The Carnivora group includes mammals
with long, sharp claws to catch prey, and
long, sharp teeth to rip it up. This group
is described over the next ten pages,
starting with the most carnivorous of all—
the cats. Some carnivores scavenge or eat the
occasional fruit or berry. But the cats are active
hunters of living prey, with large eyes to see in the
dark, and claws which (except for the cheetah) can

Leopards often drop onto their prey from a branch, then drag the
corpse back up to keep it safe from other animals, before indulging
in a treetop feast.

be pulled back into the toes, to keep them sharp. The carnivore group
also includes wolves and wild dogs, hyenas, bears, raccoons, pandas,
civets, genets, weasels, mongooses, and in the sea, seals and sea lions.

The largest cat is the Siberian type of tiger.
It can measure 10 feet (3 m) from head to
tail, and weigh 650 pounds (300 kg).

A lion pride is led by the chief male. Females
or lionesses lack the long neck mane. Cubs
lose their spots as they grow.

Cats are found around the world in
many habitats, from cold mountains to
moist tropical forests. They combine
strength and stealth with speed and
agility, using their excellent eyesight,
hearing and smell.

Cats are a uniform group, which means
they are very similar in overall body
shape and features—and also in their
hunting methods. Most live alone and
prowl at night. They stalk their prey
quietly, keeping low near the ground.
Then they make a quick dash to grab
the victim, holding it down with their
hooked claws and biting it with their
long, sharp canine teeth. The large,
sharp-edged cheek teeth or carnassials
can shear through tough skin, sinews
and gristle.

Ocelots range from southern North America
down to South America. They are expert
swimmers and climbers, catching birds in
the trees and frogs in the water.

Lions are the only cats that
live and hunt in groups,
called prides. The large,
shaggy-maned chief
male patrols the pride's
area of territory,
roaring and leaving
scent marks to
warn off

other prides. The lionesses do the work
of hunting, often as a team to bring
down a large meal such as a zebra or
wildebeest. One or two lionesses walk
toward the victim, to drive it toward the
others who are waiting in ambush.

The doglike cat
The cheetah is one of the less catlike
cats. It is built more like a greyhound
with a long, flexible back, long slim legs
and a relatively small head,
with smallish eyes and ears.
It hurls itself after its prey
with an amazing burst of
speed, rather than
stalking. It is unable to pull
in or retract its claws. The serval is a

One of the most adaptable of larger cats, the cougar can live high on mountains, in semidesert, or in swampy lowlands. It takes almost any prey, from mice to deer, and sometimes farm animals such as sheep.

rosette patches are still visible. These are called black panthers. The snow leopard or ounce is slightly smaller than the leopard and has very thick fur, to keep out the cold in its Asian mountain home. It can easily leap across an icy ravine 10 feet (3 m) wide.

Smaller cats

There are smaller cats on almost every continent. Most are about 32–44 inches (80–110 cm) long, including the tail. They live in trees, using the tail to help them balance, and hunt birds, snakes, lizards, squirrels, and small monkeys. However, the pampas cat of South America is at home on grassland, where it pursues rodents and ground birds.

The bobcat can climb, but it prefers to hunt on the ground for rats, rabbits and running gamebirds such as grouse.

Tame cats?

The many types of domestic cat were probably bred from the African wild cat, beginning in Egypt some 4,000 years ago. These first domestic cats probably caught mice in grain stores. However, even "tame" pet cats have the night-prowling, hunting instincts of their wild ancestors. In some areas, they have returned to live and breed in the wild, and are called feral cats.

smaller version of the cheetah, but has larger ears. It also lives in Africa, hunts by day and races after prey such as hares, small antelopes, lizards, and ground-living birds.

The black "panther"

The most adaptable of the seven species of big cat is the leopard. It has short legs and a muscular body, and swims or climbs after its prey. It often prowls near towns and villages and may lie on a branch, ready to drop silently on a victim passing below. Some leopards are born with almost black fur, rather than the usual tawny color, although the dark

The lynx is similar to the bobcat (above right), but larger, with bigger ear and cheek tufts. It takes larger prey such as hares and young deer. Lynx live in all northern continents.

The cheetah is the fastest land animal over short distances. It can reach speeds of more than 60 mph (95 km/h). But it gives up after about 200 yards (180 m) if the prey seems to be getting away.

CATS (FELIDS)

Big cats
- 7 species
- sharp teeth and claws
- can roar loudly

Lion
- Africa

Tiger
- South and East Asia

Jaguar
- Central and South America

Leopard
- Africa, South Asia

Snow leopard
- Central Asia

Clouded leopard
- Southeast Asia

Cheetah
- Africa, Middle East

Small cats
- 28 species
- resemble big cats, but smaller
- most cannot roar loudly

Small cats include the cougar (puma or mountain lion, the largest small cat), lynx, bobcat, caracal, ocelot, margay, leopard cat, African wild cat, European wild cat, black-footed cat (the smallest small cat)

Dogs, foxes, and hyenas

THE DOG FAMILY INCLUDES WOLVES, FOXES, AND JACKALS, as well as the familiar domestic dog, which was probably bred from the gray wolf. All of these carnivores (page 220) are strong and agile, with long legs for distance running, muscular bodies, powerful sharp-toothed jaws and keen senses of sight, hearing, and especially smell. They differ from cats mainly in that they have longer muzzles, they cannot pull their claws into their toes, and most live in pairs or larger groups called packs—apart from foxes, which dwell alone. Hyenas are also doglike carnivores, but they are not members of the dog family.

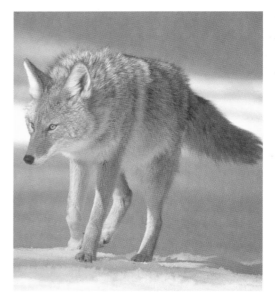

The coyote, with its mournful howl, may live alone but also gathers in packs to hunt.

The gray wolf's strength, stamina, and cunning are famed in myth and legend.

The African wild dog is an endangered species. There are only about 5,000 left, mainly in one Tanzanian wildlife reserve. They are the most efficient of all pack hunters.

Dogs have a different hunting technique from that of cats. Their long, powerful legs enable them to run well for miles. They can track prey over long distances, following the scent with their keen noses, until it tires and is caught.

The biggest dog

The gray wolf is the largest of the dog family, with a head-body length of 56 inches (130 cm). It is found in remote scrub, forest, tundra, and mountains—mainly because people have driven it away. Wolves eat a wide range of meat, from deer to mice, voles, and lemmings. They also scavenge, and even take berries and fruits. The coyote is common in parts of North America, and resembles a smaller version of the wolf.

The maned wolf lives in tall grassland in parts of South America. It has red-brown fur and such long, slim legs that it looks like a "wolf on stilts."

Jackals, like most wild dogs, convey different messages to pack members by the positions of their ears, mouth, legs, and tail.

The domestic dog

All domestic dogs, from huge great danes to tiny chihuahuas, belong to one species, *Canis familiaris*. The first dogs

A male, or dog, red fox, and a female, or vixen, chase in courtship before mating.

were probably tamed from a type of gray wolf, as long as 10,000 years ago. The dingo of Australia may once have been an even earlier, part-domesticated form of the wolf. But dingoes now roam wild across large areas of Australia. The most carnivorous dogs are the African wild dogs, whose teeth are particularly large and sharp. They feed mainly on large mammals brought down by the pack of up to 20.

Most dogs bark, yip, or yelp. But the dingo of the Australian outback rarely makes a sound.

Wily cunning

Most foxes are agile and stealthy, using a combination of stalking and running to catch prey. The red fox has a legendary reputation for cunning. It adapts to most habitats and foods, including those provided by people, so it has become one of the most widespread of all mammals. In spring and summer it feasts on eggs, young birds, and rodents. In autumn it fattens itself on fruits and berries and takes young rabbits and hares. In winter it enters villages and towns to raid trashcans and dumps. Other foxes have similar wide tastes, ranging from crabs and dead fish along the water's edge, to worms, beetles and snails, berries, and fungi.

Jackals are similar to foxes, although slightly larger, with a head-body length of 28–40 inches (70–100 cm). They eat a great range of foods, too. Unlike foxes jackals live in family groups of 4–6. They hunt as a pack to catch small gazelles and antelopes.

The master scavengers

Hyenas do not belong to the dog family. But they are similar powerful carnivores. Far from slinking away like cowards, hyenas are very aggressive and successful pack-hunters. The hyena has one of the

The arctic fox has thick fur that turns white in the winter, matching its snowy surroundings.

The striped hyena has a horselike mane that extends from head to tail. It searches at night for carcasses of large animals already part eaten by big cats.

strongest sets of jaws and teeth in the animal kingdom. It is an expert scavenger, helping vultures to clear the remains of dead animals from the African plains. The hyena eats skin, chews gristle, and cracks bones with ease. Some hyena groups do hunt and kill more than half their victims. Even lions are wary about trying to take a kill from a pack of hyenas.

The fennec fox of North Africa (left) and the bat-eared fox of southern and east Africa hunt small prey such as termites and other insects, mainly by sound, so they have very large ears.

DOGS (CANIDS)

- large, sharp canine teeth
- long snouts
- claws cannot be pulled into toes
- most can bark or yelp

Larger wild dogs
- 4 species

Gray or timber wolf
- All northern lands

Red wolf
- Southeast North America

Coyote
- North and Central America

Dingo
- Australia, Southeast Asia

Other wild dogs
- 5 species including dhole, African wild dog, maned wolf, raccoon dog, bush dog

Jackals
- 4 species
- Africa, Middle East, India

Foxes
- 21 species
- worldwide

Hyenas
- 4 species
- Africa, Middle East

Bears, raccoons, and pandas

AS CARNIVORES, BEARS ARE NOT ESPECIALLY CARNIVOROUS (page 220). They catch prey such as deer, birds, and fish. But they also scratch up worms and grubs, raid wild bees' nests for honey, and eat buds, fruits, seeds, and roots. However, like other carnivores, they have sharp teeth and strong jaws. They are big, bulky and muscular, with powerful limbs, huge paws, and dangerous claws. Raccoons are much smaller and look like a combination of bear and dog. They have bushy tails, climb well and live across North, Central, and South America. The red panda is similar to a raccoon and dwells in eastern Asia. Its cousin is one of the world's rarest yet best-known creatures—the giant panda.

Brown bears feast on the exhausted salmon that try to leap waterfalls as they swim upstream to their spawning places.

The grizzly or brown bear shows its long canine teeth in a warning snarl that few animals ignore.

Asian black bear

Bears may look friendly and cuddly, like toy teddy bears. But the larger species are massive, powerful animals, and sometimes dangerous to people—especially a mother bear protecting her young. If a bear is disturbed or surprised, it may charge as its main method of self defense. Bears were once hunted for their fur, to protect farm animals, and for "sport." Today most species are rare and live in remote places. Because of their unpredictable nature, they are best left undisturbed.

The creamy white fur of the polar bear blends in well with its snowy, icy habitat in the far north. This camouflage helps it to stalk seals on the ice without being detected. As well as very thick fur, polar bears have a thick layer of fat under their skin, to keep out the cold.

The polar bear is longer and slimmer than other bears. This mother is helping her two cubs through the freezing water.

The tree-dwelling sun bear of Southeast Asia is the smallest bear. It has a head-body length of only 4 feet (1.2 m).

Largest

The largest bears are male polar bears. They grow to 10 feet (3 m) long and 1,100 pounds (500 kg) in weight. Alaskan, Kodiak and grizzly varieties of the brown bear reach 9 feet (2.7 m).

!

A polar bear can run fast and even catch young or sick reindeer. Like other bears, it has poor eyesight and relies mainly on smell. It can scent a seal or walrus carcass 2 miles (3 km) away.

Variable bears

The Asian (Himalayan) black bear has a silky coat with a white V-shaped chest mark and large, rounded ears. It is an expert climber, eats ants and grubs as well as fruits and nuts, and often rests in the branches. The small sun bear lives in the forests of Southeast Asia, where it feeds on fruits, termites, small birds, and mammals. The brown bear species is very variable across its range, and includes the grizzly, Kodiak and Alaskan bears. The smallest variety is the European brown bear, now very rare, found in a few mountainous regions as far south as Italy and Spain.

About at night

The common raccoon, with its "bandit" face mask, is a well-known nighttime scavenger in North America. It eats fish, frogs, small birds and mammals, eggs, fruits, nuts, seeds—in fact, almost anything. The raccoon group includes coatis, from the forests of South and

Central America. The coati's flexible, elongated nose sniffs out insects and similar small prey on the forest floor.

The giant panda of China is a worldwide symbol of nature conservation. They are easily recognized, appealing, and extremely rare—with perhaps only 1,000 left in the wild. It looks like a bear, but it is not closely related to bears.

The common raccoon, like the red fox, is adaptable and comes into cities to scavenge in trash. It can climb and swim well, and handles food delicately in its front paws.

The kinkajou lives in Central and northern South America. It rests in a tree hole by day and comes out at night to feed on small animals and fruits. Its tail is prehensile, working like a fifth limb to grasp branches.

There is so little goodness in its bamboo food that it eats for up to 15 hours each day. It has an extra "thumb," an elongated part of the wrist, for splitting bamboo shoots. The red panda is related to the giant panda, but is much smaller, fox-like in shape, and with deep red fur.

The giant panda is a member of the carnivore group, but it hardly ever eats meat. It consumes mainly the stems and leaves of bamboos, which are types of grasses.

Red panda

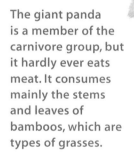

BEARS (URSIDS)
- 7 species
- large head, wide face
- poor sight but keen smell
- bulky, sturdy body
- big paws and claws
- very short tail

Polar bear
- Arctic Ocean and far north

Brown bear
- all northern lands, southern Europe

American black bear
- North America

Asian black bear
- Central and South Asia

Sun bear
- Southeast Asia

Sloth bear
- India, Sri Lanka

Spectacled bear
- South America

Raccoons and pandas
- 17 species
- mostly long-bodied, bushy-tailed
- alert, agile and adaptable
- live mainly in trees
- Americas, apart from 2 panda species

Main groups of raccoons and pandas:

Raccoons
- 6 species including crab-eating raccoon

Coatis
- 4 species including ringtailed coati, white-nosed coati

Olingos
- 2 species

Ringtail and cacomistle
- 2 species

Kinkajou
- 1 species

Pandas
- 2 species, giant and red
- East Asian

Weasels, mongooses, and civets

THE SMALLEST OF THE MAMMAL CARNIVORES (page 220) are weasels, stoats, skunks, badgers, mink, otters, and their relatives, known as mustelids. They are mostly long and slender, with low-slung bodies and short legs, keen eyes, and sharp teeth. They may be small, but when out hunting they are some of the most fearless and aggressive of all animals. However, they are otherwise shy and secretive, seldom seen in the wild except when they bound across the road. Mongooses, civets, and genets are also small carnivores; mongooses resemble stoats while civets, genets, and linsangs are catlike animals with bushy tails, found in Southern Europe, Africa, and southern and Southeast Asia.

The smallest mammal carnivore is the least (dwarf) weasel of North America, a variety of common weasel. It is less than 8 inches (20 cm) long, including the tail.

Each type of mustelid takes different prey, according to its size. Weasels are specialist hunters of mice and voles, but they occasionally eat birds, frogs, and baby rabbits. The weasel's small head and narrow body allow it to follow mice into their burrows. Stoats are larger, have a black tail tip, and hunt rats and rabbits. Pine martens are bigger still, and such skilled climbers that they can catch squirrels. The sable of Siberian forests has a head-body length of 16 inches (40 cm) and very thick, soft fur. It stays mainly on the ground, eats hares and similar animals, and also fruits and berries.

Wolverines are the largest members of the weasel family. They live in northern forests and tundra, and move quickly over loose snow with their broad feet.

The wolverine or "glutton" lives in all northern lands, but is rare in many areas. It is incredibly strong, able to drag prey as large as a deer for several miles.

The sea otter of north and east Pacific coast, floats on its back to prepare food.

The European badger's diet consists mainly of earthworms.

They scavenge on carrion but also kill prey as large as reindeer, covering up to 25 miles (40 km) in search of food.

The black-footed ferret of North America is one of the world's rarest mammals. It hunts mainly prairie dogs, and because these were killed as pests, the ferret suffered too. It became extinct in the wild in the late 1980s. But it has been successfully bred in captivity, and hopefully this species can be established again in its habitat.

A mongoose avoids a snake's deadly bite by its agility and lightning-quick reactions.

The spray from the striped skunk's glands at the base of its tail is so foul-smelling, it can stop the enemy breathing.

Badgers are mainly nocturnal and eat many foods—worms, insects, small mammals, roots, seeds, and fruits. They roam along tracks that become worn with regular use. Eurasian badgers live in family groups, in extensive burrows called setts. American badgers are fiercer and live in western North America.

At home in the water

Otters are beautifully adapted to swimming at the water's surface and below it. They paddle with their webbed feet, and swim faster by swaying the whole body and tail from side to side. Otter fur is waterproofed by plentiful oil made in the skin. The thick underfur, beneath the outer coat of long "guard" hairs, traps tiny bubbles of air. These prevent waterlogging and also keep the otter warm. The giant otter of South America has a head-and-body length of up to 5 feet (1.5 m) and a 28 inch (70 cm) tail.

Skunks live only in the Americas. The 13 species are all very similar, with black and white fur and bushy tails. They feed on insects, lizards, and other small animals, plus some fruits and berries. They are known for spraying a horrible-smelling liquid if disturbed.

The helpful mongoose

Mongooses are in some ways the tropical versions of weasels and other mustelids. They live mainly in dry country, hunting a variety of mice, insects, and other small animals, and occasionally eating fruit. Some species may tackle larger prey such as rats and even poisonous snakes. For this reason, people allow them to stay around towns and may even feed them. Most live alone, but banded mongooses and meerkats live in large family groups. Meerkats post sentries who stand bolt upright and scan the surroundings, ready to warn the others of enemies such as hawks.

Catlike civets

Civets, genets and linsangs are catlike in build and habits. They stealthily hunt small animals at night, camouflaged by their spots and stripes, and climb well. Most species live in Africa, India, or Southeast Asia, with a few in Southern Europe. The common genet, with a spotted body and striped tail, dwells as far north as France. Civets have well-developed scent glands which produce a powerful musky-smelling substance that was once collected for perfumes.

The common genet is indeed common in some areas, but shy and nocturnal, so rarely seen.

Meerkats often stand upright near their burrows to peer across the African grassland and bush, watching for danger.

Weasels and stoats (mustelids)	Cape clawless otter
• 67 species	• Africa
• small to medium size	Giant otter
• long, slim, flexible body	• South America
• short legs, medium tail	**Badgers**
• very active predators	• 9 species
• all regions except Australia, Madagascar	Eurasian badger
	• Europe to China
Groups include:	American badger
	• North America
	Honey badger (ratel)
Weasels, stoats and martens	• Africa to India
• 33 species	**Mongooses, civets and genets**
Common weasel	• 66 species
• North America, Europe, Africa, Asia	• long, flexible body
Stoat	• active, agile predators
• North America, Europe, Asia, New Zealand	**Mongooses**
Other species include American, pine and stone martens, fisher, polecat, grison, mink, sable, zorilla, wolverine (largest), black-footed ferret (rarest)	• 31 species
	• Africa, southern Asia
	• resemble weasels or stoats
	Species include Egyptian mongoose, banded mongoose, meerkat (suricate), cusimanse
Skunks	**Civets and genets**
• 13 species	• 35 species
Striped skunk	• Europe, Africa, southern Asia
• North America	• catlike
Spotted skunk	• large eyes and ears
• North, Central America	• bushy tail
	Species include African civet, common genet, African linsang, binturong, fanalouc, fossa
Otters	
• 12 species	
Eurasian otter	
• Europe, Asia, Africa	

Seals, sea lions, and sea cows

SEALS, SEA LIONS, AND THE WALRUS ARE SUPERBLY ADAPTED TO LIFE IN THE WATER. Unlike whales and dolphins, however, they rarely venture into the open ocean. They usually stay near land because they must come ashore to breed, typically on rocky, isolated coasts or on floating ice. These mammals are all meat-eaters or carnivores, taking prey such as fish and squid. Sea cows are large, slow-moving, seallike mammals that graze on water plants.

A Galapagos sea lion mother prepares to feed her youngster. Baby seals are called pups.

The Mediterranean monk seal is one of the rarest seals, with just a few hundred left. They live in remote sea caves in scattered colonies, in the Mediterranean Sea and Atlantic Ocean.

Seals, sea lions, and sea cows are all marine mammals—they live in the oceans. They all have limbs that are paddle-shaped for rowing themselves through the water. True or earless seals form the largest group, with 19 species. They do have ears, but these lack ear flaps and so are not noticeable on the outside. On land, seals are clumsy and can only slide or hump along slowly. Their rear flippers trail uselessly behind. But in water, few animals can match their speed and grace.

No crabs to eat
The most abundant seal by far, and one of the world's most numerous large wild mammals, is the crabeater seal. Some 20 million live on and around the pack ice of Antarctica. It does not eat crabs as its name suggests because there are none in this habitat. The crabeater, like the great whales, feeds mainly on shrimplike krill.

Seal-eating seal
Three other seals in the same region are the Weddell seal, the smaller Ross seal and the larger leopard seal. The first two dive to great depths, the Weddell seal descending to 1,500 feet (450 m) after fish and squid. The leopard seal, in contrast, is a sleek, fast and fierce surface predator. It grows to 11 feet (3.5 m) long and pursues mainly penguins, but it will eat large fish and even kill other seals.

A seal swims by bending its body and pushing with its rear flippers, like a fish uses its tail. The front flippers are held by its sides or used to steer and brake.

Front flipper power
The eared seals have much more noticeable ear flaps on the sides of the head. They include fur seals and sea lions. They have torpedo-shaped bodies like true seals, but their rear flippers are longer and more mobile, and their front ones larger and more powerful. They swim mainly by "rowing" with these long front flippers. On land, they can shuffle about by tucking their rear flippers under the body and propping themselves up on their front pair. They rest and breed on land at traditional sites called rookeries.

The crabeater seal (right) has few enemies, apart from killer whales and its larger cousin, the leopard seal. Many seals, like these elephant seals (left), emerge or "haul out" of the water onto rocky shores, to rest and sunbathe.

The seal with tusks

The huge walrus is more than 10 feet (3 m) long. It has a very fat, blubbery body and extra-long upper canine teeth known as tusks. Both males and females have tusks, which can grow to 2 feet (60 cm) in length. They use the tusks for grubbing in the sea bed for shellfish and other food, and to help pull themselves out from the water.

Gentle plant eaters

Manatees and dugongs are sometimes called sea cows, because they are peaceful, slow plant eaters, like cows on land. They graze on water plants in shallow tropical seas and estuaries. The dugong lives in the southwest Pacific Ocean, one species of manatee lives near the Amazon River, another around the West Indies, and a third off the coast of West Africa. These bulky animals grow to 10–13 feet (3–4 m) long. Sea cows bobbing, half-seen through ocean mists, may have given rise to sailors' legends about mermaids.

The baby harp seal is one of the most appealing of all animals. It gradually loses its fluffy baby fur and develops the dark head, dark side stripes and pale gray background color of the adult.

Like all sea mammals, the manatee (above) must come to the surface to breathe. The male dugong (below) munches sea grass, its body scarred from fights with male rivals at breeding time. A dugong has notched tail flukes like a whale; the manatee's tail is rounded.

Walruses live all around the seas and oceans of the far north. A layer of fatty blubber under skin which is 1.7 inches (4 cm) thick, protects against the intense cold.

Sea lions and seals (pinnipeds)
- 34 species
- smooth, streamlined head and bulky body
- paddlelike limbs
- sharp teeth

True or earless seals
- 19 species
- no visible or external ear flaps
- cannot tuck rear flippers under body
- inshore waters of all seas and oceans but less common in tropics
- include gray seal, common (harbour) seal, harp seal, northern elephant seal, leopard seal, Mediterranean monk seal

Eared seals (fur seals and sea lions)
- 14 species
- ear flaps (may be hidden in fur)
- can tuck rear flippers under body
- inshore waters of most seas and oceans, ice floes
- include northern fur seal, Californian sea lion, Galapagos fur seal

Walrus
- 1 species
- long tusks
- Arctic and northern oceans

Manatees and dugong (sea cows)
- 4 species
- paddlelike tail
- plant eaters
- include Amazonian manatee, West Indian manatee, West African manatee, dugong

Great whales

WHALES AND DOLPHINS ARE PERFECTLY ADAPTED TO LIFE AT SEA. In fact, they never come ashore—unless beached by accident, when they usually die. Great whales differ from toothed whales such as dolphins and porpoises (page 232) because they have comblike baleen in their mouths, for filter-feeding. Great whales were once hunted in huge numbers for their meat, fat, oil, and baleen (whalebone). The slaughter drove some species almost to extinction. Laws now prevent them from being killed in large numbers, and most are slowly recovering their populations. Great whales show complicated behavior and communicate with a wide variety of sounds and calls.

Blue whale

Largest ever

The largest animal that ever lived on Earth is the blue whale. (It is even bigger than the dinosaurs, as far as we can guess from dinosaur fossils so far discovered.) An adult female blue whale can measure more than 100 feet (30 m) long, weigh over 150 tons, and eat 4 tons of krill each day.

!

Humpbacked whales open their vast mouths and swim up to the surface, trapping small creatures inside.

Baleen whales have huge and very unusual mouths. Their jaws lack teeth. Instead, the mouth contains rows of baleen plates. These are straplike or curtainlike structures that hang down from the roof of the mouth. They have fringed edges like brushes or combs. They work as filters to sieve the small animals of the plankton from the water.

How great whales feed
These vast animals feed in different ways. Right whales cruise along with their mouths open at the surface.

A rorqual such as a blue or humpback takes a massive mouthful of sea water, so its chin expands enormously, then presses its huge tongue upward inside its mouth, to force the water out through the baleen plates. The grey whale grubs and gouges up clouds of mud from the sea bed and does the same. In all of these whales, food items such as krill and small fish get trapped in the combs or bristles of the baleen, which are tough and springy, almost like plastic. The whale then licks the food off the baleen plates and swallows it.

Gray whales feed mainly in the shallow coastal waters of the Arctic, between North America and Asia. They dive down to 300 feet (90 m) and scoop up a rich mixture of mud, to filter the small animals living in it. When the whale has a mouthful of food it surfaces to strain off the water, swallows its meal, and dives for another load.

Most whales feed and travel in loose groups called pods. Members keep in touch using an amazing variety of sounds, many too low or high for us to hear. Blue and fin whales emit ear-splitting, low-pitched grunts that are the loudest noises made by any animal. Such sounds travel for hundreds of miles through the seas.

The gray whale feeds on small creatures in the mud, leaving great holes and furrows in the seabed.

Minke whales are the smallest great whales, at 10–11 m in length.

The song of the humpback whale

Even more extraordinary are the songs of the humpback whale. These eerie, plaintive sounds plunge from high squeaks to deep wails, in a sequence that lasts half an hour or more, making it the longest, most complicated song of any animal. Usually, the singer is a male trying to attract a female at breeding time. Humpbacks also make acrobatic leaps almost right out of the water, then splash back in with an enormous crash.

Whale migrations

Many whales travel or migrate long distances between their main feeding places and the waters where the females give birth to their young, known as calves. Most great whales tend to feed in polar waters during the brief Arctic or Antarctic summer, then return near to the tropics for winter. The longest migrations are made by gray whales in the East Pacific. They travel each year from the breeding lagoons off the Californian and Mexican coasts, to feed in the rich waters of the Bering Sea, and then back again—a distance of some 9,000 miles (15,000 km). Humpbacks are also great travelers. Some spend winter in the Caribbean and summer near Greenland and Iceland.

Great whale calves stay with their mothers for up to a year. Like all mammals they feed at first on her rich milk, but gradually they learn to filter-feed for themselves. A newborn blue

Over millions of years of evolution, a whale's front legs have become flippers, used for swimming slowly and steering in the water. The rear legs have disappeared, while the tail has developed wide flukes. These swish strongly up and down to drive the mammal through the water with the power of a racing car engine.

whale calf weighs 3 tons and measures 23 feet (7 m) long. Each day it drinks 56 gallons (200 l) of milk. Female great whales usually have only one calf every two years—one reason why their numbers are taking so long to recover.

WORLD WATCH

For centuries, small numbers of great whales were hunted with spearlike harpoons from sailing or rowing boats. But in the 19th century, whaling ships were equipped with steam engines. Then came faster diesel engines and explosive harpoons. The whales could not escape. Thousands were killed yearly. By the 1950s their numbers had plummeted. In the mid 1980s mass whaling ceased at last.

DOLPHINS AND WHALES (CETACEANS)
- 76 species
- entirely aquatic, most in the sea
- long, submarine-shaped body
- front limbs are flippers
- tail flukes

The largest whales:

Baleen or great whales
- 10 species
- comblike baleen in mouth
- worldwide, mainly in colder oceans

Rorquals
- 6 species including blue whale (largest living animal), fin whale, humpback whale, minke whale, sei whale, Bryde's whale

Gray whale
- 1 species

Right whales
- 3 species including right whale, pygmy right whale, and bowhead

Dolphins and porpoises

TOOTHED WHALES INCLUDE MANY KINDS OF PORPOISES AND DOLPHINS, and also sperm whales, beaked whales, and two white whales—the narwhal and beluga. These all have more normal mouths and teeth compared to great whales (page 230). However, unlike land carnivores, a toothed whale's teeth are all similar in size and shape, designed to grasp slippery fish and squid. The largest species of toothed whale is the sperm whale. Males or bulls are up to 66 feet (20 m) long and 50 tons in weight—the largest carnivores on Earth.

Dolphins range in length from only 4 feet (1.2 m) in Heaviside's dolphin, to 23 feet (7 m) or more in the huge and powerful killer whale, or orca. Killer whales are among the fiercest predators of the sea, though they rarely pose a threat to people. With immense speed and power, they pursue their prey of fish, seals, seabirds, dolphins, and even larger whales. They hunt in groups and sometimes work together to herd a school of fish into shallow water, to feed at their leisure. Like the other dolphins, killer whales are regarded as "intelligent" animals. This is partly because they can be taught to do tricks and entertain tourists. But in the wild they also show great curiosity and adaptable behavior, working out how to eat new and unfamiliar foods.

The killer whale is the largest dolphin. It feeds mainly on seals and other sea mammals, as well as penguins and fish. It is a very fast swimmer, reaching 35 mph (55 km/h).

Many dolphins, like these bottlenoses, make spectacular leaps into the air, sometimes up to 10 feet (3 m) clear of the sea. One species, the spinner dolphin, leaps high into the air and spins like a top at the same time.

All of the dolphins are active, even playful creatures. They are sleek, powerful swimmers, and sometimes follow ships—perhaps to feast on any leftovers thrown overboard, or to save energy by swimming in the ship's wake. Most dolphins live in groups and communicate with each other using a great variety of squeals, buzzes, clicks, and grunts. They also use these sounds for echolocation or sonar, like bats (page 198) but underwater, to find prey and navigate through cloudy water. Like all whales, they breathe through their nostrils, which are joined together on the top of the head as the blowhole.

Snub-nosed whales

A dolphin has a protruding beaklike snout and a curving sickle-shaped back fin. Porpoises are similar, but lack the dolphin's beak and have a snub nose instead. They are also generally smaller than dolphins, growing to about 6 feet (2 m) in length. Most species are dark gray and feed, like dolphins, on fish and squid. Porpoises tend to stay inshore, usually in small groups of 10–15, and seldom leap clear of the water.

The biggest toothed whales

Sperm whales feed mainly on large squid, which they catch by diving deep into the ocean, regularly staying under for an hour or more. The sperm whale is gigantic, but the dwarf sperm whale is more dolphin-sized, at about 9 feet (2.6 m) long. These whales are named after the waxy, oily substance that takes up most of their bulging foreheads, called spermaceti. It may help the whale to dive very deep and also to focus the sound waves it uses for echolocation.

Beaked whales

The beaked whales are mysterious creatures that resemble overgrown dolphins. There are 18 species, but they spend most of their time diving to immense depths and so are seen at the surface much less often than other whales. They eat mainly squid. The largest is Baird's beaked whale, about 43 feet (13 m) long.

The two kinds of white whales are the narwhal and beluga. The narwhal's swordlike tusk may have inspired legends about the mythical unicorn. The beluga is tuskless but it is unusual in other ways. It is pure white when adult, and it also has a flexible neck, so it can turn its head to each side.

Belugas live in all Arctic and northern seas. They make such loud chirps, trills, and squeaks that these can be heard above the water, earning them the nickname of "sea canary."

The common or harbor porpoise finds its prey of fish, such as herring or mackerel, using a sonar system of sound clicks and listening to the echoes.

The northern bottlenose whale is a toothed whale—but it only has two teeth. These are in the lower jaw, and they may never erupt or grow above the gum.

On guard!

The narwhal grows to 16 feet (5 m) long, with mottled brown coloring. It also has a long tusk! Only the male has a tusk—a greatly lengthened upper left incisor tooth with a twisted spiral surface pattern. It grows up to 8 feet (2.5 m) long. Rival males 'fence' with their tusks at breeding time.

Freshwater dolphins

River dolphins resemble marine dolphins but live in fresh water and estuaries. They also have longer, slimmer beaks for catching mainly fish, and their echolocation is very sensitive to find their way in muddy water. They include the whitefin dolphin, one of the world's rarest mammals. There are perhaps only 150–200 left, in the Yangtze river in China.

River dolphin

Giant carnivore

The massive sperm whale is the largest predator on the planet, and also the deepest-diving of all mammals. It reaches depths of 2 miles (3 km) in search of its prey, which includes the fearsome giant squid.

small hump for dorsal fin

huge forehead filled with spermaceti oil

50 peglike teeth in narrow lower jaw

Continued from page 231:

Dolphins and other toothed whales
- 66 species
- mostly smaller than great whales
- short, sharp teeth

Groups include:

Dolphins
- 32 species
- worldwide, mainly offshore in warm seas
- beaklike snout
- includes common, bottlenose and spinner dolphins, melon-headed whale, pilot whales, killer whale (orca)

Porpoises
- 6 species
- coastal waters of northern hemisphere
- lack dolphin's "beak"
- includes common and Dall's porpoises

River dolphins
- 5 species
- fresh water
- Amazon, La Plata, Indus, Ganges, and whitefin dolphins

Sperm whales
- 3 species
- blunt forehead
- includes sperm and pygmy sperm whales

Beaked whales
- 18 species
- resemble large dolphins with beaklike snout
- includes northern bottlenose whale and Cuvier's beaked whale

White whales
- 2 species
- whitish color
- narwhal and beluga

Lemurs and bushbabies

ALONG WITH MONKEYS AND APES, THE LEMURS AND BUSHBABIES BELONG TO A GROUP OF MAMMALS KNOWN AS PRIMATES. The main primate features include a relatively large brain for the size of the body, well-developed hands with thumbs that can grasp and manipulate small items, and large, forward-facing eyes. The lemurs and bushbabies, plus the pottos, lorises, and tarsiers, are known as prosimians. This name means "early-monkeys," since their kind resemble animals that appeared on Earth before the later primates, the monkeys and apes. Many look similar to squirrels and, like them, leap around skillfully in trees.

The potto can grasp twigs between its fingers and thumb, and also between its big toe and other toes. It grows to about 14 inches (35 cm) head-and-body length.

Lemurs are found only in Madagascar. They resemble a combination of monkey and squirrel, and range in size from lesser mouse-lemurs smaller than your fist, to the large indri with a head-body length of 28 inches (70 cm). Most lemurs feed mainly at night on fruits, seeds, flowers, and leaves, which they

gather as they move through the trees. They see and hear well at night with their large eyes and ears. Most species also have long, furry tails for balancing.

The ring-tailed lemur's tail is brightly patterned with alternate rings of black and white. This species is active by day. It wipes its large tail on scent glands under its arms and chin, then waves the tail aloft to send sight and smell signals to its troop members. However, most lemur species are much less noticeable, as they hide by day and creep through the shadowy trees at night. The name "lemur" means "ghost," and some kinds make strange, eerie sounds in the darkness.

Bushbabies (below, shown life-size) have such precise hearing and fast reactions that they can hear a moth flutter past, reach out and grab it, all in total darkness.

Ring-tailed lemur mother and baby

Bushbabies live mainly in East Africa. Like lemurs, they prefer dense forests. They are small and agile, and find insects at night with their huge eyes and keen hearing. They too have long, furry tails, which help them balance as they jump. They are named from the wails they make in the darkness, which sound like a human baby crying.

The slow loris (right) is well named, since it hardly seems to move as it creeps through the thickest rain forest. It can grip a twig and hang by just one foot.

Mouse lemurs (right) are the smallest lemurs— and also the smallest primates. Yet they are long-lived for such small mammals. Some have survived 12–15 years in captivity.

PRIMATES

- 180 species
- large, forward-facing eyes
- manipulative hands
- mostly tree-dwelling

Prosimians

- 36 species
- mostly smaller than monkeys
- simple teeth with few points (cusps)

Main groups of prosimians:

Lemurs

- 10 species
- Madagascar only
- long, bushy tail

Sifakas

- 4 species
- Madagascar only
- resemble large lemurs

Dwarf lemurs and mouse lemur

- 8 species
- Madagascar only
- resemble small lemurs

Aye-aye

- 1 species
- Madagascar only
- long, thin middle finger

Bushbabies

- 6 species
- Africa
- enormous eyes

Lorises and pottos

- 4 species
- Africa and Asia

Tarsiers

- 3 species
- islands of Southeast Asia

Tarsiers live in Borneo, Sumatra, Sulawesi, and parts of the Philippines. They have huge eyes and use the sit-and-wait hunting method, watching the forest floor from a convenient low bough. When a lizard or insect ambles past, they pounce.

The tailless lorises and pottos of Africa and Asia are much more slow-moving than bushbabies. They creep slowly along branches as they feed on a range of items, from fruits and tree sap, to insects and snails, even a small bird or shrew.

The aye-aye of Madagascar (below, shown life-size) has batlike ears, large front teeth, and an extraordinary long middle finger to pick grubs out of wood. It is an endangered species.

The indri (above) is the largest type of lemur. It has a head and body up to 2 feet (60 cm) long, and weighs as much as 22 pounds (10 kg). It also lacks the typical lemur's long tail, having a short stump.

The tarsier (left, shown life-size) leaps extremely well using its muscular back legs and long, strong rear feet. It keeps its body upright as it springs from one branch to another.

African monkeys

ABOUT 40 SPECIES OF MONKEYS LIVE IN AFRICA, in habitats ranging from dense tropical forest, to open woodland and savanna, to dry rocky scrub. Most common are the guenons, with long tails. They inhabit mainly forests, traveling and feeding in groups. One of the most abundant and widespread guenons is the vervet monkey, equally at home on the ground or in trees. When feeding on the ground, vervets are always wary, and quickly rush to safety in the trees if danger threatens. Many of these African monkeys have colorful markings with different patterns of red, brown, gray, black, and white, especially around the face. These colors change to show the sex and age of each troop member.

Vervet monkeys can run, climb, and swim well, and eat most kinds of food.

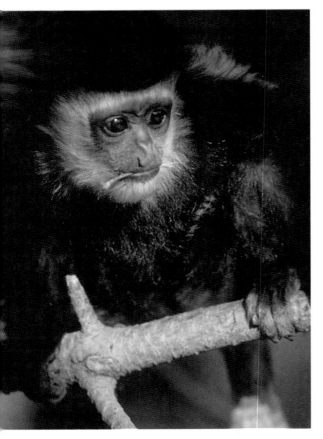

Colobus monkeys have four fingers on each hand. Their thumbs are tiny or missing.

Colobuses are some of the most beautiful and graceful of all monkeys, with their long, glossy coats and sweeping, tufted tails. They stay mainly in trees along the forest edge, and rarely come down to the ground except to feast on fallen fruits. Unfortunately, many colobus monkeys are killed for their fur, and several species are now rare or endangered. Another great threat to all monkeys is habitat loss—the clearance of their natural forest homes for farmland, buildings, and roads.

Dog-faced monkeys

Baboons are large, mainly ground-dwelling monkeys. They have doglike faces and sharp teeth. They are powerfully built, with muscular shoulders and arms, and they can run and clamber with great skill. This group includes the forest-living mandrill with its vividly colored face, and the drill with its equally colorful rear end.

Most baboons live in large groups called troops, and have close-knit social behavior. Olive baboons live in extended family groups within the larger troop. Each family usually includes offspring and also the offspring's offspring as well. The family tends to stay together and help each other if one is sick or injured. Some species of baboon even live in desert habitats with hardly any trees.

Look out!

Some monkeys have different alarm calls to indicate danger from various predators or places. One call might mean "beware above," while another means "beware on the ground." This simple language helps other group members to pinpoint the threat more easily.

The adult male mandrill has a bright red nose, with bright or pale blue patches at each side, and yellow-orange fur on the chin. Mandrills live in troops of 30–40 in West African forests. They sleep in trees, but feed mainly on the ground.

Mangabeys are closely related to baboons. They too have strong jaws and especially powerful incisor teeth, to crack open tough nuts and seeds. They also eat fruits, leaves, fungi, and small creatures such as insects, lizards, and baby birds. They are more lightly built than baboons, with tails longer than their bodies, to help balance in the treetops. Since they live among dense forest foliage they communicate not by visual signs, like baboons, but by loud whoops and cries, like most other monkeys. Mangabeys are mainly black, gray, or brownish.

White-cheeked mangabey

Largest

The mandrill and drill are the largest monkeys. Males reach 3 feet (90 cm) tall and weigh 110 pounds (50 kg).

!

Chacma baboons, a shaggy, dark gray variety of the savanna or common baboon species, can survive even in the almost waterless wastes of the Namib Desert, in southern Africa.

Olive baboons live in troops of 100 or more. The troop has a social order with leading males and females. Young males patrol the edges and act as scouts to check for danger.

WORLD WATCH

The "Barbary apes" that scamper around and entertain tourists on the Rock of Gibraltar, at the west end of the Mediterranean Sea, are not true apes. They are a type of baboonlike, tailless monkey called the Barbary macaque (page 238). They were taken to Gibraltar from their natural home in North Africa, where they have now become rare. Yet some are still captured to keep up the numbers on Gibraltar.

Primates continued from page 234:

Old World monkeys
- 133 species
- forward-facing eyes
- nostrils close together
- manipulating hands
- most have long tails

Groups of African monkeys:

Guenons
- 17 species
- slender body
- several are colorful
- mainly forests

Colobus monkeys
- 9 species
- graceful and agile
- black and white or red-brown
- woodland and forest

Baboons
- 5 species
- mainly African
- heavy body, doglike face
- some have short tails
- spend time on the ground

Mangabeys
- 4 species
- medium-sized
- graceful and agile
- forests

Asian monkeys

THE LARGEST GROUP OF ASIAN MONKEYS IS THE LEAF MONKEYS AND LANGURS. They are found mainly in southern Asia, but some live in North Africa and others in China. This group contains many species that dwell in forests, like most other monkeys. But there are also some which survive high in mountains, where it is snowy and treeless. The Hanuman (or common) langur is one of the most adaptable, ranging from gardens and towns to remote, rocky uplands. It is regarded as sacred in the Hindu faith. Even though it often raids crops, it is seldom harmed. Most leaf monkeys and langurs feed on leaves, fruits, nuts, buds, and flowers. They rarely drink, obtaining most of the water they need from their juicy food. Due to loss of their forest home, some of these monkeys are rare and a few are on the official "Red Lists" of threatened species.

Old World monkeys differ from New World or American species in various ways – including their nostrils being close together.

Hanuman langurs are bold monkeys and soon become used to people. They sometimes raid picnic sites, shops and houses to look for food.

Macaques are the most widespread monkeys, found from North Africa across the Middle East and Asia, including the Philippines and Indonesia. The habitats they occupy are equally varied, including rain forests, mangrove swamps, scrub, and even buildings such as shrines and temples. The rhesus and Japanese macaques can survive winter snow and ice, feeding on roots and tree sap.

Many macaques have hairless faces, allowing the red skin to show through.

Like many monkeys and other primates, rhesus macaques groom each other and their young. The monkey searches through the fur with its nimble fingers for bits of dirt, and for pests like fleas and lice, that it pops into its mouth. This mutual grooming helps to strengthen relationships within the family and the troop.

The crab-eating macaque was named because early scientific observers watched it eat crabs. But like many monkeys, it has a mixed diet of insects and similar small animals, eggs, fruit, buds, leaves, and almost anything else.

Waaah!
In some langurs, a young monkey is cared for by "baby-sitters" as well as by its own mother. These other females may even give their own milk to the baby. However, they may also simply put it down and walk off! The abandoned baby cries out, and its mother soon comes back.

Japanese macaques live high in mountains, where it becomes cold and icy in winter. They sometimes warm themselves by bathing in natural hot springs.

These large monkeys take their name from the flat, short nose, set back from the rounded muzzle. They also have strong arms which are almost as long as their legs. They are found mainly in forests and bamboo jungles in China, Tibet, and Southeast Asia, some species inhabiting the cloud forests high on mountain slopes. At least two species are rare or endangered, with populations of a few hundred. They can survive only if their forest habitats are protected.

Proboscis monkeys

The proboscis monkey is named after the male's prominent, protruding nose, which droops down over the mouth. The female has a shorter, more normal monkey nose, as do both sexes of the related pig-tailed monkey. Both of these species are rare and live in restricted areas—the proboscis monkey in Borneo, and the pig-tailed monkey on the Mentawai Islands off Sumatra.

The favorite habitats of the proboscis monkey are mangrove swamps along the coast, where they feed mainly on young shoots and leaves of mangroves and the fruits of other trees, such as

The pig-tailed monkey has a snub nose and distinctive thin, almost hairless tail.

pedadas. Occasionally they swim across stretches of water and they even dive from heights of 50 feet (15 m) into the sea to avoid danger.

The proboscis monkey's leafy food is poor in nutrients so it must eat large amounts. After a good meal, about half of its body weight of 30–44 pounds (15–20 kg) is the leaves in its enormous stomach.

Most primates only enter water if they must, to escape danger. Proboscis monkeys are the best swimmers in the group. They often cross rivers and creeks, even diving below the surface.

The snub-nosed monkeys of China migrate in spring up the mountain slopes, and come back down as cold autumn mists cloak the uppermost forests.

Old World monkeys continued from page 237, Asian groups include:

Leaf monkeys and langurs
- 20 species
- India, China, Southeast Asia
- long limbs and tail
- some have crestlike hairs on head
- various habitats

Macaques
- 15 species
- mostly Asian
- bulky, sturdy build
- often live on the ground

Snub-nosed monkeys
- 6 species
- China and Southeast Asia
- broad face with snub nose
- forest and bamboo groves

Proboscis monkeys
- 2 species
- Borneo, Sumatra
- bulky, rotund body
- prominent floppy nose
- rain forest and mangroves

American monkeys

NEW WORLD OR AMERICAN MONKEYS ARE FOUND MAINLY IN TROPICAL FORESTS. Most are agile and acrobatic, leaping easily through the treetops, but they are difficult to study and little is known about some species. There are two main groups, the small tamarins and marmosets, and the larger howler and woolly monkeys. They may be hard to see, but they can certainly be heard since they communicate by very loud calls. Their howls, hoots, and whoops are some of the most characteristic rain forest noises.

Howler monkeys live in forests, from the steamy tropical lowlands to the slopes about 3,000 feet (900 m) above. The six species feed mainly on fruits and young leaves. As their name suggests, they are very noisy animals. Their howling cries carry for hundreds of yards through the forest. Most of the howling happens as dawn breaks, and for the same reason that birds sing their dawn chorus. The sounds allow rival howler troops to tell each other where they are, and that their home areas or territories are occupied. This helps to avoid direct fights.

Howler monkeys live mainly in the Amazon region, in small troops of up to ten. Their large throats work as resonance chambers to make their calls so loud.

The tail of the spider monkey is so muscular and grasping that it can hold the creature's entire body weight, leaving the hands and feet free to gather food.

Shaggy sakis

Saki monkeys have shaggy fur coats, and the males tend to have bright markings around the face. Their main food is fruits, berries, and seeds, gathered as they move in small groups through the forest canopy. Some types of sakis eat small animals like bird chicks, mice, and bats, as well as eggs and the honey of wild bees.

Spiders in the trees

Spider monkeys are the most expert climbers of all monkeys. They are named from their long furry legs and grasping tail, which stick out at all angles, making them look like hairy five-legged spiders. Some species can even pick up small objects with the tail. They dangle in the highest branches, run and leap with breathtaking skill, and also swing along using their hands as hooks, like gibbons. They feed on ripe fruits.

The chief male of the brown capuchin troop follows just behind the younger males as they forage. In this position, he receives plenty of food, but he is also safe since those in front are more likely to encounter any predators.

Partly prehensile

Capuchin monkeys are medium sized, with a head and body 12–14 inches (30–35 cm) long and a tail of up to 20 inches (50 cm). They are found in most parts of Central and South America, in a wide range of forest types. They have arms shorter than their legs, and the tail is less grasping or prehensile than most other American monkeys. Their varied diet includes insects and frogs as well as fruits and leaves. Capuchins often come down to the ground to feed—which is another unusual feature of New World monkeys.

The wooly spider monkey, or muriqui, is the symbol of Brazil's conservation movement. This is the largest American monkey species, and also one of the rarest. Just a few hundred are left in the country's southeast coastal forests.

Squirrel monkeys are lively and bold, and sometimes raid fields of crops. They live in groups of 30–40 and move in the branches with great ease. Like other monkeys they use the long, thin tail as a balancing aid.

The pygmy marmoset is one of the smallest primates, with a head and body length of just 6 inches (15 cm). If a hawk or other predator comes near, it stays completely still, as if frozen.

Wooly coats

Wooly monkeys live mainly in the Amazon region. Like spider monkeys, they have a long, strong prehensile tail, which they use to hang from forest branches. They are large monkeys with a head and body length of 2 feet (60 cm) and a tail even longer. They have thick, dense fur and feed mainly on fruits and leaves.

The red uakari is one of the oddest looking of all monkeys. Its fur is white or chestnut, but its face and forehead are bald and the pale skin goes bright red in sunlight, almost as if sunburned. This monkey also has a relatively short tail. Uakaris prefer damp lowland forests, clamber rather than leap through the branches, and feed mainly on fruit.

Small and squirrel-like

Tamarins and marmosets are small, squirrel-like monkeys, found mostly in the Amazon region. Tamarins are generally bright in color, and some have long "whiskers" or a ruff of hair around the face. They eat mainly fruit and insects. Marmosets are slightly smaller than tamarins, and less brightly patterned. They use their large front teeth to bite small holes in the bark of certain forest trees. They then feed on the nutritious, sugary sap or gum that oozes out.

In grave danger

Several species of tamarin and marmoset are in danger of extinction, often because they are restricted to a particular kind of forest with certain tree species. The lion tamarin, with its golden mane of silky fur, has almost disappeared from the wild. Several zoos around the world are trying to save this species.

Small families

Titi monkeys are small, with long, bushy fur. Unlike most other American monkeys, they live in small family groups rather than large troops. Sitting side by side on a branch, they sometimes twist their dangling tails together for extra support and security. They are usually quiet, but like howler monkeys, they make loud dawn calls that last for several minutes, to defend their territory.

The owl monkey, or douroucouli, is the only monkey which is active during darkness. Its large eyes are adapted for night vision.

Monkeys continued from page 239:

New World (American) monkeys
- about 50 species
- nostrils far apart
- many have prehensile or grasping tails

Howler monkeys and spider monkeys
- 29 species
- flat faces
- most live in forests
- incudes howler monkeys (6 species), saki monkeys (6), spider monkeys (5), capuchin monkeys (4), titi monkeys (3), wooly monkeys (2), uakaris (2), night monkey (1), squirrel monkey (1)

Tamarins and marmosets
- 21 species
- most live in forests of Amazon area
- small and squirrel-like
- long, furry tail
- thumb and fingers cannot hold or manipulate items as well as larger monkeys
- feed on fruit, sap and insects
- includes tamarins (12 species), marmosets (9)

Gibbons

APES ARE LARGER THAN MONKEYS, HAVE
ARMS THAT ARE LONGER THAN THEIR LEGS,
AND LACK TAILS. They also have large heads and
strong jaws with big teeth. The ape group includes gibbons or
lesser apes, and orangs, gorillas, and chimps, known as great apes.
There are nine species of gibbon, all in the forests of Southeast Asia.
They are incredibly agile climbers, using their hooklike hands and
long, muscular arms to swing around. They also leap with great ease
and walk upright on their back legs, even along narrow branches,
holding their arms out for balance.

Like many tree-dwelling primates, gibbons are almost entirely vegetarian. Their favorite food is ripe fruit, which accounts for about two thirds of their diet, and which they travel great distances to find. They also eat flowers, buds, shoots, and leaves, and the occasional insect or other small animal. Fruit provides most of the water they need, but they also lick raindrops or dew from leaves. In a typical day, a gibbon spends about three hours searching for food, some four hours eating, and the rest of the time resting, sleeping, grooming, playing, and calling.

Arms and shoulders

The gibbon's main method of moving is almost unique among primates. Most forest monkeys have long tails to help them balance and perhaps to grasp branches. But the gibbon is tailless. Instead, it has long, muscular arms and very broad shoulders. It uses these to hang from branches and swing hand-over-hand with amazing speed and skill. This way of moving is called brachiation. The gibbon's shoulder and arm joints are very flexible, and a gibbon can hang by one arm and turn its body in a complete circle.

Gibbons, along with the orang, have the longest arms in relation to their body size, of any primate. The largest gibbon, the siamang, has an "armspan" of more than 5 feet (1.5 m). Yet its head and body are only about 32 inches (80 cm) long.

Gibbon duets

Gibbons are also famed for their loud, sometimes musical calls. These echo through the forest, especially during the dawn chorus. Gibbons use these calls to communicate with each other and with neighboring groups. Usually the female starts the call. Her mate then adds his own cries in the gaps between her sounds, so the result is a duet.

The song of a gibbon usually follows a regular pattern. It begins with a "tuning up" period where the pair practice and loosen their throats and mouths. The next stage consists of alternating sequences, as the female and male take turns. Then comes the main part—the "great call" of the female, with occasional additions from the male.

Going solo

In one species, the kloss gibbon, male and female sing separately rather than together. The male produces a loud and musical solo in the morning, for as long as two hours. The female's song is usually shorter, but even more impressive. Every three or four days she

Compared to other mammals, baby apes are cared for by their mothers for a long time. The young lar gibbon feeds on its mother's milk for up to two years.

climbs to the top of a tree to perform. Her song has some 20 different phrases, each lasting about half a minute, with long notes rising and falling. She ends with a flourish and her "great call"—during which she launches herself into the air, then rushes about tearing off leaves and snapping twigs.

The lar gibbon is also known as the common or white-handed gibbon. Its main coat color varies according to where it lives. Almost black individuals are from the Thailand region (see also below).

On Sumatra and the Malay peninsula, most lar gibbons have brownish fur (see also above). These two sites are colour-coded blue and red on the map (right), while the Thai area is coded green.

Where gibbons live

Each species of gibbon lives in a different region of Southeast Asia. This is called geographic separation. It means that they do not compete for food, since all species have similar diets. The exception is the siamang, which is considerably larger than the other species and takes larger food items.

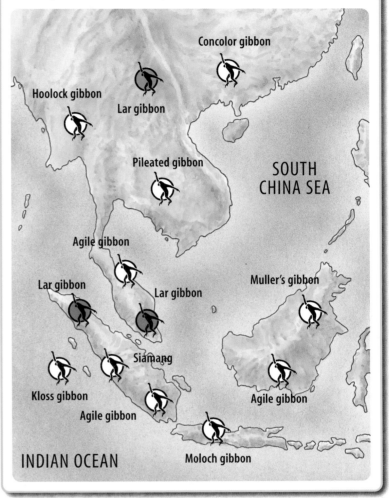

Concolor gibbon
Hoolock gibbon
Lar gibbon
Pileated gibbon
SOUTH CHINA SEA
Agile gibbon
Lar gibbon
Lar gibbon
Muller's gibbon
Siamang
Kloss gibbon
Agile gibbon
Agile gibbon
INDIAN OCEAN
Moloch gibbon

Partners for life

The duet of a female and male gibbon helps to maintain their partnership, because they pair for life. They live as a small family group with their two or three young. Baby gibbons are born about every two years, and they cling tightly to their mother's fur even as she swings at speed through the trees.

In some species, such as the siamang, the male takes over the care of the older offspring, until they are perhaps five years old. Gibbons are long-lived animals for their size, reaching about 40 years of age in the wild.

Siamangs make their calls louder by inflating their throat patches like balloons.

APES
- 13 species
- resemble large, tailless monkeys
- Africa and Southeast Asia

Gibbons (lesser apes)
- 9 species

Agile gibbon
- Malaya, Sumatra, Borneo

Concolor gibbon
- Laos, Vietnam, S. China

Hoolock gibbon
- Assam, Bangladesh, Burma

Kloss gibbon
- Mentawai Islands (Sumatra)

Lar gibbon
- Thailand, Malaya, Sumatra

Moloch gibbon
- Java

Muller's gibbon
- Borneo

Pileated gibbon
- Thailand, Cambodia

Siamang
- Malaya, Sumatra

Orangs and gorillas

THE ORANG, GORILLA, CHIMP, AND PYGMY CHIMP ARE THE FOUR KINDS OF GREAT APES, AND THE LARGEST OF THE PRIMATES. They are also the closest living relatives of ourselves, the human species. The mysterious orangs live deep in the forests of Borneo and Sumatra, in Southeast Asia. They are difficult to spot because they are rare, very shy, and live mainly on their own rather than in family groups or troops. Gorillas, the largest apes, dwell in a few restricted areas of West and Central Africa. They live in small groups. They are massive, muscular and powerful animals, yet also peaceful and gentle—unless threatened.

Largest

The orangutan is the largest tree-living mammal. Males grow to 5 feet (1.5 m) tall and weigh 200 pounds (90 kg).

!

Orangs seem to make no distinction between their arms and legs, using all of them for both climbing and feeding.

The name "orangutan" means "man of the woods." This second-largest ape has bright reddish-brown fur, which is long and shaggy. Despite their size and weight, orangs are skilled at clambering around in the trees, spreading their weight using all four limbs. They are very fond of fruit and spend many hours feasting on a tree of ripe figs or mangoes. They also eat leaves and shoots. Their big teeth and strong jaws help them to tear open even hard nuts, and pull off strips of bark to get at the sap-laden soft wood beneath. Orangs also eat insects and the occasional egg, chick, small bird, lizard, or mouse.

The long call

Orangs live in similar lowland rain forest habitats to gibbons (page 242). And like gibbons, orangs make loud calls to communicate with each other. However, it is only the male orang that does this, uttering what is known as his "long call," which lasts for a minute or two. The call starts with a series of roars, getting louder, then dying away to end with bubbling sounds.

Old male orangs develop long, shaggy fur especially over the shoulders and back, and loose, wrinkled skin on the chest and belly. They are also bigger and heavier, with larger cheek flaps than the females.

The lowland gorillas (above) have shorter, less shaggy fur than the rarer mountain gorillas (above right).

The call is not to keep in touch with family members, since orangs live solitary lives, except for a mother with her baby. The male probably makes the call to attract a female, and to warn rival males off his territory.

The massive head, neck, shoulders, and arms of the gorilla make it the strongest primate. Large males weigh over 330 pounds (150 kg).

WORLD WATCH

Gorillas are the largest primates. A mature male is 6 feet (1.8 m) tall and weighs 400 pounds (180 kg). But their size and power have not helped them survive. Rather, it has partly led to their plight. Gorillas have been shot for "sport." Their hands and feet are cut off for "trophies." They are among the most endangered of all animals, especially the mountain gorilla. Human conflicts where they live have not helped.

Gorillas are very heavily built, with a broad chest, long arms, and a large, tall-domed head (especially in adult males) with massive jaws and teeth. The nose is black, leathery, and flattened. The fur and skin is mostly black, except in older adult males, which develop a silvery-white patch on the back and flanks, giving them the name of silverbacks.

The most vegetarian ape

Gorillas are strong and muscular enough to overpower any animal in their dense forest habitat. Yet they are almost entirely vegetarian. They feed mainly on leaves, shoots, stems, and ferns, and occasionally ripe fruits. Their main feeding periods are early morning and mid–afternoon, with long rests between.

Gorillas usually sleep in nests that they make by bending and interlocking twigs and branches. Babies sleep with their mothers up to the age of about three years. These are mountain gorillas, with longer fur than the two lowland varieties.

The sleeping nest

In the early evening, gorillas climb into trees to weave nest platforms where they sleep at night. Younger gorillas spend part of the day in trees too. They weigh much less than the adults and so find climbing easier— and there are more branches that will bear their weight. But most older members of the gorilla group prefer to feed and travel on the ground. They amble along on all fours, using the soles of the feet and the bent knuckles of their hands.

Gorilla groups

Gorillas live in groups of about 5–35 animals. A typical group consists of one silverback male, one or two junior males, and several females with their offspring. Unlike most other monkeys and apes, gorillas are mostly silent, except when rival adult males meet. Then they may threaten each other. They beat their chests, thrash branches, and make barking, roaring and hooting calls.

The female gorilla is pregnant for just over nine months. When the baby is born, it cannot walk or climb, but only cling to her fur. By about three months of age the youngster is sitting up, and by six months old, it is able to climb and walk. The mother feeds it on her milk for up to 18 months.

Apes continued from page 243:

Great apes
- 4 species
- largest primates
- tailless
- fingers and thumb can manipulate small items

Gorilla
- 1 species
- tropical rain forests
- 3 varieties or subspecies: Western lowland gorilla (Cameroon, Central African Republic, Zaire/Congo, Gabon, Equatorial Guinea), Eastern lowland gorilla (eastern Zaire/Congo), mountain gorilla (Zaire/Congo, Rwanda, Uganda)
- eats leaves, shoots, buds, berries, fruits and other plant material

Orang (orangutan)
- 1 species
- tropical rain forests
- Sumatra and Borneo
- eats fruits, leaves, seeds, eggs, some small animals

Chimpanzees

CHIMPANZEES HAVE THE MOST COMPLICATED SOCIAL LIVES OF ALL THE APES. They have a huge range of facial expressions, body postures, gestures, signs, and sounds. They can work out how to solve simple problems, in the wild and in captivity. They make and use simple tools. In many ways, they seem to be a link between the world of animals and our human world. Their body structure and genes, their behavior and intelligence, and their evolution as shown by fossils, mean that chimps are our closest relatives.

There are two species of chimpanzee. These are the chimp or common chimpanzee, and the bonobo or pygmy chimpanzee. The chimp is covered with black or grey hair, except for the ears, face, hands, and feet. The face is usually pink, turning darker brown or black with age. The pygmy chimp is slightly smaller, with a lighter build and smaller teeth, and a darker face. It also has sideways tufts of hair over its ears.

The pygmy chimp, or bonobo, is only slightly smaller than the common chimp, with a head-body length of 22–26 inches (55–65 cm).

Both species of chimps are long lived. Some reach 50 years of age. More than any other animals, they show degrees of human like attributes. These include care for their kin, teamwork during hunting, sharing out food, long-lasting bonds or "friendships," the ability to learn through their lives as they acquire skills, use tools and work out problems, with a good long-term memory for individuals, places and events. A chimp also shows self-awareness. Unlike other animals, it recognizes that the reflection in a mirror is itself, not another chimp.

However chimps can also show aggression and violence that is not directed towards catching food or in self-defense against rivals, as it is in other animals. In humans, this type of aggression might be called "mindless."

The chimp's day

Chimpanzees are mainly active during the day. They rise at dawn to search for food, spending their time feeding, resting and moving on. Like gorillas, they travel mainly on the ground rather than in trees, knuckle-walking on all fours. At night, each adult makes itself a nest platform, like the gorilla's. The chimp bends and weaves together branches, twigs, and leaves, and rests and sleeps until the morning.

The two chimps

There are several differences between the common chimp and the pygmy chimp. But these are quite minor, even in overall size. Some experts suggest that the two chimps are really varieties, or subspecies, of the same species.

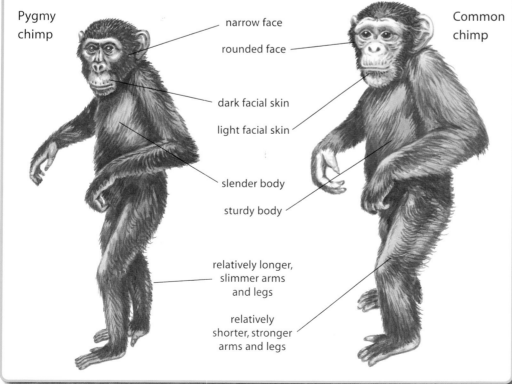

Pygmy chimp

Common chimp

narrow face

rounded face

dark facial skin

light facial skin

slender body

sturdy body

relatively longer, slimmer arms and legs

relatively shorter, stronger arms and legs

Many facial expressions made by chimps look similar to our own. However, we must be very careful about assuming that a chimp's expression that looks like our own, means the same as our version. A chimp who appears to be in a good mood and laughing (left) is really fearful, baring its teeth in defense to a threat. Chimps learn much during their long "childhood." A mother chimp (right) cares for her youngster for up to three years.

The chimp's habitat

Ideal chimp habitat includes areas with fruit trees, since fruit is their major food and they eat it for at least 4–5 hours each day. Other favored foods are young, freshly sprouted leaves, seeds, and also soft bark, sap, juicy pith wood, and flowers. They sometimes use rocks to smash open hard-cased fruits and nuts, such as those of oil palms.

Chimps are mainly vegetarian, but they also eat some animals. Their favorites include termites, ants, and caterpillars. Once a chimpanzee has found a termite mound or ants' nest, it may use a stick to probe inside. The insects crawl onto the twig, and the chimp pulls it out and licks them off. Groups of chimps occasionally work together to catch and eat larger birds and mammals, including young pigs, monkeys, and antelopes.

The raiding party

Although chimpanzees are usually gentle and careful, they are powerful animals and sometimes cause physical damage. An adult male chimp is far stronger than an adult human, with a broad chest and extremely muscular arms. Male chimps, especially, get into fights or territorial disputes. They pick up and hurl large boulders or branches with great ease. They may form a raiding party to hunt down and tear apart an animal such as a monkey, or to attack stragglers from a neighbouring rival troop. Most chimp troops number about 20–50 individuals, with one or two large, leading males, various younger males, and females with their young.

Chimp numbers have fallen rapidly in recent years, across the whole of their natural range. The main causes are habitat destruction for logging and farmland, and illegal trapping. Many of the remaining populations are small and separated, and so at greater risk of extinction. Little is known about the numbers of pygmy chimps, except that they are rarer than their larger cousins, and their habitat is under great threat too, mainly from commercial logging.

Chimps spend many hours grooming others in their family or group. They remove old hairs, bits of dirt, and pests such as fleas from each other's fur and skin. Apart from improving hygiene, this mutual grooming helps to strengthen the relationships within the troop.

Making faces

Chimpanzees use a kind of language to tell each other important information about their surroundings and intentions. They use many facial expressions, and utter various shouts and grunts. Tame chimps have learned our own sign language, using their hands to communicate with people.

Thoughtful   Pleased   Angry

Apes continued from page 245:

Chimpanzees
- 2 species

Common chimpanzee
- West and Central Africa, from Senegal to Tanzania, mainly in Zaire (Congo), Gabon, Cameroon
- forest, patchy woodland
- fruits, seeds, soft bark and other plant parts, also insects, eggs, small mammals

Pygmy chimpanzee (bonobo)
- Central Africa, only in Zaire (Congo)
- rain forest
- fruits, shoots, leaves, buds

Glossary

Abdomen The region of an animal's body that contains mainly the parts or organs for digestion, reproduction, and excretion (getting rid of wastes).

Antenna A "feeler," a long and thin part usually on or near the head, that detects touch—and perhaps smells and tastes as well.

Arthropod An invertebrate animal that has a hard outer body casing (exoskeleton) and jointed limbs, such as an insect, crab, spider, centipede, or millipede.

Asexual reproduction Producing offspring without sex (*see* Sexual reproduction). For example, some simple animals simply split in two (fission). Some grow "buds" that detach to form new individuals (vegetative reproduction). Some female animals produce eggs that develop into young without being fertilized by the sperm from a male (parthenogenesis).

Camouflage When an animal is shaped, colored, and patterned to blend in with its surroundings, so that it is less likely to be noticed, especially by its predators or prey.

Canine teeth Long, sharp teeth, like spears or daggers, near the front of the mouth of a mammal. They are well developed in meat eaters such as dogs and cats.

Carapace A large, hard, shieldlike covering over an animal's body. The upper part of the shell of a turtle is a carapace. So is the top part of the shell of a crab.

Carnivore An animal that eats the meat or flesh of other animals. Most carnivores are predators or hunting animals.

Carrion "Dead meat"—the dead and dying bodies or carcasses of animals, which are usually eaten by scavengers.

Cilia Microscopic hairlike parts that coat many outer surfaces and inner linings of animals and their body parts, such as the body surface of a tiny worm or the inside of the intestine. Cilia wave to and fro like tiny oars to cause movement.

Compound eye An eye made up of many separate light-detecting units, like a mosaic, rather than one larger unit, like our own eye. Insects have compound eyes.

Courtship behavior The movements, actions, sounds, and scents made by a male and/or female animal of the same species, when they come together to mate.

Detritivore An animal that feeds on detritus—the dead, dying, and rotting bits of animals, plants, and other once-living things.

Digestion Breaking down bits of food into tiny pieces, by squeezing and squashing it, and pouring powerful chemical juices onto it. The pieces or nutrients are small enough to be taken into body tissues, for growth and life processes.

Digit A toe or finger or a similar part on the end of a limb.

Dorsal On the top, upper side or back of an animal, like a fish's dorsal fin.

Echolocation A system of sending out sounds, listening to the echoes that bounce back, and then working out the size and position of nearby objects. Bats, dolphins, shrews, and some birds use echolocation.

Egg A single living cell produced by a female animal for reproduction. Some eggs are microscopic. Birds' eggs are large and enclosed in a hard shell. (*See* Sexual reproduction.)

Endoskeleton A strong supporting framework on the inside of the body, such as our own bones.

Evolution The changes in living things through time, due to changing conditions or environment. New species appear, and existing species that are not suited or adapted to the conditions, and which cannot change or evolve, die out or become extinct.

Exoskeleton A strong supporting framework on the outside of the body, such as an insect's body casing.

Extinction When all the members of a particular group of living thing, usually a species, die out so that the species disappears forever.

Eye A body part that detects light rays and produces nerve signals that go to the animal's brain. (*See also* Compound eye.)

Filter-feeding When an animal feeds by filtering or sieving lots of tiny particles, usually from water, using body parts shaped like combs, brushes or feathers.

Flagellum A long, whiplike part sticking out from a microscopic cell. It lashes to and fro to cause movement.

Food chain and web The connections or links between different living things, according to how they get their food. A simple food chain is when a rabbit eats some grass, and a fox eats the rabbit: Grass > Rabbit > Fox

In nature, many animals eat a variety of foods, so food chains link into a complex network known as a food web.

Genes Instructions or blueprints to make living things, in the form of chemical codes of the substance DNA, found inside cells. A living thing develops in shape, size, and color, and carries out its digestion and other body processes, according to its genes.

Gills Body parts specialized for absorbing oxygen dissolved in water. They are usually delicate and feathery.

Gland A body part that makes a certain product, usually a liquid, for use by the animal. A salivary gland makes saliva (spit), a venom gland makes poison, and a mucus gland makes slimy mucus.

Habitat A type of natural place with characteristic plants and animals, such as a pond, an oak wood or a rocky seashore. Some animals, such as penguins, live only in one habitat. Others, such as the red fox, range across many habitats.

Herbivore An animal that eats mainly plants or their parts and products, such as leaves, fruits, or roots.

Hermaphrodite An animal that has both female and male sex organs, so it can produce both eggs and sperm.

Hibernation When a warm-blooded animal goes into a "deep sleep" during adverse conditions. Its body temperature falls drastically and its heartbeat, breathing and other body processes almost stop.

Incisor tooth Long, sharp-edged, chisel-like teeth, at the front of the mouth of a mammal. They are well developed in rodents (gnawing animals) such as mice, rats, and beavers.

Insectivore An animal that eats mainly insects, especially ants or termites, and often other small prey items too, such as worms, spiders, and slugs.

Invertebrate An animal without a backbone, more accurately, without a vertebral column (*see* Vertebrate). The vast majority of animals, both in numbers of individuals and numbers of species, are invertebrates such as insects, crabs, starfish, snails, and worms.

Kingdom One of the five main groups of living things. Animals make up the biggest kingdom, Animalia.

Larva The very active growing and feeding stage in the lives of certain animals. It usually follows the egg stage. A larva does not look like its parent.

Lungs Body parts specialized for absorbing oxygen from air.

Metamorphosis When an animal changes its body shape dramatically as it grows. For example, a butterfly begins life as an egg, hatches into a caterpillar (larva), then turns into a chrysalis (pupa), and finally into the adult butterfly.

Migration A long journey to find food or more suitable conditions. Some migrations are regular, to and fro along the same route, at the same time each year. Others are occasional, as when lemmings run out of food and set off in almost any direction.

Molar teeth Wide, flat teeth at the back of the mouth of a mammal, for chewing. They are well developed in herbivores such as zebras, antelopes, and elephants.

Mucus A slimy, usually sticky substance made by many animals, for uses such as protection, trapping bits of food, deterring enemies, or easing movement.

Muscle A body part of an animal specialized to get shorter, or contract. Muscles make movements.

New World The continents and nearby islands of North and South America. They are separated from the Old World by the Atlantic and Pacific Oceans.

Nutrients Substances such as minerals that a living thing takes in as food, so it can grow, maintain, and repair its body, and use energy for life processes.

Old World The continents and main islands of Europe, Africa, Asia, and Australia. They are separated from the New World by the Atlantic and Pacific Oceans.

Omnivore An animal that eats many kinds of food, including meat and plants.

Oxygen An invisible gas, with no taste or smell, that makes up one fifth of the air around us. Oxygen is needed by living things because it is a vital part of the chemical process which breaks down food to get energy. Most animals obtain oxygen through their gills or lungs, or by absorbing it through the body's surface.

Parasite A living thing that exists on or in another, known as the host. The parasite gains something, such as shelter or food, and causes harm to the host.

Parthenogenesis *See* Asexual reproduction.

Pheromone A chemical substance, like a scent, that an animal releases into the air or spreads on the ground. Each pheromone causes a certain reaction in others of its species, such as getting ready to breed, or following the pheromone trail to food.

Predator An animal that hunts or actively pursues other creatures, its prey, for food.

Prehensile A body part that is flexible and muscular, and which can be used for grasping and holding. Some monkeys have prehensile tails.

Prey Any animal that is pursued or hunted as food, by a predator.

Proboscis A movable stalklike part on the head of an animal, usually with the mouth on it or near it.

Pupa The seemingly inactive, resting stage in the lives of certain animals, such as insects. It usually follows the larva stage and is sometimes called a chrysalis or cocoon.

Sexual reproduction When a sperm cell joins with an egg cell to make a fertilized egg, which develops into a new individual. This usually involves a female and male of the same species mating (having sex). (*See* Asexual reproduction.)

Species A kind or type of living thing, such as the tiger, the golden eagle or the common octopus. Members of a species can breed with each other, but not with members of other species.

Sperm A single living cell, usually shaped like a microscopic tadpole, produced by a male animal for reproduction. (*See* Sexual reproduction.)

Symbiosis When two different kinds or species of living things exist closely together and benefit each other in some way, such as giving protection or sharing food.

Territory An area or place that an animal occupies and defends against rivals of its species. Some territories are for feeding, some are for breeding, and some are for both. A tiger's territory covers dozens of square miles of forest. A limpet's territory is just a few square feet of seashore rock.

Thorax The region of an animal's body that contains mainly the parts for moving, such as legs or wings, and often those for breathing and pumping blood (the heart). In the human body it is called the chest.

Torpor When a cold-blooded animal becomes inactive, usually because the temperature falls, as at night or in winter.

Vegetative reproduction *See* Asexual reproduction.

Ventral On the underside or belly of an animal, like a fish's ventral fin.

Vertebrate An animal with a backbone, more accurately, with a vertebral column— a row of bones or cartilages called vertebrae. The main groups of vertebrates are fish, amphibians, reptiles, birds, and mammals. (*See also* Invertebrate.)

Viviparous When a female animal gives birth to babies ("live young"), rather than laying eggs.

Warning colors Bright colors and patterns on an animal's body, which warn others that it is dangerous or harmful in some way. It may have a sting, or a poison bite, or a horrible taste. Red and black or yellow and black are common warning colors, found on bees, wasps, beetles, frogs, snakes, and various other animals.

Index

marlins 101, 122, **124-125**
black 125
blue 125
striped 125
marloos 194
marmosets 240, 241
pygmy 241
marmots 210, 211
alpine 211
marsupial mammals **194-195**
martens 226, 227
pine 226, 227
stone 227
martins 189
American purple 188
house 188
sand 189
matamatas 140, 141
mayflies 82-83
meadowlarks 189
medusas 24, 25, 31
meerkats 227
megapodes 173
menhaden 109
mice 6, **206-207**
birch 207
harvest 206
house 206
jumping 206, 207
marsupial 195
New World 207
Old World 207
pocket 207, 211
pygmy 206
yellow-necked 206
midges 80, 81
midshipman 115
miliota 15
millepora 31
millipedes 6, 71, 72, 73, **98-99**
pill 98
polydesmus 98
mink 226, 227
minnows 113
mites 72, 94, 96, 97
flour 97
giant red velvet 96
moas, giant 162
mockingbirds 183
mole rats 191
African 207
naked 207
moles 191, 196, 197
golden 197
marsupial 194, 195
mollusks 41, **54-55**
bivalves 62-63
cephalopods 64-65
seashells 60, 61
sea snails 59
mongooses 220, **226-227**
banded 227
Egyptian 227
monito del monte 195
monitors 131, 139, **152-153**
Gould's 153
Nile 152, 153
sand 152
monkeys 7, 9, 191
African **236-237**
American **240-241**
Asian **238-239**

brown capuchin 240
capuchin 240, 241
colobus 236, 237
guenon 236, 237
howler 240, 241
leaf 238, 239
New World 240-241
night 241
Old World 237, 238, 239
owl 241
proboscis 239
saki 240, 241
snub-nosed 239
spider 240, 241
squirrel 241
titi 241
vervet 236
wooly 240, 241
wooly spider 241
monkfish 102
monotremes 191, **192-193**
moonrats 196, 197
moorhens 173
moose 213
morepork 179
mosquitoes 80
filaria 51
malaria 13, 72
mosquitofish 118, 119
moss animals **16-17**
moths 71, **76-77**
agrippa 76
bogong 77
clearwing 77
silkworm 72
sphinx 79
mouflons 214, 215
bighorn 214
mouthbrooders 7, 126
Nigerian 126
mudpuppies 132, 135
mudskippers 128, 129
muggers 145
mullets, red 123
muriqui 241
muskellunge 111
musk oxen 215
mussels 6, 41, 54, 55, 60, 62
bitterling 112
pea 63
pearl 63
swan 63
mustelids 226, 227

N

narwhals 232, 233
nautiluses 54, 65
paper 65
pearly 65
needlefish 118, 119
silver 119
nematodes 50, 51
nemerteans 52, 53
neotony 135
nettle animals **24-25**
newts 131, 132, 133, **134-135**
eastern 135
great crested 133
striped 135
warty 135
nightingales 186, 187
nightjars **178-179**
nudibranchs 57
yellow-spotted red 57

numbats 195
nuthatches 189
nyala 215

O

obbelias 30, 31
ocelots 220, 221
octopuses 54, 55, **64-65**
blue-ringed 65
odd-toed ungulates 212, **216-217**
oilbirds 179
okapis 213
olingos 225
olms 135
onychophorans 99
opossums 195
American 195
shrew 195
Virginia 194, 195
orangs 242, **244-245**
orcas 232, 233
orioles 183
Baltimore 183
orthopterans **82-83, 86-87**
oryxes 215
ospreys 170, 171
osteichthyes 103
ostracods 93
ostriches 161, 162, 163
otters 226, 227
Cape clawless 227
Eurasian 227
giant 227
sea 226
otter shrews 197
ounces 221
owls **178-179**
barn 179
eagle 178, 179
elf 178
fishing 179
great horned 178
horned 8, 178
little 179
short-eared 179
snowy 178
oxen, musk 215
oystercatchers 63, 166
oyster drills 59
oysters 41, 54, 55, 60, 62, 63
cockscomb 62
pinctada pearl 63

P

pacaranas 209
pacas 209
paddlefish **106-107**
pandas 220, **224-225**
giant 224, 225
red 224, 225
pangolins 200, 201
tree 200
panthers 221
black 221
paramecium 17
parrotfish **126-127**
blue 127
rainbow 127
parrots 6, 161, **174-175**
African gray 174
kakapo 162
partridges 172, 173

swamp 173
passerines 182, 183, **186-187**, 188-189
seed-eating 184
pauropods 99
peacocks 161, 172
peccaries 213
pedalias 19
pelicans 161, 166, 167
brown 167
white 166, 167
penguins 8, 9, 161, 162, 163
emperor 163
perch **122-123**
Nile 122, 127
perching birds 182, 183, 188-189
perchlike fish 122-123, 126
peregrines 170
perenties 152
peripatuses 99
periwinkles 58, 59
petrels 164, 165
storm 165
phasmids 86, 87
pheasants 172, 173
argus 172
common 172
monal 172
Reeves 172
pickerals 110, 111
piddocks 63
pigeons 6, **174-175**
crowned 174
pigs 191, **212-213**
wild 213
pikas **202-203**
large-eared 203
northern 203
pike **110-111**
gar 106
northern 110, 111
pilchards 108, 109
pillbugs 93
pinnipeds 229
pinworms 51
pipefish 116, 117
pipits 188, 189
cuckoo 176
meadow 176
piranha, red 113
pisces 103
placental mammals 199
placozoans 21
plaice 120, 121
planarians 46
crenobia 47
dugesia 47
polycelis 47
planigales 195
plankton 11, **14-15**
plantain-eaters 176
plasmodia 13
platyhelminthes 47
platypuses 192
duck-billed 192
plovers 166
polecats 227
pollocks 114
pollution 39, 107, 137
polykrikos 15
polyps 24, 25
colonial 28, 29
coral 11, 36, 37, 38, 67

hydroids 30
sea anemones 32
polyzoans 17
pondskaters 84
porcupinefish 120, 121
porcupines 208, 209
American 208
crested 208
ground 208
New World 208
tree 208
poriferans **21**
porpoises 191, **232-233**
common 233
Dall's 233
harbour 233
possums 195
brushtail 194, 195
honey 194, 195
pygmy 195
ringtail 195
potoos 178, 234, 235
pouched mammals **194-195**
pouts 114
prairie dogs 210, 211
black-tailed 211
prawns 71, 72, **90-91**
primates 234, 235
apes 242
gorillas 245
great apes 244
macaques 238
pronghorns 215
pronking 215
prosimians 234, 235
protists 6, 11, **12-13**, 17
coral 38, 39
floating **14-15**
protozoans 12
pseudoscorpions 96
ptarmigans 173
pufferfish 120, 121
puffins 6, 161, 165
pumas 221
pupfish, Devil's Hole 119
pythons 131, 138, 139, **154-155**
green 154
Indian 155
reticulated 154, 155

Q

quails 172-172
painted 172
queleas 185
red-billed 185
quolls 195

R

rabbits 6, 191, **202-203**
volcano 202
raccoons 220, **224-225**
common 225
crab-eating 225
racerunners 150, 151
radiolarians 14, 15
ragworms 42
rails 162, 168, **172-173**
rainbowfish 118, 119
raptors **170-171**
ratel 227
ratfish **104-105**
ratites 162, 163
rats 6, **206-207**

Acknowledgments

The publishers wish to thank the following artists who have contributed to this publication:

Janet Baker (Julian Baker Illustrations), Andy Beckett (Illustration), John Butler, Kuo Kang Chen, Wayne Ford, Chris Forsey, Roger Gorringe (Illustration), Ron Hayward, Roger Kent (Illustration), Stuart Lafford (Linden Artists), Mick Loates (Linden Artists), Alan Male (Linden Artists), Matt Nicholas (David Lewis Agency), Jane Pickering (Linden Artists), Terry Riley, Mike Saunders, Sarah Smith (Linden Artists), Christian Webb (Temple Rogers), David Webb (Linden Artists), Martin Wilcock (Illustration).

The publishers wish to thank the following photographic sources for the use of their photographs in this publication:

OSF = Oxford Scientific Films; NHPA = Natural History Photographic Agency

Page 12 (T/R) Peter Parks/OSF; 14 (B) Peter Parks/OSF; 16 (T/R) Karen Gowlett-Holmes/OSF; 17 (B) Harold Taylor/OSF; 18/19 (T/C) Peter Parks/OSF; 19 (B/L) M.I. Walker/NHPA; 23 (T) Richard Herrmann/OSF; 26 (B) Frederik Ehrenstrom/OSF; 29 (T/R) A.N.T./NHPA; 30 (T) Peter Parks/OSF; 34-35 (B) Norbert Wu/NHPA; 36 (T/R) A.N.T./NHPA; 39 (B) David B. Fleetham/OSF; 45 (T/R) David Fox/OSF, (B) Rodger Jackman/OSF; 46 (B) G.I. Bernard/NHPA; 48 (B/L) London Scientific Films/OSF; 50 (T/R) London Scientific Films/OSF; 53 (B/L) Image Quest/NHPA; 55 (B/L) Peter Parks/OSF; 56 (C/L) Colin Milkins/OSF; 57 (T/L) Rudie H.Kuiter/OSF; 59 (C/L) H.L. Fox/OSF; 63 (T/R) Norbert Wu/NHPA; 64 (T/R) Audie Kuiter/OSF; 67 (T/R) Peter Parks/OSF; 68 (T/R) Pam & Willy Kemp/OSF; 69 (T/R) Frederik Ehrenstrom/OSF; 75 (B) Kjell B. Sandved/OSF; 76 (C) London Scientific Films/OSF; 78-79 (B/C) D.M. Shale/OSF; 83 (T/R) Bob Fredrick/OSF; 85 (T/L) Colin Milkins/OSF; 86 (B/L) Alastair Shay/OSF; 88 (C) Alastair Macewan/OSF; 90 (B) Jan Aldenhoven/OSF; 92 (L) J.A.L. Cooke/OSF; 94 (C/R) A.N.T./NHPA; 96 (B/L) Peter Parks/OSF; 99 (B) Michael Fogden/OSF; 106 (B) Hellio & Van Ingen/NHPA; 109 (C) Kathy Tyrrell/OSF; 111 (C/R) Agence Nature/NHPA, (B/L) Peter Parks/OSF; 112 (C/R) D. Heuclin/NHPA; 115 (T) B. Jones & M. Shimlock/NHPA; 117 (T/R) David B.Fleetham/OSF; 118 (B) Richard Herrmann/OSF; 119 (B/L) Kathie Atkinson/OSF, (T/L) Max Gibbs/OSF; 121 (C) NHPA; 122 (T/R) Tobias Bernhard/OSF; 122/3 (C) G.I. Bernard/NHPA; 125 (T/R) A.N.T./ NHPA; 128/9 (B/C) Dr. Ivan Polunin/NHPA; 135 (B/L) Robert Erwin/NHPA; 136 (T/R) G.I. Bernard/NHPA; 137 (B/L) Stephen Dalton/NHPA; 138 (T/R) Martin Harvey/NHPA; 140-141 (T/R) Daniel Heuclin/NHPA; 142 (B) Jany Sauvanet/NHPA; 145 (C/R) Daniel Heuclin/NHPA; 146-147 (T/C) Stan Osolinski/OSF; 148 (B) Stephen Dalton/NHPA; 149 (T/L) Stephen Dalton/NHPA; 150 (B/R) Haroldo Palo Jr./NHPA; 155 (T/L) Jany Sauvanet/NHPA; 156-157 (C) Daniel Heuclin/NHPA; 158 (B) Stephen Dalton/NHPA; 163 (C/R) Tui de Roy/OSF; 165 (T) Bill Coster/NHPA; 168-169 (C) David C. Fritts/Animals Animals/OSF; 173 (B/L) Roger Tidman/NHPA; 175 (T) L. Hugh Newman/NHPA: 176-177 (C) Martyn Chillmaid/OSF; 180 (T/R) Robert Tyrrell/OSF; 182 (B) Michael Morcombe/NHPA; 185 Maurice Tibbs/Survival Anglia/OSF; 186 (R) Ralph & Daphne Keller/NHPA; 193 (T/L) A.N.T./NHPA; 196 (T/R) Raymond A. Mendez/Animals Animals/OSF; 198 (B/L) Richard la Val/Animals Animals/OSF; 199 (C) Stephen Dalton/NHPA; 201 (T/R) Michael Fogden/OSF; 203 (B) Manfred Danegger/NHPA; 204 (T) Survival Anglia/OSF; 206 (T/L) Andrew Thomson; 207 (B) Raymond A. Mendez/Animals Animals/OSF; 210/11 (T/C) Nick Bergkessel/Photo Researchers/OSF; 215 (C) Anthony Bannister/NHPA: 222 (B) Peter Pickford/NHPA; 226-227 (T/C) Daniel Heuclin/NHPA; 229 (B/L) A.N.T./NHPA; 232 (B) Konrad Wothe/OSF; 236 (B/C) Brian Hawkes/NHPA; 239 (T) Norbert Wu/NHPA; 241 (B/L) Stephen Dalton/NHPA; 243 (B/L) Martin Harvey/NHPA; 245/6 (T/C) Martin Harvey/NHPA; 246 (T/R) Martyn Colbeck/OSF.

All other photographs from MKP Archives.